Dear Professor Dyson

*Twenty Years of Correspondence Between Freeman Dyson and
Undergraduate Students on Science, Technology, Society and Life*

Dear Professor Dyson

*Twenty Years of Correspondence Between Freeman Dyson and
Undergraduate Students on Science, Technology, Society and Life*

Editor

Dwight E Neuenschwander
Southern Nazarene University, USA

World Scientific

NEW JERSEY · LONDON · SINGAPORE · BEIJING · SHANGHAI · HONG KONG · TAIPEI · CHENNAI · TOKYO

Published by

World Scientific Publishing Co. Pte. Ltd.

5 Toh Tuck Link, Singapore 596224

USA office: 27 Warren Street, Suite 401-402, Hackensack, NJ 07601

UK office: 57 Shelton Street, Covent Garden, London WC2H 9HE

Library of Congress Cataloging-in-Publication Data
Names: Dyson, Freeman J., author. | Neuenschwander, Dwight E., editor.
Title: Dear Professor Dyson : twenty years of correspondence between Freeman Dyson and
    undergraduate students on science, technology, society and life / editor
    Dwight E. Neuenschwander, Southern Nazarene University, USA.
Description: Singapore ; Hackensack, NJ : World Scientific Publishing Co. Pte. Ltd., [2016] | 2016 |
    Includes bibliographical references and index.
Identifiers: LCCN 2016000010| ISBN 9789814675840 (hardcover ; alk. paper) |
    ISBN 9814675849 (hardcover ; alk. paper) | ISBN 9789814675857 (pbk. ; alk. paper) |
    ISBN 9814675857 (pbk. ; alk. paper)
Subjects: LCSH: Dyson, Freeman J.--Correspondence. | Physicists--Correspondence. |
    Undergraduates--Correspondence.
Classification: LCC QC16.D95 A4 2016 | DDC 530.092--dc23
LC record available at http://lccn.loc.gov/2016000010

British Library Cataloguing-in-Publication Data
A catalogue record for this book is available from the British Library.

Printed in Singapore

To the grandchildren

L to R: (front row) *Aidan, Tess, Jack, Charlie, Clara, James, George;*
(middle row) *Lucy, Randy, Marcus, Max;*
(back row) *Liam, Bryn, Lauren, Mitchell, Donald.*
(photo courtesy of Freeman and Imme Dyson)

Teegon, Claire, Sophie (author photo)

**and to the grandchildren of the future we will never see.
We are borrowing this planet from you.**

Introduction

In August 2013 the Institute of Advanced Studies at Nanyang Technological University in Singapore hosted the "Conference in Honour of the 90th Birthday of Professor Freeman Dyson." [Phua *et al.*(2014)] In a session entitled "Remembering Freeman," I had the honor of telling the audience about extended correspondence between Professor Dyson and a generation of students from a small university in Oklahoma. The Singapore talk was expanded into this book.

Alice Calaprice, editor of *The Quotable Einstein*, recalls a conversation with Helen Dukas, who was Albert Einstein's secretary from 1928 to 1955. The conversation turned to Freeman Dyson, who came to the Institute for Advanced Study as a permanent member in 1953. Dukas recalled, "He is a great man. My one regret is that he did not meet Professor Einstein. In the '50s the professor mentioned that he had heard of this interesting young man. I told him that I could arrange a meeting, but the professor said, 'Oh, no, I don't want to bother such an important man!' " Calaprice added, "Unlike the polite Professor Einstein, I dared to bother this man— to ask him to write a forward for this book; and I am deeply grateful that he readily agreed." [Einstein and Calaprice(2005)]

For nearly thirty years in our university's general education capstone course "Science, Technology, and Society" (STS), Professor Dyson's memoir *Disturbing the Universe* has been our primary textbook. [Dyson(1979a)] Like Alice Calaprice, my students and I dared to bother this great man. Our correspondence with him has always been warm and cordial. As in the Singapore speech, this book will not focus on Professor Dyson's well-known achievements. Here, we focus on his integrity, his humanity, and how he has become a wise grandfatherly mentor to some three thousand students in Oklahoma.

Courses like STS exist to celebrate science and technology, and to question their consequences in our high-tech, mass-produced, noisy, militarized, convenience-and-efficiency-driven, perpetually entertained, automated, franchised-and-corporatized world. As a class, we strive to look at everything with eyes that are both appreciative and critical. Professor Dyson shares with us his thoughts on diverse topics about science and technology, and about life. To make this book work it will not do to merely quote the letters. As in the telling of any story, context must be presented.

In order to see behind the letters to what we were reading and discussing, you, the reader, have just been made a part of our class, without the burden of paying tuition. This chronicle describes not only what Professor Dyson said to us in his letters, but delves into the thoughts in our minds, and the discussions in our classroom, that he stimulated.

About a decade ago I began assigning the students the task of imagining the course to be a journey during which they promised to write a weekly letter to someone at home. They were to reflect on what they have recently encountered in the journey and relate it to their personal experiences.[1] A presentation of the correspondence with Professor Dyson would not be complete without sampling the students' thoughts expressed in their own words. The students' comments selected for inclusion represent all the others.

This book is the confluence of five streams: our correspondence with Professor Dyson, passages from *Disturbing the Universe*, passages from Professor Dyson's other writings and the writings of other authors, highlights of classroom presentations and discussions, and reflections by individual students. Different streams of input are distinguished by different fonts. In citing references, page numbers are denoted with square brackets, such as [Dyson(1979a)][7], which means page 7 of *Disturbing the Universe*.

As I write this, Professor Dyson is ninety-two years old and still going strong. My students and I wish him well. We are blessed to call him our mentor, and honored to be counted among his friends.

December 2015

---

[1] Excerpts from a sample of the student letters are read aloud to the class (the authors remain anonymous) the week after they are handed in. Sharing letters with everyone in this way brings out some of the course's best moments. The students learn much from each other, and I learn much from them.

Acknowledgments

This book should have about three thousand authors, the students past and present in the "Science, Technology, and Society" course described herein. It was written to express our collective gratitude to Professor Dyson, who has been our textbook author, wise counselor, and steadfast correspondent. Through his letters he has given generously of himself for more than two decades. From the students' testimony, it is clear that their engagement with Freeman Dyson profoundly touched their lives, as he has touched mine.

This book was also written with appreciation for Imme Dyson, ever so gracious, and for the Dyson children and grandchildren. We hope it will show to Professor Dyson's family the depth of his influence on the lives of so many young people they will never meet.

For their input and encouragement, I also thank a variety of guest speakers, other correspondents, and colleagues. These include Raghunath Acharya, Victor Alpher, Efrain Chacón and the Chacón family, Daryl Cox, Jim Cullumber, George Dyson, Randy Ehrlich, Brent Eskridge, Leo Finkenbinder, Zana Finkenbinder, Kenneth Ford, Karl Giberson, David Gordon and North Carolina Public Radio, John Goulden, Loren Gresham, Gwen Ladd Hackler, Nancy Halliday, Nancy Howie, Harlan Moore, Mark Portney, Phillip Schewe, Douglas Strickland, Dudley Strickland, Jirair Tashjian, Gary White, Austin Wilson, Ron Wilson, Mark Winslow, Sharon Young.

For permission to use images, I acknowledge with gratitude Freeman and Imme Dyson; Leo Finkenbinder; Old Oregon Photos; Marco Saborio; the Museum of London; students, friends, and family members.

The administrators of the general education program at Southern Nazarene University deserve credit for conceiving STS in the mid-1980s and, equally significant, for never micromanaging it. I am thinking especially of Randall Spindle who asked me to teach the course when it was new, and, more recently, Heather Clemmer and Dennis Williams who have overseen our university's "Gen Ed" curriculum and academic policies in recent years. If STS had been bureaucratically managed from the top down, it would have been just another forgettable required course. Instead, the content and culture of STS was allowed to flow from the identities of the participants.

I thank The Catalysts, an organization of SNU science alumni, for their support and encouragement.

To my wife Rhonda, and to our sons Charles and Steven, I express my appreciation for their encouragement across the STS years. I am grateful to Rhonda for her love and support throughout this long adventure.

Whoever concerns himself with big technology, either to push it forward or to stop it, is gambling in human lives.
—Freeman Dyson (1979)

It is easy to become so immersed in technology that we ignore what we know about life.
–Sherry Turkle (2011)

Contents

Introduction   vii

Acknowledgments   ix

1. Walking with Grandfather
   Letters of Introduction   1

2. Living in the Questions
   Real Questions Having Few Answers   10

3. A Hexagonal Mountain
   Three Reasons to Hate Science, Three Reasons to Love It   37

4. Martha and Mary
   Advice to Young People Choosing Their Life's Work   57

5. Engines with Souls
   Discussions about Our Machines   84

6. Steered from Afar
   Conversations about Identity and Conformity   103

7. The Swamp Angel
   Letters on Ends and Means   116

8. Rapid Rupture
   Letters about Nuclear Weapons   138

9. Arsenals of Folly
   Correspondence on the Militarization of the Economy   165

10. To Touch the Face of the Stars
     Letters on Our Place in the Universe   194

11. Silence
     On Seeking Serenity and Peace of Mind   212

12. The Chainsaw and the White Oak
     Letters about the Environment   222

13. "Why Should I Care?"
     Discussions about Values and Ethics   248

14. Playing God
     Letters on Genetic Engineering   266

15. Bonds of Kinship
     Thoughts on Relationships   286

16. Two Windows
     Letters on Science and Religion   311

17. Doubt and Faith
     More Letters on Science, Religion, and Honesty   328

18. Dreams of Earth and Sky
     Thoughts on Meaning   349

19. Family First
     Letters on Priorities   372

Bibliography   385

Index   393

1 Walking with Grandfather

Letters of Introduction

"And the oldest of the Grandfathers spoke with a kind voice and said: 'Come right in and do not fear... Your Grandfathers all over the world are having a council, and they have called you here to teach you.'" –Black Elk[2]

***

For twelve weeks forty-six students have been reading and discussing *Disturbing the Universe*, the textbook for our "Science, Technology, and Society" class. The professor asks if they would like to correspond with the author, Professor Freeman J. Dyson of the Institute for Advanced Study in Princeton, New Jersey. Eyes go wide. Yes, they say, we would like that. A committee of students drafts a letter. After collective in-class editing the professor types their letter on university letterhead:

> *April 6, 1993*
> *Professor Freeman J. Dyson*
> *Institute for Advanced Study*
> *Princeton, NJ 08540*
>
> *Dear Professor Dyson,*
> *We are using your elegant book "Disturbing the Universe" as our textbook this semester, in my section of the course "Science, Technology, and Society" at Southern Nazarene University. STS is a general education requirement of all degree-seeking students at SNU. Taken in the junior or senior year, it is to be a cross-disciplinary view of issues and the relations between science, technology, society, and the individual. "Disturbing the Universe" is a perfect text for such a course.... It is a rich book, profound yet accessible to all readers, and a joy to read. For additional background, interpretations, and for following interesting tangents, we occasionally supplement the text with passages from other books and journals, and with films.*
>
> *My students and I thought that, as an author, you might enjoy some feedback from your readers. Enclosed you will find from each student a paper which contains one comment and one question. If you could find the time to respond to one or perhaps two of them, we would be very honored. We appreciate that*

---

[2][Neihardt(1961)][25]

1

your calendar is most demanding, so it is with some hesitation that we ask even this much of you. Our request merely reflects how much we have enjoyed and learned from you through "Disturbing the Universe."

Each student signs their name, lists their academic major, and attaches their comment and question. We stuff the letter and attachments into an envelope, post it and hope for the best. Professor Dyson is a busy and important man. He has never heard of our little school on the prairie, which sits on US Route 66 in the center of what used to be called Indian Territory.

To our delight, within a week we receive a letter, typed on letterhead of the Institute for Advanced Study, School of Natural Sciences. At the next class meeting, Professor Dyson's reply is read aloud and photocopies are distributed:

April 9, 1993
Dear Professor Neuenschwander,
The best reward for writing books is to receive a letter like yours. Warmest thanks to you and to your students for your friendly response. Your remarks and your questions uplift my old grandfather spirit. I am sorry I cannot reply at length to each of you. Instead I will give you some brief answers to a few of the questions and send some of my recent talks that touch on the same questions...

The talks became valuable supplements to later class discussions. For example, a 1993 speech called "The Scientist as Rebel" contains an encouraging message of thoughtful rebellion:

Science is an alliance of free spirits in all cultures rebelling against the local tyranny that each culture imposes on its children....

Professor Dyson's letter of reply was uplifting because he spoke to us as a wise grandfather. In the cultures that were sent to Indian Territory, grandparents were respected for their experience, accomplishments, and wisdom, and characterized by their humility. In 2005, in the small wisdom-packed book *Walking with Grandfather*, the Lakota writer Joseph Marshall III recalled his grandfather, and explained "One has to live a long life to gain wisdom, and it is regarded as life's gift by some who finally achieve it. It is, many also realize, a gift they cannot keep to themselves. It must be given back to life." Marshall's editor added, "How do they share this precious gift? Through the power of their presence and in the vehicle of story." [Marshall(2005)]

Professor Dyson gives of himself to us by going beyond answering our questions to include relevant stories. Much of our class discussion consists of sharing personal stories. In our first letter exchange, rather than answering "one or perhaps two" of our questions, Professor Dyson gave lengthy replies to six of them.[3] Grandfather Dyson's friendly style and informal closing comments made us feel like we had known him for years:

> ... *My apologies to all those whose questions I did not answer. Now it is past midnight and time for me to go to bed. With thanks and good wishes to all of you,*
> *Yours ever,*
> *Freeman Dyson*

and included his signature.

Despite the lateness of the hour, on the first page of the letter he added a hand-written note:

> *P.S. I am glad to see that several of you are studying nursing. The brightest of my daughters is a nurse. It is a splendid profession and gives you the flexibility you need if you want to raise a family. This daughter is also interested in souls as well as bodies and she is a part-time seminary student, intending eventually to be a Presbyterian minister as well as a nurse.*

The class met then, as it does now, one evening per week for three hours. In the Spring 1993 class of forty-six students, about half were nurses. While the nurses were flattered by Professor Dyson's note, we interpreted his comment about his "brightest daughter" in terms of Garrison Keillor's Lake Wobegone, where "all the children are above average."[4] For the Dyson family this is not hyperbolic talk. Professor Dyson and his first wife Verena Huber are parents of Esther and George, who joined stepsister Katarina. Professor Dyson and his second wife Imme are parents to Dorothy, Emily, Mia, and Rebecca. Besides the daughter who is a nurse and pastor, the other daughters include a cosmonaut and venture capitalist who set up a

---

[3]In later correspondence we generally tried to keep the number of questions to about six.

[4]Garrison Keillor's radio program *A Prairie Home Companion* (National Public Radio) features the weekly "News from Lake Wobegone." Keillor closes this part of the program with "And that's the news from Lake Wobegone, where all the women are strong, all the men good-looking, and all the children are above average." Lake Wobegone and its characters come from Garrison Keillor, *Lake Wobegone Days* (1990).

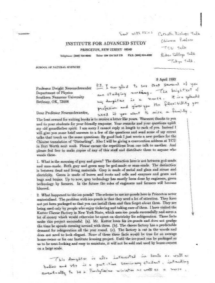

Fig. 1.1   *Page 1 of Professor Dyson's first letter to us.* (author photo)

private foundation concerned with health care; a veterinarian; a radiologist; a cardiologist.

Their outnumbered brother George is a craftsman who can build anything with his hands. As a teenager he migrated to the Pacific Northwest. There he worked on fishing boats and lived in a tree house. Not an ordinary tree house, but a solidly constructed house with a shingled roof, glazed windows and a fireplace, ninety-five feet aloft in a Douglas fir. Back on the ground George builds ocean-going kayaks in the traditional Aleutian design, the *baidarka*. [Dyson(1997a)] More recently, he has written books on the history of technology, including the evolution of global networks of machines that think [Dyson(1997b)], a spacecraft powered with nuclear bombs [Dyson(2002b)], and the building of the first electronic programmable computer [Dyson(2012)].

In a follow-up thank you letter to Professor Dyson of May 10, 1993 we expressed our "apologies for any lost sleep that we may have caused you" along with an added note:

> *May 11, 1993*
> *Dear Professor Dyson,*
> *... It has been a joy to once again teach our Science, Technology, and Society course, using "Disturbing the Universe" as the text. Perhaps when you wrote this book you did not have in*

mind its use as a college text on the relations between science, technology, and society. However, "Disturbing the Universe" has proved itself to be the ideal text for this course. Unlike the usual textbook expositions of issues and events, "Disturbing" is <u>alive</u>. Standard texts... cannot hold a candle to the memoirs of someone who was actually there, and who writes with passion, grace, and an elegant, profound simplicity....

It was interesting... to see how, on many significant occasions in your life, poetry was the most effective medium for expressing that for which normal prose was inadequate. Thank you for sharing that important component of your life. The poetry... [illustrates] that scientists are not one-dimensional people, in contrast to a misconception which many students bring to the STS course....

Thank you so much for sharing your life and insights with us....
Warm regards, DEN

To our letters of May 10 and 11, Professor Dyson made this hand-written reply on IAS stationary:

May 18 1993
Dear Professor Neuenschwander,
Thank you very much for your warm letter and thanks even more to the students for theirs. Please give the students my greetings and tell them that I am busy being a grandfather since our daughter organized a very special party for Mother's Day.
Yours ever,
Freeman Dyson

He enclosed a special announcement:

Unofficial Birth Announcement
Donald Dyson Reid, 4 pounds 14 ounces
George Freeman Reid, 5 pounds 4 ounces
made their entrance six weeks early on May 9, 1993.
Dorothy and both kids are doing fine.

When we received this announcement the summer school session had started, but the summer school students admirably carried the ball by sending Professor Dyson some Father's Day cards, along with a cover letter:

June 7, 1993
Dear Professor Dyson,
... Congratulations to you and all your family! We are glad to hear that mother and babies are doing fine.

Extracurricular Encounters

Several months before suggesting to the class the possibility of a letter, I sat in an audience of physics teachers who listened as Professor Dyson delivered his acceptance speech for the Ørsted Medal (or Oersted Medal), the highest honor presented by the American Association of Physics Teachers. Professor Dyson's acceptance speech, "To Teach or Not to Teach," [Dyson(1991)] was delivered in the plenary awards session in 1991 at the annual January AAPT meeting, which took place in San Antonio, Texas. After hearing many award speeches over the years, one expects the distinguished recipient to swoop in on the great day, pose for the grip-and-grin photo, deliver a brilliant speech—then disappear after the award session. On this day, Professor Dyson posed for the obligatory photo and delivered a profound speech. But after the award session he did not disappear. He remained at the meeting and participated in the parallel sessions, another physics teacher mingling with colleagues from high schools and universities. He was approachable.

He is still approachable. Twenty-two years after his Ørstead Medal speech, in November 2012 the quadrennial convention of the Sigma Pi Sigma physics honor society took place in Orlando, Florida. [Feller and Sauncy(2013)] Of the eight hundred attendees, over six hundred were boisterous, enthusiastic undergraduate physics majors. Professor Dyson was one of the featured speakers, scheduled to deliver a plenary talk on Saturday morning. He nonchalantly appeared in the lobby the preceding Thursday evening, and was instantly surrounded by crowds of students—and physics society CEOs and Nobel Laureates—who wanted to shake his hand, collect his autograph, and have their photo made with him.

For the next two days, during every break between sessions, long lines quickly formed of students who wanted to greet Professor Dyson. The young people waited with the patience one would see in a receiving line for a head of state, but the lines formed with the speed of a crowd of fans surrounding a rock star.[5] It did not stop until after 10 PM on Saturday, the last day of the conference. At that hour Professor Dyson was still standing in the lobby, talking to the last lingering students while staff took down the registration booth in the nearly-deserted convention center. Of course,

---

[5] In his biography of Professor Dyson, [Schewe(2013)][67–68] which appeared the following year, Phillip Schewe drew a fitting analogy between Beatlemania of 1964, and "Dysonmania" of 1949 when Freeman Dyson unified the various ways of doing quantum electrodynamics [Dyson(1949)].

Fig. 1.2 *A typical scene between sessions at the 2012 Congress: long lines of students waiting to greet Professor Dyson.* (author photo)

he was much younger then—merely 88, going on a spry 89. Although he seemed to have more energy than the young people who swarmed around him, I was glad for him when they finally let him return to his hotel. For these past twenty years, I hope my students and I have not taken his patience for granted.

The Fall 1998 semester class asked about the origin of their STS textbook:

> *3 December 1998*
> *Dear Professor Dyson,*
> *What motivated you to write "Disturbing the Universe?"*
>
> *5 December 1998*
> *Dear Dwight and STS class,*
> *... I was invited by the Sloan Foundation to write a scientific autobiography, as one of a series that they were publishing. I was glad to accept the invitation, because I enjoy writing. I had done enough interesting things and known enough interesting people, so I knew I had material to make a book. The most important thing when you are writing a book is to have something to say. I had something to say. Also the Sloan Foundation paid me a substantial advance, which helped to put my daughters through college. Since we have five daughters, college bills were a strong motivation.*
> *... Happy Christmas and New Year to you all.*
> *Yours sincerely,*
> *Freeman Dyson*

The students needed no further explanation about college bills.

> March 22, 2005
> Dear Professor Dyson,
> The name "Dyson" may be scarcer than my own surname, so
> may I ask [if you are] related to Sir Frank Dyson who, together
> with Arthur Eddington, organized the 1919 solar eclipse expe-
> ditions that confirmed Einstein's prediction of starlight deflec-
> tion?... [Also] I am frequently asked by students if you are re-
> lated to the gentleman who markets the Dyson vacuum cleaner.

> 7 May 2005
> Dear Dwight,
> Answering your question about Dysons. I am not related to Sir
> Frank Dyson, but he came from the same part of Yorkshire as
> my father, and his father, who was a Baptist minister, mar-
> ried my grandparents. My father knew Sir Frank, and I heard
> a lot about his activities when I was a child. His fame certainly
> stimulated my interest in astronomy and science... I am also
> not related to James Dyson [the British inventor and industrial
> engineer], but I once appeared side-by-side with him on a tele-
> vision program when we both happened to be in New Zealand. I
> liked him very much....

One of our more recent letters was sent to Professor Dyson a few days
before his ninetieth birthday:

> 4 December 2013
> Dear Professor Dyson,
> On behalf of the Fall 2013 semester Science, Technology, & So-
> ciety class, we thank you once again for being part of our lives...
> In less than two weeks you will have completed 90 laps around
> the sun. For this we congratulate you! You are in excellent
> health, you still lead a robust and active life, and your services
> are still in demand. You are inspiring! With the view from 90,
> what advice do you have for university students in their early
> 20s, which would help them live a life not only as long, but even
> more important, lived with meaning and fulfillment?
>
> ...We hope that you and your family had a joyous Thanksgiving,
> and are looking forward to happy gatherings over the upcoming
> holidays. Best wishes to Mrs. Dyson, to your son and daughters
> and their families, and enjoy those wonderful grandchildren!
> Warm regards,
> The STS class of Fall 2013

Two days later we received his e-mailed reply:

> *6 December 2013*
> *Dear Dwight and class,*
> *...Thank you for your congratulations, but being ninety has not made me any wiser than I was before. My advice to you young people is still the same. Avoid making choices too soon, be ready to grab at unexpected chances when they appear, work hard at acquiring skills like programming computers or writing clear English that are always useful, make the best of whatever job you are doing, be ready to switch careers when necessary, be a good team player, and try to leave the world a better place than you found it. I like to repeat the advice that our daughter Esther puts on her E-mails: Always make new mistakes.*
> *Happy New Year to all of you,*
> *Yours ever,*
> *Freeman*

Thus it has gone for over twenty years, a wonderful mix of curricular and personal exchanges. In September 2014 a student named Ryan wrote, "They have written each other and this class has asked him questions since before I was born!"

2 Living in the Questions

Real Questions Having Few Answers

"Be patient toward all that is unsolved in your heart and try to love the questions themselves....Live the questions now." – Rainer Maria Rilke[6]

***

On the first Tuesday of a new semester, a university student searches for a classroom:

```
First day of this class...where's the classroom for
''Science, Technology, Society?'' This course sounds
dreadfully generic. Another general education course to get
out of the way so I can graduate in May. I'm not keen on
science. Let's get this over with. Ah, here it is, room 10.
Heading in... What's this? I hear music--could that be
''Time'' from Pink Floyd's Dark Side of the Moon''?
```

> *"...You run and you run to catch up with the sun but it's sinking*
> *Racing around to come up behind you again..."*[7]

```
This is not what I expected.
```

Students gather and find seats as the music plays. At the front of the room, a black-and-white photograph, taken in 1916, appears on the screen. It shows a family of the Coeur D'Alene tribe in traditional dress, seated in a Chalmers automobile.

A heading on the photo says "Welcome to Science, Technology, and Society." The song ends and the STS professor introduces himself. He sips coffee from a mug that says "Potawatomi Nation." The picture on the screen is interesting, he says, for two reasons. First, the family appears to embrace new technology without it changing who they are. Second, the picture recalls the long and bitter collision that took place in North America between cultures whose technologies and values and ways of understanding the world were drastically different. To Native Americans the land was sacred and was to be treated with reverence. The people were part of nature; they considered the bison and coyote to be their relatives. To the

---

[6][Rilke(2011)]. Ch. 4.

[7]Pink Floyd, "Time" from *The Dark Side of the Moon* (Capitol Records, 1973.)

Fig. 2.1 *The Wildshoe family of the Coeur D'Alene tribe, in their Chalmers automobile near Spokane, Washington. Front seat: Phillip Wildshoe, his wife Eugenia and baby Eugenia; middle seat: sons David (in bonnet) and Vincent; back seat: daughters Rosie and Anne (child) and an unidentified woman, probably from the Kootenai-Salish tribe. Photo by Frank Palmer of Spokane, Washington, 1916.* (courtesy of Old Oregon Photos)

newcomers the land was a commodity to be possessed and exploited, nature was an opposing force to be conquered, and the bison and coyote were pests to be eradicated. The Native Americans and Euro-Americans could have learned much from each other. From the Euro-Americans the Native Americans could have learned written language and science and "gray technology" such as metallurgy. Indeed, they quickly adapted European horses and firearms, and around 1820 Sequoyah introduced a syllabary for the Cherokee language.

Reciprocally, the colonists and settlers could have learned much from the Native Americans, such as "green technology," to work with the animals and plants that were already adapted to this continent, instead of trying to replace them. They might have learned to respect the land and all its creatures, seeing human beings as part of nature and not above it.

To those facing west, the conquest of the North American continent was heroic. To those facing east, the conquest was tragic. [Brown(1971)] The heroism and the tragedy are both true. For those facing west, their numbers were leveraged by technology. For those facing east, courage and gallantry were not enough. The dominance of a highly technological invasive society over indigenous ones is not exclusively a North American phenomenon. Which society you happen to be born into is a matter of luck. Professor Dyson's opening remarks in *Disturbing the Universe* include the role of luck: "Science and technology, like all original creations of the human spirit, are unpredictable...Whoever concerns himself with big technology, either to push it forward or to stop it, is gambling in human lives...." [Dyson(1979a)][7]

> *April 6, 1999*
> *Dear Professor Dyson,*
> *Once again our Science, Technology, and Society class has re-duced about a hundred proposed questions to five. If we may impose upon your graciousness once again...*
> *... What would you say is the greatest invention of mankind?...*
> *... On behalf of the nearly 50 students in our class, I thank you for contributing so much to our learning and to our lives.*
> *Warm regards,*
> *DEN on behalf of the students*
>
> *10 April 1999*
> *Dear Dwight,*
> *Thanks for your message, and thanks to the class for their good questions. It is a wet Saturday in Minnesota, with rain blowing horizontally all day long, a good day for staying indoors and answering letters....*
> *What is the greatest invention of mankind? Language. After that, domesticating plants and animals. After that, writing. After that, religion. After that, science. I am in the middle of reading an excellent book, "Guns, Germs and Steel: the Fates of Human Societies," by Jared Diamond. I recommend it to you and your students. It deals with these questions on a very broad basis: which inventions were most important and why some societies made them and others did not. Diamond is a field biologist who spent a large part of his life among the prim-itive people in New Guinea and elsewhere. He says he knows by direct experience that these people are at least as smart as we are. The fact that we made the important inventions and they did not has nothing to do with our being smarter. We were just luckier. It was accidents of geography that gave us our advan-tage. I think he proves his case very convincingly.*
> *... Thank you for reducing the questions from a hundred to five. All good wishes to the class. And to you, from Freeman.*

Diamond suggests two reasons why New Guineans may be smarter than Westerners. The first reason is society: avoiding a violent early demise in a wild environment without police or judicial systems selects for alert intelligence. The second reason is technology. Traditional New Guinea children have few opportunities for passive electronic entertainment. Instead, they "spend almost all of their waking hours actively doing something, such as talking or playing with other children or adults." [Diamond(1999)][2–7]

Our new student feels a flash of panic upon hearing an announcement:

> The professor is about to call the roll--and he wants each
> student, when called, to give a one-word description of what
> we expect this course to be about! I thought he was going to
> tell *us* what this course is about. He's giving us a few
> minutes to discuss candidate words with our neighbors...

During the roll call and student introductions, each person contributes a word. They are recorded on the white board. Change. Ideas. Industry. Observation. Reality. Understanding. Some words suggest upbeat optimism: Discovery. Exploration. Innovation. Knowledge. Progress. Other words sound dubious or cautious. Conflict. Consequences. Pollution. Uncertainty. Most words trigger a few moments of discussion, especially the ones with multiple shades of meaning.

For instance, "progress" is a loaded word. In the Oklahoma town where I live the Chamber of Commerce sign used to say "Welcome to Piedmont—Open Spaces and Friendly Faces." About ten years ago, that painted plywood sign was torn down and replaced with a natty brick one saying "Welcome to Piedmont—Winds of Progress." The faces are still friendly, but the open spaces and distinctive town identity are disappearing. Progress means increased tax revenue for the town, which has resulted in good things including a new library and road repairs. But it also means congested traffic, garish signage, light pollution and cookie-cutter franchises identical to what already exist within a twenty-minute drive to nearby towns. Something gained, something lost. Winds of Progress.

After each student presents a word, the professor uncovers two words that were written on the whiteboard before class, that he wishes to add to our list. They are "appreciation" and "awareness." "These words are not better than yours," he says, "But they are motifs that help me navigate the range of topics implied by science and technology and society." To illustrate what he means, he changes the image on the screen. Half the screen lights up to show a sports car. "For example," he says, "our automobiles are marvelous machines that will, at any time, carry us across the continent quickly and reliably and in comfort. Even if you have only a humble high-mileage well-used sedan, you still have at your service a machine that Louis XIV could not have at any price." We should appreciate what our technology makes possible.

The other half of the screen lights up with a photo of gridlock on an urban highway interchange. The professor continues: We should also be aware of the consequences of millions of these marvelous machines operating daily around the globe. We pay a steep price for our dependence on them. Do we own our machines, or do they own us? This course celebrates technology–and questions it.

Other words, the professor says, will be added later. Caring. Respect. Reverence. All in due time.

STS History

The Science, Technology, and Society course (Natural Science 3043), or STS, was created when our university revised its general education requirements in the mid-1980s.[8] Teaching a section of this new course was an assignment I accepted with enthusiasm. NS 3043 fulfills a liberal arts requirement for all our students earning a bachelor's degree. They take it during their junior or senior year, and come from all academic majors, which enables me to meet a cross-section of the student population.

From the moment I was asked to teach STS I knew that *Disturbing the Universe* would be an essential component in the course. In his closing chapters Professor Dyson eloquently relates his resolution to a struggle that I felt deeply for a long time but did not know how to articulate–

...In the silence I gradually become aware that the questions I had intended to raise with him have been answered... [Dyson(1979a)][261]

Having been in their place, I knew that many students coming into the STS class would bring similar struggles and questions with them. They, too, would wish to live divided no more.

Thirty years after it started, STS is still a part of our university's general education program, and the timeless *Disturbing the Universe* still forms an essential part of it. Upon meeting the book Ciara V. commented,

---

[8]When started in 1986 the course was called "Man, Science, and Technology," and was still known as MST when our class first wrote to Professor Dyson in 1993. Starting with the 1994–95 academic year, the name was changed to "Science, Technology, and Society."

Dear Mom, In one of my classes we are reading a book called *Disturbing the Universe* by Freeman Dyson that I was nervous about reading, but have found it not as scary as I had built it up to being. He begins by talking about a book that he read as a child, *The Magic City* by Edith Nesbit. He goes on to point out how when the people in this city wish for machinery, they are stuck with it for life... Thinking about how this applies to my life brought that truth into broader focus [with] all the machines that I have come to see as something I can't live without. Like my iPod that you frequently say I need to put down so I can hear the whole conversation, ...or the cell phone that I can't seem to part with for a second.

Leslie C., who loves literature, wrote in the beginning of the semester,

I have noticed that Dyson begins almost every chapter with a reference to literature.... Because Dyson is not just SCIENCE SCIENCE SCIENCE, I take him a little more seriously. Because he's open-minded and well-rounded. The short and long of it: I can respect his opinions about science (or technology or society) because he respects MINE about literature.

Freeman Dyson writes about science by telling stories from his personal experiences.

I am trying in this book to describe to people who are not scientists the way the human situation looks to someone who is a scientist. Partly I shall be describing how science looks from the inside. Partly I shall be discussing the future of technology. Partly I shall be struggling with the ethical problems of war and peace, freedom and responsibility, hope and despair, as these are affected by science. These are all parts of a picture which must be seen as a whole in order to be understood. It makes no sense to me to separate science from technology, technology from ethics, or ethics from religion... [Dyson(1979a)][5]

Early one semester a student named Jessica wrote in her weekly letter,

I was worried that everything [Professor Dyson] said would go right over my head, but it really hasn't.... I was delighted to read that he is specifically talking to people who are not scientists. He also explains that he is writing from his personal experiences. In many ways, I respect Dyson more than I ever thought I would. I honestly had no intention of reading the book, but I have found the reading very interesting and insightful.

> 20 November 2012
> Dear Professor Dyson,
> It was so good to see you at the Sigma Pi Sigma Congress in Orlando.... Your patience with the long lines of students at the meeting who wanted to meet you was impressive.... But you did not turn away a single student who wanted to speak with you.
> ... In our class discussion... several questions to you were pro-posed.... However, we don't want to trade on your reluctance to turn students away... we trust that our questions will not get in the way of your Thanksgiving time with your family....
> What is a non-science issue with which you have had to strug-gle, and what conclusions did you reach?...

> 25 November 2012
> Dear Dwight,
> Thank you for your friendly message. It was good to see you in Orlando. I forgot to ask you how you are recovering from the tornado, which hit you a hell of a lot harder than the hurricane hit us...
> I am alone in Princeton so it is a good time to answer your student's questions. The day after Thanksgiving my wife Imme nobly flew to England to spend a week with my sister Alice who is...ailing in an old people's home. I am selfishly staying home, with the excuse that I already made two visits this year. Imme is now at the end of her first day in Winchester, which is per-petually grey and usually raining at this time of year. Alice is always happy to see us, and talks coherently about the past, but forgets almost everything of the present. Thank God she is not unhappy, but she is no longer the sister I have known for 85 years. I hope when my time comes my heart will quit before my brains.
> Now it is time to begin with your questions.
> What non-science issues have I had to struggle with? I have been so lucky in my personal life that I never had to struggle hard. Like many scientists, I reached a mid-life crisis at the age of forty when it was obvious that I was no longer smart

enough to compete with the young people at the cutting edge of science. It was clear that I must find another line of work. At the Institute for Advanced Study where I had a permanent job, I was supposed to do research and was not required to teach. So I decided to resign my position at the Institute and move to a university where I would spend the rest of my life as a teacher. I had good invitations from Yeshiva University in New York and at Northwestern University in Chicago. But when I discussed the possibility of moving with my family, they voted unanimously against it. They did not want to live in New York or Chicago. I did not have the moral strength to go against the family's wishes. So I stayed at the Institute and started a new career writing books for the general public. Writing books is my way of teaching. For the second half of my life, I was a writer rather than a scientist, doing research as a side-line, working on unfashionable problems which did not require me to be competitive. I found writing to be an enjoyable and rewarding activity, and through my books I came to know a much wider variety of people than I had known as a scientist. Now at age 88 I am reviewing other people's books instead of writing my own.[9]

On an intellectual level, I had another struggle, adapting my socialist principles to a capitalist society. In England during World War Two, I lived in a socialist society that functioned well. That was perhaps the highest point that socialism ever reached. Money did not matter. Everyone got the same rations of food and clothes and soap and other necessities. The rationed stuff was cheap, and there was nothing else to buy. Cars were not allowed any gasoline except for official business. It was a wonderful time to be a socialist, so long as the war lasted. Rich and poor people were all in the same boat. We tried to continue living the same way after the war ended. But gradually, as the rationing was abandoned and more things became available, money started to matter. Rich and poor became different. Inequalities became sharper. When I started to raise a family, I discovered that my socialist principles gave way to my responsibilities as a father. As a father, I needed money to take care of my wife and kids, and the more money the better. The theoretical idea of equality faded, as the kids needed a good home in a good neighborhood with good schools. The final blow to my socialist ideals came when my oldest daughter became a successful venture capitalist, using her wealth to rescue small companies and start new enterprises. She taught me that capitalism can

---

[9]At this writing, Professor Dyson has just released two new books: *Birds and Frogs* (World Scientific, Singapore, 2015) and *Dreams of Earth and Sky* (New York Review of Books, 2015).

> *be creative. She became a generous friend and role model to her numerous nephews and nieces.*

Although *Star Trek* enthusiasts have heard of the "Dyson sphere," most students entering STS have never heard of Freeman Dyson or quantum electrodynamics, number theory, the Triga nuclear reactor, adaptive optics, the Jasons, Project Orion, random matrices, spin waves, dark matter, serious studies on the colonization of space, or cosmological eschatology. Introductions are needed. While geographical logistics prevent Professor Dyson from making a dramatic entrance in person on the first day of class, I share with the students a summary of his career and accomplishments, his life and family, including photographs they graciously provided.

"I really appreciated the overview of Freeman Dyson," wrote Patty J., "I had never heard of this man before... You've got to appreciate a man whose scientific genius is fully balanced by an intact and healthy family..." Ben S. observed, "Getting to know Freeman Dyson was quite an approach. Having this unconventional textbook is one thing, but knowing its author is another. It is nice that our author is an actual human."

Many Questions, Few Answers

"The answer, my friend, is blowin' in the wind, The answer is blowin' in the wind..." –Bob Dylan[10]

The STS syllabus begins with a disclaimer: "This course is not about finding answers. Rather, it is about understanding the questions." By way of foreshadowing and overview, and to make connections with entries in the student-created word list, questions that cut broadly and deeply across STS issues are suggested during the first class session. Introducing them takes much of our first three-hour session. Let us review them here.

1. What is science? This broad question raises a host of sub-questions, such as: What are "facts?" What are "theories" and how do they differ from "hypotheses?"

Some activities have the trappings of science but are not science. Since the Sun and Moon affect our lives on Earth, to ancient and medieval minds it stood to reason that the "wandering stars," or planets, could affect our

---

[10] "Blowin' in the Wind" (1962) by Bob Dylan, Columbia Records; made famous in 1963 by Peter, Paul and Mary.

lives too. From the motions of the planets the stargazers claimed to fore-
tell your future. Your birthday defines the constellation along the zodiac
that applies to you. For example, if your birthday falls in December, you
were born under the sign of Sagittarius. Look at today's horoscope under
Sagittarius to find today's astrological prediction that applies to you.

Do a little experiment. Take a newspaper or magazine horoscope and
cut out all the predictions, one for each sign of the zodiac. Cut off the
names—Pisces, Gemini, Aquarius, and so on. Now mix up the slips of
paper. Select the papers at random. Could each one apply to you? Without
their labels can you distinguish which one applies to Gemini, to Cancer,
to Scorpio? When I do the experiment, I find the predictions are so broad
that all of them apply perfectly to me! They are so right they cannot be
wrong! As predictions they are meaningless. Even though astrologers and
astronomers both look at the sky, astrologers are not doing science.

Next let's turn to an example of someone doing science. In June 1905
a twenty-six-year-old clerk at the Swiss patent office published an article
in *Annalen der Physik* that resolved a long-standing paradox about light,
electromagnetism and motion. To resolve the paradox the clerk laid out
the foundations of what we now call the special theory of relativity. His
name was Albert Einstein.

The paper on special relativity was followed in September by a short
note, presented as an afterthought. [Stachel(1998)] Einstein imagined a
body at rest giving off two pulses of light simultaneously, where, as seen by
an observer relative to whom the body is at rest, the light pulses move with
speed c in opposite directions, each carrying half the light energy. Using
some results from his June paper about the relativity of energy as observed
from different frames of reference, Einstein performed a simple calculation
and made a quantitative prediction:

From this equation it directly follows that–
If a body gives off the energy E in the form of radiation, its mass diminishes
by E/c^2....

This is the famous $E = mc^2$. It became science when Einstein suggested how to test it against the real world. Unlike horoscope predictions,
Einstein's prediction could be shown to be wrong if it was not right:

It is not impossible that with bodies whose energy-content is variable to a
high degree (e.g. with radium salts) the theory may be successfully put to the
test.

Radium is an especially radioactive element, discovered in 1898 by Marie and Pierre Curie, after Marie realized there was more radioactivity in uranium ore than could be accounted for by uranium.[11] Measure the energy given off by a radium sample during a specific time, then compare the sample's final mass to its initial mass. To the precision that the measured mass change and the measured E/c^2 agree, we have confidence that Einstein's ideas describe a reality in nature. And Einstein *was* right, so now the energy budgets of radioactivity and nuclear reactions make sense: nuclei convert a tiny fraction of their mass into enormous energy.

As an informal description, science seems to be the art of creating and testing a network of concepts, in terms of which the physical world becomes comprehenisble. Science explores *nature*, and any explanations forthcoming from science appeal only to mechanisms that operate *within* nature. Nature's doings range from sub-atomic particles to the entire universe. That's a wide field! Even so, some have suggested that science has pushed about as far as it can go.

> *3 December 1998*
> *Dear Professor Dyson,*
> *At the risk of imposing on your past graciousness, I have gath-
> ered questions from every student in my 50-person "Science,
> Technology, and Society" class this semester. From that set
> [we] have narrowed the field to the most recurring few. If you
> have the time to respond to one or two of them, the class would
> be most appreciative....*
> *Do you foresee boundaries to science and technology? How far
> can or will science go? What happens when we reach the limit?*
>
> *5 December 1998*
> *Dear Dwight,*
> *Thank you for your message. Please give my greetings to your
> students and tell them I am glad to see their questions ....*
> *We cannot possibly see from here whether there are any limits
> to science or to technology. Responding to John Horgan's book,
> "The End of Science,"[12], my son said, "How can he know about
> the end of science when we are still so close to the beginning?"
> What my son says is true. We are still close to the beginning
> of science. My own guess is that science of some kind will
> continue to develop so long as the human species survives. But
> the science of AD 4000 will probably be as different from our*

---

[11] Curie first discovered polonium, followed by radium. [Segrè(1980)]

[12] John Horgan, *The End of Science: Facing the Limits of Knowledge in the Twilight of the Scientific Age* (1996).

*science as our science is from the science of Aristotle. It might
be so different that we would no longer call it science. But I
cannot imagine how we could "reach the limit." So long as
there are people, there will be new things to explore and new
questions to answer.
... Happy Christmas and New Year to you all.
Yours sincerely,
Freeman Dyson*

2. What does it mean to say a society is—or is not—"scientific"?

In *Disturbing the Universe* Professor Dyson addresses the non-scientist majority of the public: "...I am talking here to unscientific people who ultimately have the responsibility for guiding the growth of science and technology into creative rather than destructive directions." [Dyson(1979a)][5] How do unscientific people control science and technology? In a market economy, citizens strongly influence the direction of technology by their choices in discretionary spending. Automobiles and televisions and smart phones dominate our lives because we eagerly buy them. "...In our world, thousands of scientists play with millions of toys, but only a few of their toys grow big." [Dyson(1979a)][7] The marketers strive to convince you, the "consumer," that you deserve the newest model automobile or smart phone, even though your old one works fine. Yesterday's luxury becomes today's necessity. A challenge for each of us arises in distinguishing wants from needs.

The public also steers scientific research agendas through government policies and research grants funded by agencies such as the National Science Foundation, the National Institute of Health, NASA, and branches of the military.

The last thing that society or science needs is for scientists to be perceived as come some high priesthood, or white-lab-coated Dr. Frankenstein caricatures.[13] The closing episode of Jacob Bronowski's television documentary and accompanying book *The Ascent of Man*[14] carries this challenge:

---

[13]Literature professor Gwen Ladd Hackler has presented to STS guest lectures on Mary Shelly's *Frankenstein*.
[14]*The Ascent of Man* traces significant stepping-stones in human intellectual development, such as the invention of agriculture, architecture, mathematics, relativity, the discovery of the atom, evolution, DNA.

This is a world run by specialists: is not that what we mean by a scientific society? No, it is not. A scientific society is one in which specialists can indeed do the things like making the electric lights work. But it is you, it is I, who have to know how nature works, and how (for example) electricity is one of her expressions in the light and in my brain. [Bronowski(1973)][435–436]

Nevertheless, a mystique hangs about the practice of science. Professor Dyson recalls the economist John Maynard Keynes saying, in a lecture on Isaac Newton, that "traditional mythology links the figure of the scientist with that of the Magus...." Professor Dyson then noted the appearance of "a new magus," the writer Robert Pirsig with his book *Zen and the Art of Motorcycle Maintenance*. "His book explores the dual nature of science, on the one hand science as dedicated craftsmanship, on the other hand science as intellectual obsession." In the end, Newton and Pirsig "settled for a more limited area of understanding." [Dyson(1979a)][8–10] Science may never reach an end, but it has limitations.

A sub-question that keeps emerging across the years, when thinking about science, technology and society, asks what it means for a society to be "civilized." Is technology the hallmark of civilization? For instance, Amish and Mennonite communities are content to run their farms with 19th century technology, but no one considers them uncivilized. On contrast, Hitler's Third Reich had the latest technology of the time, including the first jet airplanes and the V-1 and V-2 rockets. But they were built to serve a regime that was considered by the rest of the world to be antithetical to what we mean by civilization.

3. How do science and technology affect our engagement with the world? Through science we see our species and our planet in time and space, the better to understand our place in the great bloodstream of life and in the cosmos. Through technology we use our scientific understanding of nature to make things. In recent years, phenomenal new things have included personal computers, CT and MRI scans, laproscopic surgery, robotic manufacturing, night-vision goggles, the Internet, flat-screen television, and so on. Because of technology we can easily travel, communicate across large distances, enjoy air-conditioned houses and enhanced life expectancy. It must also be noted that through technology we also have anthrax and nuclear weapons, which says more about the human condition than it does about technology.

Because of technology, we spend much of our lives in artificial environments. Unmodified nature becomes something we go to see at the museums called national parks. Thomas Lovejoy wrote in 2010,[15]

We need to move from thinking of nature as just something set aside in a protected area in the midst of a human dominated landscape, to a vision of humanity and its aspirations embedded in the planet's natural infrastructure. [Lovejoy(2010)]

Furthermore, as our technologies become increasingly complicated so we cannot see how a device works by looking at it, and as our technologies become more and more automated so that we interact hands-on with real things less and less, we become disconnected from our technology too. In some STS classes we listen to a recorded interview with photographer David Plowden.[16] His famous images include portraits of steam locomotives photographed "in their very eleventh hour." [Plowden(2007)] With fondness he recalls each locomotive as an individual, saying "What other machine could you look at and see how it works?" The MIT psychologist Sherry Turkle, who studies relations between people and computerized technology, tells of a retired engineer named Jonathan. He approaches the robot called My Real Baby. He wants to understand how it works. "With permission, he takes apart the robot as much as he can, but as with all things computational, in the end he is left with mysteries. When everything is laid out on a table, there is still an ultimate particle whose workings remain opaque: a chip." [Turkle(2012)][111]

The physicist and motorcycle restorer Matthew Shepherd expresses a similar frustration with electronic gadgets layered on top of machines to make them "smart," which risks dumbing down the people who use them:

Consider the angry feeling that bubbles up in this person when, in a public bathroom, he finds himself waving his hands under the faucet, trying to elicit a few seconds of water from it in a futile rain dance of guessed-at mantras. This man would like to know: Why should there not be a handle?....
It's true, some people fail to turn off a manual faucet. With its blanket presumption of irresponsibility, the infrared faucet doesn't merely respond to this

---

[15] Thomas Lovejoy was executive vice president of the World Wildlife Fund–US, originator of the debt-for-nature swaps, and was founding science advisor to the public television series *Nature*.

[16] "Disappearing America," interview with photographer David Plowden by Dick Gordon on "The Story," 7 December 2007, North Carolina Public Radio.

fact, it installs it, giving it the status of normalcy. There is a kind of infantiliza-
tion at work, and it offends the spirited personality. [Crawford(2009)][54–56]

The spirited engagement that gave us technology in the first place has
come around to producing spirit-diminishing technology that disengages us
from nature and from our own stuff. The irritating thing is that a distant
anonymous someone else decides what we need, and pushes it on us even
when do not ask for it. The Cold War Communists merely treated us as
the enemy (which implies a measure of respect), but Silicon Valley treats us
as incompetent nincompoops who need their benevolent help ("there's an
app for that") for every little task in life. In contrast to the Silicon Valley
ideology of solutionism, dealing with problems and struggles ourselves are
the making of an authentic human being. [Morozov(2013)]

As our dependency on technology becomes more indelible, as our de-
tachment from hands-on engagement with real things becomes more complete, do we even care? Robert Pirsig observed, "It occurred to me that
there is no manual that deals with the real business of motorcycle maintenance, the most important aspect of all. Caring about what you are
doing..." [Pirsig(1999)][34] If motorcycles are not your passion, replace "motorcycle maintenance" with whatever your task or passion happens to be.
Zen and the art of nursing. Zen and the Art of being a drummer. Zen
and the art of teaching third grade.... The principles are the same. The
real business of doing them right is *caring*. Whether it be performing brain
surgery or cleaning a stable, whatsoever is rightly done, however humble,
is noble.

Pirsig identifies two modes for seeing a motorcycle, the "classic" and the
"romantic" modes. The classic mode sees underlying form, through tools
and maintenance schedules and circuit diagrams. When your motorcycle
won't start you have to see the machine through classical eyes. The romantic mode sees the gleam of the chrome, the unity of rider and machine as
you bank into a turn—the sensory experiences that drew you to motorcycling in the first place. Both ways of seeing the motorcycle are important,
but they are not the same. Reconciling these two modes of understanding
forms the thesis of Pirsig's book. His pivotal word is "Quality" which he
uses as a proper noun. Long before Prisig wrote *Zen*, Professor Dyson was
living by similar principles in his own life. "Much of the joy of science
is the joy of solid work done by skilled workmen.... The essential factor
which keeps the scientific enterprise healthy is a shared respect for qual-

ity." [Dyson(1979a)][9–10] Pirsig describes how Quality cannot be defined, even though you know it when you see it. [Pirsig(1999)][205–206] We ran this notion by Professor Dyson.

> *7 May 2002*
> *Dear Professor Dyson,*
> *... Another question that we raise relates to Pirsig's book since you mention "Zen and the Art of Motorcycle Maintenance" in "The Magic City:" How do you define (or describe or characterize) "Quality?" Thank you for your consideration, and for being a presence in our class....*
> *Dwight, on behalf of the STS class*

> *20 May 2002*
> *Dear Dwight and students,*
> *I don't try to define quality. If you need to define it, then you don't understand it. Defining quality is a futile exercise, like defining good and evil or beauty and ugliness. I mean by quality a hoe-plough that someone in Idaho sent as a present to my wife, a simple hand-tool that makes it easier and pleasanter to weed a garden. Or a mountain-bike that she likes to ride into town to do the shopping. Or a neat piece of writing like Pirsig's "Zen."*
> *... I don't know whether you are aware that Pirsig's son Chris was murdered as soon as he was grown up. A senseless death on a street in San Francisco. Apparently a random act of madness without any motivation. This must have been a crushing blow for Pirsig. It reminds me how lucky I am to have a son who is nearing fifty and still alive and vigorous....*
> *All good wishes for the summer to you and the students. And thanks for sending the questions.*
> *Yours ever, Freeman.*

4. How should we think about our stuff—the products of technology? Dalamar, Nevada, is a ghost town. Gold mining occured here between 1885 and 1900. Today only ruins remain, foundations of buildings and collapsed mines. In Dalamar I came across another relic, a car in ruins, that somehow ended up here.

It is the carcass of a 1954 Cadillac Sedan de Ville. The car had been burned and riddled with hundreds of bullet holes. Feeling like someone tending the dead after a massacre, I gathered its scattered parts and reassembled them into their proper places as best as I could, then took the

Fig. 2.2 *The remains of a much-abused 1954 Cadillac Sedan de Ville in Dalamar, Nevada.* (author photo)

car's photo. The image shows more than a rusted hulk of what was originally a beautiful car. The photo shows lack of respect towards the machine, and towards the people who made it and took care of it. I have a problem understanding anyone who takes delight in gleefully destroying something they cannot make themselves.

Before someone could heap such abuse on this car, they had to convince themselves that it had no value. This attitude extends oh so easily beyond machines—to animals, to ecosystems, to another person, to another ethnic group. Before you can bulldoze a forest or fire-bomb a city, you must convince yourself that the forest or the city—and their inhabitants—are expendable objects.

Of course, if no cars were ever scrapped we would be smothered in them. But when a car must be scrapped, a house demolished, or a horse euthanized, let it be done in a way that shows respect. Because of what it does to the gleeful destroyer, destruction should not be a spectator sport or a behavior indistinguishable from showing contempt. Joe B. wrote in his first letter of the semester,

```
    I have been pondering quotes that I heard in my STS
class... ''How can you gleefully destroy something that you
yourself cannot create?'' and ''Power in the hand of a
non-thinking mind is dangerous.'' Something that both of
these quotes brings to mind is a chainsaw....When felling a
```

tree takes 30 seconds to a minute, one puts much less thought
into cutting it down than if it must be cut down with an axe.
What is it that makes destroying things so fun?

Thanks to science and technology, our lives are awash with *stuff*. Technology has brought more stuff, but has it brought more *meaning*? Does the sheer volume of our stuff cause us to lose appreciation for what we have? Conversely, do we let our stuff be the measure of who we are? A question worth repeating thirty times each semester asks, "Do you own your stuff, or does your stuff own you?" In a weekly letter one student wrote,

Whatever technology we choose, we are stuck with it--the
Magic City.... Also, technology seems to now be
economic-driven rather than help-driven. Take i-pods. About
every month a bigger, better model comes out. Would it not
be more beneficial to make a new one only once a year? This
only feeds consumerism...

Have we gone too far with our technology? Should we return to a simpler time?

> *12 November 2007*
> *Dear Professor Dyson,*
> *We hope that the 2007 Thanksgiving season finds you and all your family doing well.... We enjoyed seeing photos of George's 6-person baidarka and his tree house, and pictures of some of your grandchildren.... We know that you have many correspondents around the world, but if you could answer some of our questions we would be much obliged. Thank you for your consideration.*
> *...Reading your book makes it appear that you have a very distinct notion of the evils that technology can achieve. Do the good deeds that technology makes possible still vastly outweigh the evils? Should we have not pursued technological advancement as a society at all, and maintained a simpler way of life, free of the possibility of nuclear war or genetic monsters?*
>
> *23 November 2007*
> *Dear Dwight,*
> *Thank you for your letter of November 12 with questions from the STS class.... Each of the questions would take several pages to answer adequately. These responses are just comments and not answers.*

...The choice whether to adopt a technological lifestyle was made by our ancestors ten thousand years ago when they invented agriculture. Agriculture was technological from the start, and led directly to civilization, with all its advantages and disadvantages. Yes, I think the advantages greatly outweigh the disadvantages. Before agriculture, we were hunter-gatherers living in small bands and incessantly fighting our neighbors. Paleontological evidence indicates that we were dying violent deaths then, much more frequently than we are today. There was never a time when we were living a simpler way of life without violent quarrels and slaughter. To get rid of nuclear war and genetic monsters will not be easy, but it will probably be easier in a civilized world than in an uncivilized world. The idea that we could go back to a peaceful world by getting rid of technology is an illusion.

5. What are the real—and often hidden—costs of maintaining our modern lifestyle? Have you ever noticed that housing subdivisions and shopping centers are typically named after what was destroyed to make way for them? There are no more open meadows in Rambling Acres. At Windmill Acres the antique Aeromotor windmills have been pulled down and replaced by a scaled-down fake one at the entrance. I have looked, and no quail are found at Quail Springs Mall. Deer Spring subdivision has no more deer. The dolphins at Sea World have *their* world reduced from the open sea to a few tanks.[17]

The sellers of new technologies skillfully extol their products' advantages. Smart phones keep you connected. Autonomous cars correct your mistakes. Self-serve checkouts save you time. Spell-check corrects your typos. GPS helps you find your destination. All of these claims are true. But it is also true that smart phones can become a leash that allows you few moments to yourself. As Thoreau said, "If the bell rings, why should I run?" [Thoreau(1960)][67] Autonomous cars means people will lose driving skills. Self-checkouts deprive cashiers of their jobs. Spell-check means I no longer have to know how to spell. GPS means I can forget how to take visual clues from my surroundings.

---

[17]Ever since the release of the 2009 film documentary *The Cove*, one cannot help but wonder if the captive performers are survivors from the pods of terrorized animals that were herded into a Japanese cove, a few to be captured for sale and the rest slaughtered. Recently Sea World has produced television ads emphasizing how well they care for their animals.

We rightly celebrate what technology does for us. But we are negligent if we overlook what technology displaces. The new is not necessarily the best. Efficiency is not always humanizing. Just because we *can* do something, does it follow that we *should*?

6. What are our stewardship responsibilities towards other lives with whom we share this planet? Voltaire famously wrote "With great power comes great responsibility."[18] Technology has given us tremendous power. Whether we are up to the responsibility remains an open question. Without technology we are prey animals, but with technology we are capable of authoring the mass extinctions of entire species. Recent reports indicate that humans are wiping out about 1 percent of all other species every year, that one of the "great extinction episodes in the Earth's history is underway.' [BBC News(2008)] A one percent extinction rate may not sound like much, but it means half of the remaining species will be gone in seventy years.

The reservation Lakota depended on the buffalo (or bison) for their survival. In order for the people to live, they recognized the necessity for some animals to die. As part of the hunt, the Lakota conducted ceremonies to thank the bison and apologize to them. As a matter of respect as well as economy, even when buffalo were abundant, every part of each slain animal was used. The meat provided food, hides became clothing and blankets and tipis, bones and horns became utensils and tools, sinew provided bowstrings. Being fed and clothed by the buffalo, the Lakota saw themselves as relatives of the "buffalo nation." A Lakota coming across a buffalo skull on the prairie would turn it to face the east so the spirit of the animal could greet the rising sun. [Standing Bear(1933)], [Marshall(2002)] Modern society does not think in terms of buffalo spirits. But we might do well to take a lesson in respect.

When I bite into my Big Mac or my chicken strips, do I mentally thank the steer who spent the last weeks of his life in the muck of a crowded feedlot, or the chicken who spent its entire life in a wire cage the size of a truck battery, destined to become lunch in a Styrofoam box and forgotten before being digested? If for the sake of economy and convenience we are complicit in the unnecessary suffering of any creature, can we justly call our society civilized?

Globally the tropical forests are being cut down today at a rate of about one acre per second. The United States "develops" about half an acre of

---

[18] *Euvres de Voltaire*, Volume 48.

Fig. 2.3 *Retired plutonium bomb casing, 1945 "Fat Man" design, Bradbury Museum, Los Alamos.* (author photo)

land every minute. Our manicured habitats cost other species their habitat; the stars are increasingly washed out and the lives of nocturnal creatures disrupted by relentlessly growing light pollution. If we hold title to a piece of land, do we also own the lives of the creatures who were there first?

What do we owe the creatures who were here first and who value their own lives? What do we owe our descendants? When does development become a form of theft, stealing from our grandchildren the vistas and experiences we enjoy? Ultimately, do we really own *anything*? Whatever we have, someday we will leave it all behind. We merely borrow it from our grandchildren.

7. What ethical dilemmas are raised by the applications of science? The above photograph is projected on the screen in the classroom. When asked what it is, one or two students suggest that it looks like a bomb. It is the casing from a decommissioned plutonium bomb like the one that fell on Nagasaki, Japan, on August 9, 1945. When I stooped down to take its picture, I felt like the bomb was looking back at me and asking,

"Now that you humans are clever enough to build nuclear weapons, are you wise enough to manage them responsibly?"

The double helix of DNA offers another iconic image of promise and peril in the applications of science. If genetic therapies will eliminate cancer and Alzheimer's disease and prevent birth defects, it would seem perverse to not use them. But when we engineer our children's genes to enhance their ability to play the piano or football, will their high-level skills be their own? Will there be any personal fulfillment in the purchase of genetically-engineered accomplishment? If we engineer genetic freedom from melancholy, will we also quench the creative spirit? If we can make birth defects and serious diseases obselete by genetic therapies, will these remedies be as accessible to poor as they will be to the rich? [Fukuyama(2002)][43], [McKibben(2003)][44]

All technologies have unintended consequences. The study of science, technology, and society inevitably becomes the study of ethics. On the eve of Thanksgiving holiday, the fall 2004 class sent a provocative cartoon to Professor Dyson.

> *23 November 2004*
> *Dear Professor Dyson,*
> *We trust that you and your family are doing well as 2004 winds down. For another semester, "Disturbing the Universe" has provided a springboard for fruitful discussions....*
> *Attached is a cartoon showing Ethics following in the large footsteps of Science, and Ethics shouting, "Wait Up!" Is there a practical way to slow down the advances of science so that ethics can catch up?*[19]

> *30 November 2004*
> *Dear STS class,*
> *Thanks to you all for the Thanksgiving message and the three questions that came with it. Nobody has found a better way to say thank you than the old Anglican prayer-book: "We thank Thee for our creation, preservation, and all the blessings of this life..." It does not say anything about roast turkey and stuffing. Here are some tentative answers to your questions:*
> *Is there a practical way to slow down the advances of science so that ethics can catch up? My answer to this question is Yes. The picture shows science as a huge monster and ethics as a puny creature getting left behind. It is interesting that many people see it that way. Since I am a scientist, I see it differently.*

---

[19]The cartoon was drawn in 2001 by Scott B. Stantis of the *Birmingham News* of Alabama, and originally distributed by the Copley News Service.

Fig. 2.4   *"Is there a practical way to slow down the advances of science so that ethics can catch up?"* (Scott B. Stantis cartoon. Multiple good-faith but unsuccessful efforts have been made to find the present copyright owner.)

> *I see science as a collection of explorers trying to find their way through difficult country, with ethics as a distant beacon on the far horizon. There are many practical ways to slow down science. The easiest way is to stop providing the money that scientists need. The next easiest way is to impose rules and regulations that make scientists miserable. The third way is to hire lawyers and attack scientific enterprises with lawsuits. The fourth way is to attack laboratories physically and destroy experiments. All these four ways to slow down science have been used successfully. As I see it, the problem is to keep science moving ahead rather than to slow it down. Ethics should be a guide to keep it moving in the right direction, not a brake to slow it down. Of course science can be dangerous, but science guided by ethics offers much more hope than danger.*

As Professor Dyson wrote in our textbook, "In the long run, the technological means that scientists place in our hands may be less important than the ideological ends to which these means are harnessed." [Dyson(1979a)][7]

8. Can science and religion both be true? Science offers one lens for examining the world and our place in it. Literature, the arts, philosophy, and religion offer other lenses. Can one look at the world through more than one lens without seeing contradictory images? For a tighter version of this question we ask, can science and religion both be true?

At least since the time of Galileo, science and religion have frequently been seen as opponents. Some of our students raised in pious homes come to us bewildered, asking which one is true: *Genesis* or evolution? But that is not the question. A more relevant set of questions might ask what issues are addressed by *Genesis* and how do they differ from the questions addressed by evolution. What does each accept as criteria for truth? Can there be more than one kind of truth?

In a 1939 contribution to a collection of essays written to honor Albert Einstein on his seventieth birthday, the Danish physicist Niels Bohr described two kinds of truth: "simple truth" and "deep truth." According to Bohr, the opposite of a simple truth is false, but the opposite of a deep truth is also true. [Schlipp(1970)][240] Bohr's insight cautions us that demanding simple yes–no, black–white binary choice answers to deep questions is equivalent to trivializing them. Rather than being *contradictory* world views, perhaps *Genesis* and evolution *complement* each other.

Bohr's statement is not a word-game, but came straight from the laboratory. In our world that has become so dependent on electronics, we overlook the fact that the simple question, "What is an electron?" does not have a unique answer. Television picture tubes were designed by assuming each electron to be a localized pellet, a "particle." But the designers of the transistors in computer chips must treat the electron as a spread-out cloud that sloshes about like a wave. So what is an electron *really*? Physicists have found that if you probe the electron in some ways it behaves like a localized particle, but if you probe its doings in other ways it behaves like a spread-out wave. That is the best we can do. We do not know, in some ultimate sense, what an electron *really is*; the best we can do is to describe what it is *like*—wave or particle—and what it's like depends on how we interact with it. There are limits to what we can *know*.

> *20 November 2012*
> *Dear Professor Dyson,*
> *...The Gospels tell us that when Pilate asked Jesus, "What is truth,"' Jesus gave no answer. If someone asks you "'What is truth?" how would you respond?"*

> *25 November 2012*
> *Dear Dwight,*
> *Thank you for your friendly message....*
> *...What is truth? This is a question of words rather than substance. Jesus, according to John 18:37 said, "To this end I was born, and for this cause came I into the world, that I should bear*

witness unto the truth. Every one that is of the truth heareth my voice." And then Pilate said, "What is truth?" and did not stay for an answer. Pilate had no idea what Jesus had in mind. As usual, Jesus did not explain himself. I imagine that what he meant by truth was a clear vision of things as they are. But that is my own interpretation, and Jesus may have had a different notion of truth. Pilate's previous question was, "Art thou a king?" Jesus said, "My kingdom is not of this world." So his notion of truth may have been a vision of a different world. Each of us has a personal set of beliefs that we consider to be the truth. For me, truth is not absolute or permanent. It changes as we learn or as we forget. Truth is a convenient way of organizing our fragmentary understanding of the world. The beautiful thing about science is that almost everything we believe turns out to be wrong. Science is perpetual learning, perpetual bumping into fresh surprises.

One of the most unexpected questions ever put to me along these lines was asked by a retired prospector. Two friends and I were driving off-road in the desert east of Phoenix, Arizona. We came across an elderly man enjoying his remaining years in peaceful solitude, living in an old Airstream trailer with a ramshackle lean-to built alongside it. We stopped the jeep and approached his dwelling on foot as he sat in a chair under his lean-to, tossing bread scraps to a great-tailed grackle who responded to the name of Peter. The man motioned for us to join him. Our host sat in the calm retirement of a man who knows who he is, has all that he needs and is content. As we settled on some crates he lit his pipe while looking at us through round spectacles with bright merry eyes. He took his time. When the pipe was going to his satisfaction, he leaned back in his chair and said, "Well now, tell me: What do you boys know *for sure*?"

If physicists cannot know for sure what the mundane electron "really" is, how can we hope to have exact knowledge on much deeper questions? Recognizing the limits of knowledge and living with uncertainty are essential to science—and a liberating recognition of reality for anyone.

In our first letter April 6, 1993 the class asked Professor Dyson, "What effect does science have on your religion?" His reply of April 9 has echoed through all our classes across the years: "...I consider science and religion to be two windows through which we look out at the world. Neither window by itself gives a complete view...." No single way of looking at the world is rich enough or versatile enough to capture all the dimensions of our existence. We are like the blind men in John Godfrey Saxe's parable of the elephant.

The man who grabbed its trunk declared the elephant to be like a snake; another who found the tail said the creature was like a rope, and so on:[20]

> *And so these men of Indostan*
> *Disputed loud and long,*
> *Each in his own opinion*
> *Exceeding stiff and strong,*
> *Though each was partly in the right,*
> *And all were in the wrong!*

Three Observations

When reflecting over several semester's worth of STS readings and class discussions, some recurring lessons emerge.

1. Life's important questions seldom, if ever, have black-and-white answers. Instead, we typically find vast areas of gray. Perhaps the best we can do is to understand the questions. Understanding the questions may be more important than answering them.

2. Nature works on timescales unfathomably longer than the timescales of human events. The horizons of human events are measured in semesters, quarterly reports, the next election, a few decades, and, for historians, a few centuries. Seldom do we give much thought to how our actions today will impact other lives five hundred or five thousand years from now.[21] Mountains look permanent, but on a timescale of a billion years the Himalayas are as ephemeral as clouds. Species come and go on a timescale of tens of millions of years. Thus on the geological time scale, the appearance of the human race is but a blip. From our perspective, the natural landscapes do not change much in the lifetime of a civilization, unless we do something to them. In our gaze of the world, they provide a point of apparent stability.

> *...You run and you run to catch up with the sun but it's sinking*
> *Racing around to come up behind you again*
> *The sun is the same in a relative way but you're older*
> *Shorter of breath, and one day closer to death...*[22]

---

[20]From "The Blind Men and the Elepant" by John Godfrey Saxe (1816–1887).
[21]Of course, nature also has processes that work on very short timescales, such as the decays of unstable elementary particles.
[22]"Time" by Pink Floyd.

In the long view, the Earth does not need us. But on the timescale of human events, oh how we need the Earth!

3. STS issues are ultimately about *values* and *relationships*. In the end, technology is not about things, science is not about methods, and society is not about economics or politics. Something deeper cuts across them all: relationships between ourselves and other creatures with whom we share this planet; relationships between cultures; relationships with generations past and future; relationships with the ecosystems that sustain us; relationships between ourselves and our possessions; the relationship between my inner self and my place in the grand scheme of things as I reflect on my limited existence in a large and impersonal universe.

In trying to make sense out of science, technology, and society we are really trying to understand ourselves—our passions and desires, our identities, our yearnings and our fears. Science and technology are tools that work two ways: we shape them, and they shape us. What matters are the values residing in the minds to which those tools are connected.

3 A Hexagonal Mountain

Three Reasons to Hate Science, Three Reasons to Love It

> *"It is no wonder that a majority of our children have turned away from science. The more you tell them that science is useful, the more they are turned off. They know what useful means."*
> –Freeman Dyson[23]

***

Because the STS course title includes the word "science," some students come into it with fear and loathing. In Professor Dyson's 1991 Ørsted Medal speech he listed three reasons why some young people hate science, and three reasons why they could find science worthy of their devotion:

> *The generation that is now young has three good reasons for turning away from science. Science is presented to our young people as a rigid and authoritarian discipline, tied to mercenary and utilitarian ends, and tainted by its association with weapons of mass murder. These three reasons for hating science are real and serious.... Our task as educators is to show our children that science is a hexagonal mountain with six faces, with three beautiful faces in addition to the three ugly faces. The beautiful faces of science are, science as subversion of authority, science as an art form, and science as an international club. The way to attract young people into science is to show them all six faces and give them freedom to explore the beautiful and the ugly faces as they please.* [Dyson(1991)]

These six faces of science have been explored in every STS section since Professor Dyson delivered this speech in 1991.

Three Beautiful Faces

Subversion of authority: Professor Dyson is not calling for anarchy, but reminding us that the spirit of science says "Is that so, eh? How do you know? What's the *evidence*?" Tyrants and dictators cannot survive open inquiry because science is antithetical to authoritarianism. We do not have to go back to the 1633 trial of Galileo before the Holy Office of the

---

[23][Chaisson and Kim(1999)][55].

Inquisition, or the 1925 Scopes Trial in Tennessee to find examples. More recently, in 1989 Chinese students launched a protest demanding human rights and basic freedoms for all Chinese people. Fang Lizhi was a physics professor at Beijing University at the time. He and his students were among the leaders of the protest.

Why have physics students always conflicted with Communist authorities? The answer is quite simple: The general spirit and method of physics and other fields of science are in direct conflict with the ideology of tyranny. [Lizhi(1990)]

Art form: Art and science share the broad goal of interpreting human experience. Both use analogies, metaphors, and symbols; both explore distinctions between reality and appearance; both occasionally undergo revolutions, where new paradigms are adopted and new problems are presented to be solved. Both live with ambiguity. Ambiguity in art allows the viewer to engage the full range of emotions and plasticity of mind—part of the charm of Johannes Vermeer's *Girl with a Pearl Earring* is that the girl's story remains unknown, so each viewer can supply one for her. Athough science tries to spell things out as much as possible to minimize confusion, ambiguity in science can lead to new discoveries, such as seeing mass as a form of energy. Science and art depend on creative ways of seeing.

International Club: At the annual International Physics Olympiad, a competition for pre-university students, during the closing banquet the participants are invited to an open microphone. When Norway hosted the 1996 competition, the students from the People's Republic of China and the students from Taiwan ascended the stage together, put their arms around one other's shoulders, and sang in unison. Drawn together by physics, they were part of something that transcended political arrogance and national provincialism.

> *4 December 2013*
> *Dear Professor Dyson,*
> *...You have traveled over so much of the world, visited so many countries, and have friends in so many cultures, may we ask what are your favorite places, and why?*
>
> *6 December 2013*
> *Dear Dwight,*
> *I do not have a favorite place, because each country has unique qualities, and each is enjoyable in a unique way. The best thing*

about this planet is that different cultures and different ways of living still survive. I will mention just a few places that I found delightful.

The place that I visited most recently is Singapore. That is a wonderful place because it is a socialist welfare state with a flourishing capitalist economy. It combines two very different heritages, the Chinese heritage of capitalist work ethic, and the British heritage of socialist government. It succeeded in preserving the best bits of both heritages. It is a living proof that socialism and capitalism can work together.

Another wonderful place is Switzerland, which has a big diversity of cultures and languages in one small country. I lived in Zürich which is an old-fashioned city with electric street-cars and clean streets. When our first baby was due to be born, my wife arrived at the hospital almost too late, with labor already started. The guard at the door would not let us in until we had given him two names for the baby, one for a girl and one for a boy. In Switzerland you are not allowed to be born without a name. We had to decide quickly. It was Oliver or Esther, and she turned out to be Esther.

Another place that we loved was the United States of sixty years ago, when we came to live at Ithaca in New York State. In those days, the United States was friendlier than it is now, students did not have cars, and we all helped each other to survive in the snowy winters. We were not afraid to hitch-hike or to pick up hitch-hikers on the highways. Nobody was homeless and nobody kept their house-doors locked. Rich people were not so rich and poor people were not so poor as they are today. The war-time ethic of sharing the hardships still prevailed. The biggest need of this country today is to restore the ethic of sharing hardships. We have a lot to learn from other countries such as Singapore and Switzerland.

Three Ugly Faces

Although the three beautiful faces of science are more fun to discuss, the three ugly faces of science are equally real and important.

May 6, 2004
Dear Professor Dyson,
The students in our spring 2004 semester section of our Science, Technology, and Society class enjoyed reading "Disturbing the Universe" and discussing the issues it raises...
You clearly developed a love for science at a young age, and

experienced early its "three beautiful faces" as described in your
AAPT speech. When and under what circumstances did you
begin to see the "three ugly faces" of science?

6 May 2004
Dear Dwight,...
Thanks to you and the class for a good set of questions....
The three ugly faces of science are (a) a rigid and authoritarian
discipline, (b) tied to mercenary and utilitarian ends, and (c)
tainted by its association with weapons of mass murder. When
did I first see the three ugly faces? I think (a) came when I was
about twelve years old and forced to slog through endless bor-
ing exercises in geometry and algebra. Probably (b) came from
reading the novels of H.G. Wells, especially "Tonobungay" and
"The Island of Doctor Moreau," when I was a teenager. The
final chapter of "Tonobungay" is especially memorable, with the
title "Night and the Open Sea." The narrator of the story, after
the commercial empire of Tonobungay has totally collapsed, es-
capes on his high-speed warship ready to sell to the next highest
bidder. He stands on the deck of his warship, watching the lights
on the shore fade into the distance, his ship swiftly heading into
the darkness. Certainly (c) came from my family's memories of
World War One, which was a chemists' war, fought with poi-
son gases as well as chemical high explosives. When I was a
teenager I also read Aldous Huxley's "Brave New World" which
begins with a war fought with anthrax bombs. In those days we
expected World War Two to be a biologists' war fought with bio-
logical weapons. We knew about anthrax. Anthrax was another
gift that we owed to science.

The second and third ugly faces of science will greatly occupy us later. Here we focus on the first ugly face of science. Although science is antithetical to rigid authority, the ugly face of science *presented as* a rigid, authoritarian discipline hits close to home for many STS students. Jessica recalled, "Back in middle school teachers were always boring and never took time to make science interesting."

Science is not perceived that way at the beginning of a child's educational career. Over the years we have collected science questions from second and third graders: What makes light? How can the planets orbit the sun when they're on nothing? Does space ever end? How does electricity get through the plug? How do magnets work? How does gravity work? What makes the Sun shine? Ashley, a second-grader, wrote "Some times the moon is full and sometimes it's half a moon. Do they just cut it in half?"[24] It is easy to smile at Ashley's statement, but consider what she has done. She has made an observation and proposed a hypothesis. Instead of saying "How ridiculous!" to Ashley, we should say, "OK Ashley, suppose the moon *were* cut in half. What should we look for to test this idea?" Ashley is already halfway there in a research program. So were the rest of us when we were second-graders. Let us overhear a reading of Allison C.'s letter:

> This last week we talked about the outlook that second and
> third graders have on life and science. They are not afraid
> to ask questions.... I remember the time in my life when I
> was one of these kids. I was never afraid to ask questions.
> I never worried about how dumb it sounded or what other
> people thought. I was just curious about how the world
> worked and wanted answers. Now, as adults we are told to
> accept what is taught and not ask too many questions.... For
> the most part, I believe in what is being taught.... I wish
> I still had the thirst to ask questions. I have found myself
> just accepting what is taught and moving on. This is no way
> to learn... There is a lot to be learned from children.

Most of our STS students were educated in American schools. A typical STS class roster includes half a dozen elementary education and early childhood majors. A few STS students are parents already, most want to be someday, and many already have young nieces and nephews. Through these perspectives, the STS participants are invested in educating the young. This interest shows up repeatedly in our questions to Professor Dyson. At the end of the fall 2000 semester, we asked him how he ignites a hunger for knowledge in his students:

> *4 December 2000*
> *Dear Professor Dyson,*
> *Our Science, Society, and Technology class wishes you and your*
> *family a joyous Christmas season.... As a professor, what ways*
> *have you found most effective to spark the hunger for knowledge*
> *in others?*

His answer was quite candid:

---

[24]These young student's questions are discussed in "Motorcycle Maintenance and the Art of Physics Appreciation," *Radiations*, Fall 2007, 5–11.

7 December 2000
Dear Dwight,
Thanks for your message. This time the students' list of questions is shorter than last year. I suppose you told them to avoid repeating last year's list, and now they are beginning to run out of questions. Anyhow, here are my answers. Since there are fewer questions, my answers will be a bit longer....
I don't know whether I ever sparked the hunger for knowledge in anybody. That is not my main purpose when I am teaching. When I am teaching, I treat the students as grown-ups and try to engage them in discussions. I am not trying to spark their hunger for knowledge. I am trying to get them to think. I assume that if they were not hungry for knowledge they wouldn't come to my classes, and in that case they probably shouldn't be in college in the first place.
I have done two very different kinds of teaching. Recently I have mostly been teaching "Science and" courses, such as "Science and Society," "Science and Literature," "Science and the Environment" to mixed classes of humanities and science majors. Earlier I was teaching mostly technical physics courses to science majors. In the technical courses, the students have to do problems. In the non-technical courses, they have to write essays. For me, the problems and the essays are the most important part of teaching. By forcing the students to solve the problems or write the essays, and then criticizing and discussing their efforts, I am teaching them to think. That is the best way I know to get them to think. Also, to think clearly and write clearly are the most important skills that they will need when they are out in the real world. I don't think this has much to do with sparking their hunger for knowledge.
I have only been teaching university students. For an elementary school teacher, sparking the kids' hunger for knowledge is the main object of the game. Some of the teachers who teach my grandchildren do it very well. I don't know how they do it.

Professor Dyson certainly makes us think! A student named Caleb G. wrote,

I have been reading a book by Freeman Dyson called *Disturbing the Universe*. After reading a little about Dyson's college life I feel like he and I have become closer. I also feel as though I now have a better idea of how to read and understand this book. I would compare this book to *I and Thou* by Martin Buber. Both books should be read as though you were having coffee with the writer. These men are not trying to rebuke us. But they are asking us to think. In the case of Freeman Dyson, I believe he is trying to help us understand the results of our actions... Will we ever be responsible enough to handle what our minds are capable of?

By the time most children reach the seventh grade—sometimes by the fourth grade—their wonder and curiosity about nature have largely dissipated. Reasons for this loss of interest, according to STS students' recollections, include having science taught to them as a checklist recipe called "The Scientific Method," and perpetually facing standardized tests that restrict teaching options. Who mourns the loss of instinct for exploratory play that comes so naturally to children—and is so essential to art and poetry and scientific research? As children grow and the pressure increases to conform, could the loss of interest in practically everything be a natural part of personal development?[25]

> *1 May 2000*
> *Dear Professor Dyson,*
> *Here once again, if we may impose on you for a few moments of your time, are selected questions from the Spring 2000 Science, Technology, and Society class.*
> *...Lisa A. asks, "What causes children to lose their fascination with science? I remember loving science in my first few years of school... I looked forward to the field trips to science and marine centers. My sister and I would beg our parents to take us there when we were not in school. However, now that I am older, I can hardly stand to sit through a science class. I even changed my major so I would not have to take so many science hours. From talking to students, it sounds like this is a common feeling among many. Looking back, I cannot remember a specific time or class that made me lose my interest in science. I know that not everyone is going to be a scientist, but [now it seems] there should be at least some tolerance for it. Do you think it is just a natural part of growing older that one forgets how to be curious about the world? Or is it maybe the way science is presented in schools that cause children to turn away from it? Do you have any suggestions for keeping children interested in science?"*

Professor Dyson's response came back the same day:

---

[25]Stephen Jay Gould describes how most adults know more science than they give themselves credit for. [Gould(1997)] Gardeners and fishermen know a lot of biology, construction workers and mechanics know a lot of physics, and so on.

1 May 2000
Dear Dwight,
Luckily I have a few short days left before your term ends. The relentless Templeton time-table begins again with a new series of interviews in London and Washington....
Lisa A. Yes, the way you describe it rings true. Children are naturally curious up to the age of ten and then lose it. A month ago I was teaching a class of fourth-graders and they were wonderful, full of curiosity and enthusiasm. I know that if they had been seventh-graders a lot of them would have been bored. Every science teacher knows this. I don't blame this on the way science is taught in schools, because it happens even when science is taught well. Certainly kids are turned off even faster when science is taught badly, but many of them get turned off anyway.
I don't think science is different from music or drawing in the way children grow out of it. My grandsons are in an elementary school with an excellent art teacher. We recently went to the exhibition where the kids show their stuff. Amazingly good paintings and drawings done by hundreds of kids. The art teacher knows every one of the 500 kids in the school by name. A large majority of them do great stuff up to the age of ten. But then, as they become teenagers, most of them lose it. Only a small minority keep on drawing and painting and keep their talent. And it is the same with science. And with music and mathematics. I think it is part of human nature that we start out as children interested in everything, then become specialists as young adults, and then broaden our interests again in later life. There is nothing wrong with being bored by science if you don't happen to be scientifically gifted. What is wrong is for teachers to have to try to stuff science into people who are bored with it. So my recommendation for education in science is, give it to young children who take to it naturally, and to old people who come to it fresh in later life, and make it optional for teenagers and college students, just as we do with art and music. The idea of forcing everyone to be "scientifically literate" does not work. As Tolstoy said a hundred and fifty years ago, "All that the greater part of the people carry away from school is the horror of schooling."[26] So it is no surprise that the attempt to force people to think scientifically gives them a horror of science. Most of us are just not built that way.

The American public educational system, though largely funded by local property taxes, is partially funded by state government budgets, which

---

[26][Chaisson and Kim(1999)]

receive federal funding whose payout depends on the state conforming to federal curriculum and assessment standards. Thus the classroom teacher must teach to a test imposed by legislators, among whom few have ever taught children in a class setting themselves. Teacher evaluations and contracts depend on how their pupils perform on standardized tests, even though public school teachers cannot recruit their students. There is no time to look at sunspots through pinhole cameras or examine insect wings under microscopes, not even for the children who take to it naturally. Such responses to natural childhood curiosities must be bypassed because they are, in the teacher's words, "not on the test."[27]

The STS students are given the option of signing a "Grade Information Waiver." So far in every section in which it has been offered over the past decade, about 90% of the students sign it. They get written comments on their work, but no grades are revealed during the course. The phenomena merits study by education researchers, but it appears that taking grades off the table releases some kind of brake. Perhaps by not knowing if you're getting by, you have to become more engaged. The idea of not knowing one's grade along the way takes some getting used to. Laura P. observed,

```
    Most classes nowadays have an intense and detailed grading
policy in which students feel the need to check their grade
after every assignment.  So sometimes if a student is doing
well in a class, they feel as though they can slack off.
This grading policy also encourages memorization of
information over actual learning of the information.  Prof.
N has a waiver I can sign that states I will not ask to see
my grade through the entire semester and, ironically, as a
reward I will receive 2 % extra on my overall grade.  I think
this policy will really challenge me because although I am
smart, I tend to be ''people smart,'' figuring out what the
professor wants and delivering that and no more.  My emphasis
[has been] on producing what the professor wants instead of
learning the actual material.
```

23 November 2004
Dear Professor Dyson,
We trust that you and your family are doing well as 2004 winds down. For another semester, "Disturbing the Universe" has provided a springboard for fruitful discussions in our Science, Technology, and Society class....

---

[27] As this is being written, some push-back is coming from teachers and the grassroots, as states start realizing the down side of assessment as tyranny.

Another book we read this semester was Robert Pirsig's "Zen and the Art of Motorcycle Maintenance." Pirsig describes teaching composition at Montana State University. When he withheld grades, so that grades were no longer a superficial goal, the students' creativity was able to flourish. Is there a similar principle that applies to the relationship between government regulations and developments in science or education?

Thank you for your time, and for your contribution to our lives through your book and other writings. We wish you and your family a Happy Thanksgiving!

30 November 2004

Dear STS class,

Thanks to you all for the Thanksgiving message and the questions that came with it .... Here are some tentative answers to your questions: ...

Do government regulations have a stifling effect on science and education? I have no first-hand experience that I can bring to bear on this question. I think that the answer is generally no. The best way to answer the question is to look at different countries that have different ways of running science and education. For example, consider France and the USA. In France, the government runs science and education with a tight control, in the USA both science and education are mostly run locally without detailed control by the federal government. The French system produces science and education that are on the average better than the USA. The USA system produces very uneven quality. The best American science and education is better than the French but the worst American science and education is far worse. So it is a question of values, whether you value fairness above freedom or freedom above fairness. The French system is more fair, the American system is more free. Of course, both systems put too much emphasis on grades, so we still need more teachers like Robert Pirsig.

That's all I have to say. Happy Christmas and New Year to you all, and especially to Dwight.

Yours ever, Freeman Dyson.

Pirsig tells of visiting a former colleague, Robert DeWeese, a professor of sculpture. Before Pirsig arrived, DeWeese spent an afternoon assembling a rotisserie by following a frustrating set of instructions. Wanting to see the instructions thoroughly damned, he showed them to Pirsig, who edited technical manuals. Pirsig found nothing technically wrong with the instructions, but observed something deeper: [Pirsig(1999)][166–167]

What's really angering about instructions of this sort is that they imply there's only one way to put this rotisserie together—their way. And that presumption wipes out all the creativity....

But if you have to choose among an infinite number of ways to put it together then the relation of the machine to you, and the relation of the machine and you to the rest of the world, has to be considered... the art of the work is just as dependent upon your own mind and spirit as it is upon the material of the machine.

Professor Dyson closed his Ørsted Medal speech by saying "A dream of a better future; that is what our kids need. And that is what science, if we don't confuse science with SAT scores, can give them." [Dyson(1991)]

> *24 April 2014*
> *Dear Professor Dyson,*
> *If you could change anything about K-12 science education, what would it be?*
> *Most of the students in this semester's STS class came up through the standardized testing that steers public K-12 education today. In class we discussed how many parents, students, and teachers are frustrated by the fact that the curriculum is not allowed to follow the children's insatiable curiosity. Investigations that could follow from questions in a third-grader's mind (e.g., "What holds the moon up when it's on nothing?" "Why are people different?") are, as the teachers say, "not on the test." The teachers unfortunately have no time to spare for going on interesting tangents, even though that would stoke pupil interest and make learning fun and promote education appreciation even higher in the long run (we think). The teachers' job security, student promotion to the next grade, and district funding are all tied to the test scores. The theme that initiated this discussion was the "six faces of science" which you articulated in your AAPT speech "To Teach or Not To Teach." The ugly face of "science presented as a rigid authoritarian discipline" generalizes to a lot of disciplines as delivered in K-12.*

As he does so often, Professor Dyson's response introduced broader dimensions of the problem for us to consider:

> *28 April 2014*
> *Dear Dwight and Students,*
> *Thank you very much for your questions. These are good questions and the discussions that came along with them are very helpful. You have already gone deeply into each of them. I*

will disagree with some of your opinions, but I do not expect to change your minds.

What would I change in K-12 education?

We all hate the tyranny of the testing system in American schools, but the system has one important virtue. It is fair. I happen to live in Princeton, New Jersey, where the Educational Testing Service (ETS) produces and administers the tests. I remember vividly a day when the Minister of Education of the Soviet Union came to visit Princeton. He visited three institutions, the Institute for Advanced Study where I work, the University nearby, and ETS. He was not much interested in the Institute and the University, but he was intensely interested in ETS. He said the Soviet Union had good Institutes and Universities but had nothing like ETS. He said the education system in the Soviet Union was grossly unfair. To get into a good university and have a chance of a good career, a child must have parents with good connections. Success depended on good connections, not on hard work. He said he would try to introduce something like ETS in the Soviet Union. Of course this never happened. The education system in Russia today is as unfair as it was in the Soviet Union in the old days.

I grew up in England where the system was unfair in a different way. I got a free education in an excellent private high-school. To get the free education beginning at age 12, I had to sit for three days taking ten written examinations in ten subjects including Latin and Greek. The examinations were intensely competitive. Only the top 13 out of hundreds of boys got in. Girls were not invited to compete. In theory the system was supposed to be fair because rich and poor boys were treated equally. In reality it was grossly unfair because only upper-class kids had a chance of being prepared with knowledge of Latin and Greek. The boys who got in were all like me, sons of well-educated upper-class families.

When I came to America and saw my kids taking the ETS tests in American public schools, I was delighted to see that the tests were fair. Also the kids did not need to spend much time preparing. The tests were rather trivial, being designed for average kids and not for the intellectual elite. I felt that the tests did less harm than the elitist British system or the corrupt Russian system. Now that my grandchildren are in American schools, I still feel the same way.

So finally I must answer your question. The main thing I would change in the American system is the number of hours that the kids spend in class. In my last year in the English high-school I spent seven hours a week in class. The rest of the time was free, for me and for the teachers, so that I could get an educa-

tion as I chose and they could give me help when I needed it. The school had a good library, a music building with practice-rooms, a museum, a carpentry-shop and a book-binding shop, not to mention football and cricket fields. Sitting in class all day is not the best way to learn or to teach. If the kids and the teachers had more free time, the tyranny of the testing system would not be so harmful.
Yours ever, Freeman

STS students were also thinking about these matters before 2014:

1 May 2001
Dear Professor Dyson,
Once again as we near the semester's end, our Science, Technology, and Society class sends greetings to you and your family. ...How would you recommend that we educate K-6 students about science?...

3 May 2001
Dear Dwight, thank you for the May Day message and thanks to the students for their list of questions....
I don't know much about educating kids about science. My own grandchildren seem to be picking up a lot of science, but I don't know how much comes from school and how much from parents and friends. We are lucky to have a number of excellent museums in this area, and kids probably learn more in museums than they do in school. They love to go on trips to museums. Recently I picked up a crinoid fossil when I was hiking in Arizona. I gave it to one of my grandsons and he said at once, "Oh yes, that was living on the bottom of the sea before there were dinosaurs." I asked him how he knew that and he said he had seen one in a museum. It is amazing how much they pick up. The main thing to avoid is turning them off science by forcing them to learn a lot of dull stuff in school. If I were in charge of public education, I would campaign for more museums and fewer classrooms.

In the museum, there it is in front of you, a real *tyrannosaurus rex* skeleton; the actual *Columbia* capsule that took the Apollo 11 astronauts to the Moon and back.... *There it is.* In its presence, a relationship occurs that that cannot be duplicated by looking at images.

1 May 1998
Dear Professor Dyson,
...Is there a dream of yours that remains unfulfilled?

> *2 May 1998*
> *Dear Dwight and Class,*
> *Many dreams remain ...unfulfilled. I suppose the most impor-*
> *tant is the dream of Samuel Gompers, that the United States*
> *should become a society of schools, books and leisure instead of*
> *a society of jails, guns and greed.*[28]
> *Yours ever, Freeman*

Samuel Gompers (1850–1924) was the founder and first president of the American Federation of Labor. Under his leadership the AFL sought economic security and higher wages for its workers, and was not interested in the revolutionary ideologies sweeping across Europe during his lifetime. In San Antonio there stands a monument to Gompers, bearing the lines from one of his speeches that Professor Dyson paraphrased. Labor, Gompers said, wants "more school houses and less jails, more books and less guns, more learning and less vice, more leisure and less greed, more justice and less revenge. We want more opportunities to cultivate our better nature."

In an essay on education called "Tolstoy, Napoleon and Gompers," Professor Dyson described two models of education, personified by Napoleon and Leo Tolstoy. [Chaisson and Kim(1999)][53–59] When Napoleon considered a society managed by an Imperial government, he established a rigid top-down educational system whose "basic pattern is centralization, standardization and rigorous testing by examination." In contrast, "Leo Tolstoy... worked from the bottom up. He organized a school for the children of the peasants on his estate at Yasnaya Polyana. He taught the children himself." Before organizing his school, Tolstoy traveled across Europe to observe Napoleon's model in action, and judged it a colossal failure. That is why he wrote "All that the greater part of the people carry away from school is a horror of schooling." After assessing both models Professor Dyson came to a conclusion that echoes Bohr's principle of complementarity:

Napoleon and Tolstoy both proclaimed important truths about education. Napoleon proclaimed that the essence of education is discipline. Tolstoy proclaimed that the essence of education is freedom.... How can both of them be true?... For Napoleon, education meant the training of an intellectual elite who would find careers in the institutions of a technically organized society. For Tolstoy, education meant opening the eyes of ordinary children to the wonders of the world around them.... In the modern world,...both kinds of education are necessary.... Only Napoleon can give us a cadre of technically trained ex-

---

[28][Mantsios(1998)][51]

perts to make our society economically competitive. Only Tolstoy can give us a population of culturally and scientifically literate citizens who may possess the wisdom to save our society from Napoleonic follies...We have a long way to go.

Hay Bale Research

Most STS students have little personal scientific experience beyond introductory survey courses. To appreciate in a shared experience how science is done, they conduct some research themselves. Each STS class completes an assignment called "A Question to Nature." Working in groups, the students measure something on campus that cannot be measured directly, but must be inferred from measurements that *are* accessible. Various classes have measured the distance between the base of a catalpa tree planted by the class of 1926 and the summit of the radio tower on the roof of the science building; other classes have estimated the number of tennis balls that could be stuffed into the rooftop observatory, or the number of hay bales that could be loaded in our campus administration building, and so on.

The given instructions are minimal. "Estimate the number of $2' \times 2' \times 4'$ hay bales that would fit within the exterior surfaces of Bresee Hall. You may not ask anyone about the building; you are to put the question to the physical system itself." The groups are left to their own devices on how to proceed. Some step off distances, others count bricks or use triangulation. Some estimate heights in improvised units such as "Jennifers." Some use GPS or satellite photos or laser range finders. The strategic variety is impressive, and they amaze themselves, these young people who told themselves they could not do science.

On a designated day we hold a "Meeting of the American Association of Campus Geodesy." Each group presents its methods, results and an estimate of uncertainty. The session has a printed program, a moderator, time limits and questions from the audience. As audience members the students have a job to do. They are given a worksheet with guidelines for peer-reviewing the talks, using a five-star system. Presentation styles range from elegant seriousness (e.g., collared shirts with jackets and neckties) to hilarious (e.g., puppets). The culture of the meeting is our own, and emphasizes freedom. We say, take the work seriously, but do not take yourselves seriously. The exercise is considered a success if everyone gave it their best shot and had a good time. When all the groups have presented their results, a bar graph of class data is sketched on the whiteboard and

we have a plenary discussion. Let us listen to some student comments
afterwards:

```
   I had no idea how we were going to come up with the
measurement to figure out the volume of the building.
Luckily my group members were very creative in this
aspect....  I was surprised at how many techniques were used
to gather data....  It turned out to be a fun project...
--Hannah A.
```

```
   Dear Dad, This week I felt like a scientist....it was kind
of fun measuring, calculating, converting [units], and
gathering data...  In the past, learning has been a guided
tour of how to do things, but now it is about figuring things
out...  --Kayla C.
```

```
   This week after presentations, we talked about all of the
[assumptions] that went into our research.  The question of
how we measure [distances] from the Earth to planets was
brought up.  It had never occurred to me that we may not know
the exact measurements to the different planets...  --Emily
B.
```

```
   Dear Mr. French (my high school geometry teacher):  You
were right.  I'll say it again, you were right.  We actually
do use geometry in the real world...  --Cait E.
```

```
   ...We were able to break out of the mold of science we've
been taught...  in doing this class project we were able to
be creative and use what we had to form an answer...
--Elijah D.
```

```
   At first,...  I did not see the significance of Science in
doing this project....  As we started to collaborate and
crunch the numbers, someone in our group said, ''I feel like
the group working on the Manhattan project.''  At that point,
the whole project made sense in my mind.  We were...  a group
of scientists putting our minds together to try solving a
very complex puzzle.  The fact that we were using math to
```

reach our answer was not the point of the project but merely
one of the tools we needed... --Cameron M.

   ...The layout of the building was odd.... The fact that we
were not able to ask anyone anything about the building made
it tougher as well. We had to take our own measurements and
do our own research... However, I was relieved to discover
that the majority of all the other groups came up with
relatively the same answer as we did... --Amanda A.

During our plenary discussion, inevitably someone raises their hand and
asks "What's the answer?" The professor turns around and looks at the
graphed data, with its class average and the spread around the average.
"This," he says, pointing to the board, "is our answer. This is what we
know, and how well we know it." The students find this response disappointing. They have been conditioned to expect that every question has a
precise answer. But that is not the way of science. In any measurement,
uncertainty always exists. An "exact" answer means knowing the quantity
to an infinite number of decimal places, and no measurement can achieve
that, not even in principle. Doing science means living with uncertainty.
The room gets quiet, and to give the thought time to sink in the professor
takes another sip of coffee from a mug that says "Fermilab."

   ...we wanted to get as accurate of an answer as possible.
Once in class, we were pleased to see that the answer we got
was in the general ballpark of what everyone had gotten. We
were, however, frustrated when we found out we were not going
to get a definite answer. As I have thought about this the
last few days, it seems fitting, though.... For instance,
though we know the general area a hurricane may hit, we never
know the exact location. It seems like there are many things
like this in nature... --Chase H.

Although our answer is not exact, it is authentic. According to our
data, the answer lies between this number and that number, in the sense
that two-thirds (say) of our data lands between those two numbers. We
discuss ways the measurement could be improved, gleaning ideas from one
another about effective practices to consider and pitfalls to avoid. If the
number of hay bales that could be stuffed into Bresee Hall was crucial to

know with higher precision, then after our presentations and discussions we would go out and make measurements all over again, and when coming back the second time should see improved precision and accuracy with a much smaller spread in the uncertainty. Science is an iterative process done in community.

The professor commends the students on a job well done. The compliment is sincere. Then the professor says, "But I don't buy it." The faces are shocked and the students sit in stunned silence. The professor lingers over another sip of coffee. "I don't buy it, because all of this is only a theory, right?" Pause. "Have you ever heard anyone say 'Don't believe that, it's only a theory'?" When someone says that, they mean "That's a speculation," but scientists mean the opposite by the word "theory." Scientists use the word in contexts such as "antenna theory" or "nuclear theory," which means an organized framework for a body of knowledge that can be used with justified confidence to predict what a specific system will do in a given circumstance. The professor asks, "Do you realize how theory-laden your measurements are?"

The students made assumptions galore: space is Euclidean; metersticks do not stretch when held vertically; volumes are additive; light travels in straight lines, and so on. Those who used the global positioning system have little idea of the principles of special and general relativity on which their instrument relies. Everyone's measurements depend on the work of previous generations of experimenters and theorists and instrument makers whose methods and results were checked and rechecked by skeptical colleagues. Under what conditions does light travel in a straight line? How large an area can be measured without having to take the curvature of Earth's surface into account? We discuss the role of modeling, the making of conceptual representations of the system under investigation, as when treating the buiilding as a set of boxes when estimating its volume. Tayler S. wrote,

Dear Mom, This past week we were posed with an interesting question: How many hay bales can be placed inside of one of the buildings on campus? This question seemed rather simple when I imagined doing it in my head. However, when the time came to measure the building we weren't sure how we were going to calculate the height of the building. We tried a number of different methods...It wasn't until after we measured and were looking at our data did we realize how many more assumptions we had to take into consideration to come to a conclusion....

To complete this exercise as a science, one more step should be taken. Bresee Hall houses the office of the university president. After our Geodesy Conference, he receives an email:

11 March 2014
Dear President Gresham:
In the Science, Technology, and Society course the students have presented a question to nature, made some measurements and reported on their estimates of how many $2' \times 2' \times 4'$ hay bales would be required to fill Bresee Hall. The class average was 18,533 plus or minus 5,000 (a broad distribution). That, of course, was the theory side of our question to nature.
Now we need to do the experimental side of the research program. How soon can everyone and everything be evacuated from Bresee Hall, so we can see how many hay bales can, in reality, be put inside it?
We need about $180,000 to purchase the hay, more if the actual number of bales required lies near the top end of the distribution in our theoretical estimate. Please deposit the necessary funds in the Physics Department budget.
Your cooperation would be greatly appreciated as we investigate this important science question.
Respectfully submitted,
DEN, Professor of Physics

11 March 2014
Dear STS Class:
LOL! I'm not sure that many hay bales wouldn't collapse old Bresee!
Sincerely, President Gresham

A crucial question the professor asks the students is, "Did you have fun in this project?" Tayler S. continued, "Once we got our number (20,599) of hay bales we thought to ourselves how fun it was to do something where there wasn't a definitive answer. Also, we weren't constrained by a certain method and it allowed us to do whatever we wanted to come up with an answer..."

Research is a form of creative but purposeful play. The holy curiosity of a child's simple but profound questioning has never left Professor Dyson across his ninety-plus years. May it never leave the rest of us. As Allison said, "there is a lot to be learned from children."

> *Time seems to stand quite still*
> *In a child's world it always will...*
> *Yesterday's dreams*
> *Are tomorrow's sighs*
> *Watch children playing*
> *They seem so wise.*
> –The Moody Blues[29]

---

[29] "The Morning" from the album *Days of Future Passed*, Decca Records (1967).

4 Martha and Mary

Advice to Young People Choosing Their Life's Work

"The mass of men lead lives of quiet desperation.... Grow wild according to thy nature, like these sedges and brakes, which will never become English hay." – Henry David Thoreau[30]

***

When I was a young assistant professor in a large state university, one Monday afternoon, a young man entered my office and asked me to sign some forms. He was withdrawing from the university. I signed the forms and he went on his way. The following Thursday, a young man committed suicide in our building by diving down an eight-story stairwell. The next day the campus newspaper reported that, earlier in the week, the suicidal young man had withdrawn from the university.

Every year about a dozen university students out of one hundred thousand commit suicide. [Neuenschwander(2004)] Every semester about midway through the term one or two students come to my office who want to quit. Discouraged, overwhelmed and fed up, they have just about had enough. Ever since that sunny but dark Thursday afternoon, I tell them, if you need to withdraw, that's fine—but before I sign the form I must know where you're jumping *to*. It *is* my business.

Getting through university presents significant intellectual and emotional challenges. The challenge of mastering a discipline's content is only part of it. Learning to manage yourself, to set priorities and handle crises presents another set of problems that, for some students, become overwhelming. The most valuable part of one's education comes from knowing thyself, as Socrates observed.

To enroll in STS a student must have reached their junior or senior year. Thus they come into STS already heavily invested in university life, including a specific major which they hope will open doors to desired career options. About one quarter of them receive their diplomas on the Saturday commencement following their Tuesday STS final exam. Some are having second thoughts about what they want to do with their lives. Of course such doubts are not unusual, and are generally not as fateful as imagined.

---

[30][Thoreau(1960)][143].

As our correspondence with Professor Dyson has progressed, on numerous occasions he has offered wise insight for undergraduate students who are trying to understand themselves and look to the future.

His own preparation for a career began with unusual early focus.

At the age of seven, he was observed reading one of his father's books, Arthur Eddington's *Space, Time, and Gravitation*.... [At Winchester] Freeman studied Russian. He also studied Latin... and Greek. He dabbled in biology and considered a possible medical career. Because there was no course in physics, Freeman taught himself this subject using a textbook by Georg Joos.[31] As a protest against compulsory Latin and soccer, he helped organize a science club... [Schewe(2013)][3]

Freeman realized that if he wanted to become fluent in Einstein's relativity he would have to learn differential equations. He recalls,

A year before the beginning of the Second World War, I got hold of a copy of Piaggio's "Differential Equations." This did not come from my teachers... I was too busy during the school term to give my attention to it, so I saved it for the Christmas vacation...

My school vacations were mostly spent at a cottage on the shore which my father had bought as a holiday home. He was a musician.... His best-known work is "The Canterbury Pilgrims," a setting of the Prologue of Chaucer's Canterbury Tales for solo voices, chorus and orchestra. It was first performed at Winchester when I was seven years old. It is dedicated "to M.L.D., who prepared the words." That is my mother, who shared with him an intense affection for Chaucer and for the characters that Chaucer immortalized. [Dyson(1979a)][11–12]

"The first mature flowering of Dyson's music came while he was the Director of Music at Winchester College," writes a modern commentator.[32] "Here not only was he an organist, but he had a choir and an orchestra, as well as an adult choral society... Choral societies responded from the first, and *In Honour of the City* (1928) and *The Canterbury Pilgrims* (1930) quickly established him as a vibrant musical voice of considerable personality."

---

[31] *Theoretical Physics*, first published in 1934.

[32] Program notes by Richard Hickox, pp. 6–7, with the CD *The Canterbury Pilgrims* by George Dyson, London Symphony Chorus and London Symphony Orchestra, Richard Hickox, Conductor; Chandos Records Ltd. (1997).

11 June 2001
Dear Professor Dyson,
During the final exam of the regular semester with 50 students,
I had them spread out among several rooms to take the exam.
As they wrote the exam one group of students wanted me to
play for them your father's "Canterbury Pilgrims," which I did
on the CD player. I had been using parts of it before class for
some background music after they "met" your father early in
the book.
Thank you again for your responses to our questions. I hope
we don't wear out our welcome.
Warm regards, Dwight

We continue with Professor Dyson's Christmas holiday recollection: "I arrived at the cottage on the coast with my precious Piaggio and did not intend to be parted from him.... I started at six in the morning and stopped at ten in the evening, with short breaks for meals... Never have I enjoyed a vacation more." [Dyson(1979a)][13] This passage motivated a student named Aaron R. to think about his own goals and what it would take to reach them:

I enjoyed these first few chapters very much. The main point I liked that jumped out at me was the part where he talked about having to learn differential equations.... He wanted to learn the math so badly that he spent his entire Christmas break reading this book fourteen hours a day. He worked hard on this so that he could later read Einstein. I can relate to this because I am just now starting to learn to play the cello. I already sing and play guitar, but I have always wanted to learn to play a classical stringed instrument. I want to jump right in playing cello suites and large pieces, but my entire first lesson was all about how to hold the bow. I have to spend a lot of time on small things so I can work my way up to the more complicated procedures.

Another student, Stan W., wrote:

...You see, the main thing I have taken from Dyson's readings is learning about the way he spent his time in his youth. Although there wasn't TV or internet for him to waste his time with, he definitely could have wasted it. Instead, he took to understanding the depths of mathematics. He appreciated beautiful poetry, foreign languages, and meaningful music.... My brother came in and saw me reading one day and thought the TV was broken. It is an absurd idea in our world for people to actually spend their time away from mainstream technology.

The account of Christmas with Piaggio continues:

After a while my parents became worried. My mother looked sadly at me and quoted from Chaucer's Clerk of Oxenford:

> *Of study took he most care and most heed,*
> *Not a word spake he more than was need.*

She warned me that I would ruin my health and burn out my brains if I went on like this.... I was in love with mathematics, and nothing else mattered. [Dyson(1979a)][13–14]

Every semester when those one or two students come into my office, discouraged with burned-out brains and wanting to talk, we have a conversation about mental maintenance. When the young Freeman was approaching the end of Piaggio's seven hundred examples, he began to skip a few of them, and even set aside an hour for a walk with his mother.

...She was well prepared...
My mother was a lawyer by profession and intensely interested in people. She loved the Latin and Greek poets.... She began her lecture with a quotation from the play "The Self-Tormentor" by the African slave Terentius Afer, who became the greatest Latin playwright: "I am human and I let nothing human be alien to me." ...She understood my impatience, and my passion for the abstract beauties of Piaggio. But she begged me not to lose my humanity in my haste to become a mathematician. You will regret it deeply, she said, when one day you are a great scientist and you wake up to find that you have never had time to make friends. What good will it do you to prove the Riemann hypothesis, if you have no wife and no children to share your triumph?...
I listened to all this carelessly, knowing that I had no use for it yet but could come back to it later. After my mother had finished with Terence the African, she began again with Goethe's Faust... [Dyson(1979a)][11–15]

This scene reminded Jamie M. of her relationship with her mother and their conversation on the same topic:

My mom loves taking walks, and over the last couple of years walking has become ''our'' time. It is her time to be a mom, taking in all the worries I have and offering advice, even in the moment when I would least like to hear it. Dyson's mom uses a quotation from the play ''The Self-Tormenter...'' My mom and I were walking this past Saturday. I was sharing with her how I feel like this semester is going to be extremely challenging, and how I feel like I am not going to have enough time to get everything finished that I need to. She gently reminded me, in that tone all mothers use, that I need to make sure that I make time for the important things in life.... She is trying to enlighten me on how she wishes she had done things a little differently while she was in school. I am totally the type of person that will skip hanging out with friends simply to get an A. I love the fact that my mom challenges me to look at things through a different perspective, and it isn't trying to tell me to stop applying myself. Rather, she encourages me to remember the important things in life. Reminding me that a GPA will fade away, but friendships and memories will remain with me for a lifetime.

The foregoing passage in Professor Dyson's book motivated a student named Blake J. to address his weekly STS letter to a younger brother. "...All of this has been vague, my brother, but it leads me to one lesson taught to Dyson by his mother, which is that we are relational beings. Even if we fulfill every material dream we have, it will not provide us happiness if we cannot share it with the ones we love. I have not been the greatest example of this, but it is my hope that these words can create a step in the right direction..."

> *4 December 2000*
> *Dear Professor Dyson,*
> *Our Science, Society, and Technology class at SNU wishes you and your family a joyous Christmas season.*
> *...What other works was your mother fond of quoting besides Chaucer's works, Goethe's "Faust," and Terentius Afer's "The Self-Tormenter?"*

7 December 2000
Dear Dwight, thanks for your message...
When my sister and I were small children, before we ever heard
of Goethe's Faust or Terentius Afer, my mother used to recite
a poem every night when she put us to bed. She knew a lot of
poems by heart. The one I remember best is "'Tis gone that
bright." We liked that one best because it was the longest. It
was so long that there was a good chance we would be asleep
before it finished. I don't even remember who wrote it. It is
a hymn and was probably written by some nineteenth-century
hymn-writer. It begins:

> *'Tis gone, that bright and orb'ed blaze,*
> *Fast fading from our wistful gaze...*

and it goes on for a long time describing the evening turning
into night. Then comes a sudden shift to another theme:

> *Sun of my soul, my Saviour dear,*
> *It is not night if thou be near.*
> *O may no earthborn cloud arise*
> *To hide me from my Saviour's eyes.*

After that there are many more verses but I don't remember
how it ends. When my mother was in a hurry, she would begin
with "Sun of my soul" instead of "'Tis gone that bright" and
we would be disappointed.
When we were older, another book that my mother liked to quote
from was "1066 and All That," by Sellar and Yeatman, two
school-teachers who wrote the book as a spoof of English history
as it was taught in schools. The book was written in the 1930s
and was a best-seller. I only remember the last sentence of the
book: "In 1920 America became top nation and history came
to a stop." Before that, of course, England was top nation and
that was what history was about.

I know from personal experience, having learned the relevant lessons the
hard way, that the challenges of academic and professional life are not well
met by maximizing time spent in the office. Instead, one needs to max-
imize one's effectiveness. Maximizing effectiveness requires setting aside
time each week for mental maintenance. [Neuenschwander(2004)], [Neuen-
schwander(2014)] Many a class session has veered aside into an important
tangent here, where we swap stories against the background of Mildred
Dyson's lecture to her precocious son. Most of the STS students are about
20 to 23 years old, on a track to graduate with a specific major within a

few months. Many of them are still wondering what they will do with their lives.

While I was never precocious, I know that my students see me as a professor of a highly mathematical subject, and assume that in high school I surely completed Advanced Placement Calculus. They are astonished to learn that my entire high school mathematics career consisted of a generous D in ninth grade algebra. They are also astonished to learn that I felt like quitting more than once in my university student career, and that I acted on those feelings more than once. I tell them (because I firmly believe it to be so) that getting a degree is mostly about persistence. We do not need another Einstein or Beethoven. We already have Einstein and Beethoven. I say to them, we need you to be *you*, because you are the only *you* that will ever exist in the history of the universe. Each person has a combination of talents, passions and experiences that are unique, and therefore has something to offer that would not otherwise be contributed.

For several years, Professor and Imme Dyson have sent our classes a copy of their "New Year Letter, Dyson Family Chronicle." One section of their letter for the 2013 New Year described a 2012 performance of *The Canterbury Pilgrims*:

> ...while the Olympic Games were attracting most of the tourists to London, Imme and I were in Hereford for the Three Choirs Festival. The three cathedral choirs of Gloucester, Worcester and Hereford join together and take turns to host the festival. When my sister Alice and I were children before World War 2, we went to the festival every year, and Hereford was the place we liked best. Our father composed and conducted a new choral work for the festival each year, and we got free tickets. This year his "Canterbury Pilgrims" was performed at Hereford, and Imme and I were invited to hear it. The cathedral was packed, with not a single empty seat, and the performance was as magnificent as I remembered it from 75 years before. The choirs and soloists evidently enjoyed it as much as we did. One of the people who was with us in Hereford was Paul Spicer, an English conductor who has written a biography of my father. The biography is finished but not yet published. It brings my father vividly back to life, and incidentally draws a dramatic portrait of English society through a century of rapid change.[33]

> *12 November 2007*
> *Dear Professor Dyson,*
> *We hope that the 2007 Thanksgiving season finds you and all your family doing well....*

---

[33]Paul Spicer's biography, *Sir George Dyson* has since been published (Boydell Press, Woodbridge, UK, 2014).

> *You speak of art, opera, music, and literature in parallel with science in your book. [We were] curious as to where your love for the arts began in your life and who some of your favorite artists, musicians, and authors were?*

> *23 November 2007*
> *Dear Dwight,...*
> *I was exposed to a great deal of music as a child, as my father was a professional conductor and composer. I was dragged to many concerts. I was more interested in the musicians than the music. When I was about five years old, one of the ladies at a concert said to me, "Aren't you lucky to get to hear so much music?" and I replied, "Music is very nice but too long." She told that to my father and he was highly amused. After that he always supplied me with a score so I could read along instead of listening to the music. Music has always been a foreign language to me, interesting to observe but basically incomprehensible. The same is true of art and opera.*
> *Literature is different. Literature speaks to me directly. I acquired a taste for literature from my mother, who was even more tone-deaf than me. As a child I disliked boy-stories and loved girl-stories. My favorite books were "The Wizard of Oz," "Alice through the Looking-Glass," "Little Women," "The Secret Garden," all with girls for heroes. "The Magic City" was an exception, but the real hero of that story is the nurse-maid and not the boy. Later when I had children of my own I loved to read aloud "Charlotte's Web." I was always more at home with literature than with art or music. I enjoyed writing more than drawing or playing the violin. In the end I slipped easily from doing science to writing books.*

Let the record show that, as a student in Winchester College, despite his self-diagnosed tone-deafness, young Freeman Dyson played violin in school performances, and he played it well. [Schewe(2013)][11], [Schweber(1994)][480]

> *1 May 2001*
> *Dear Professor Dyson,*
> *...What book was the most influential in your life?*

> *3 May 2001*
> *Dear Dwight, thank you for the May Day message and thanks to the students for their list of questions....*
> *The most influential book was probably Eric Bell's "Men of Mathematics," a collection of biographies of mathematicians*

written in a readable and racy style.[34] *A large proportion of the mathematicians of my generation were seduced by Bell's book into becoming mathematicians. The great thing about Bell's book is that the characters are real people with many faults and weaknesses, so the stories ring true. If this collection of jerks and fools could do great mathematics, then so can you.*

3 December 1998
Dear Professor Dyson,
...Which individual has had the greatest influence on your life, and why?

To answer this question Professor Dyson divided his life into three eras:

5 December 1998
Dear Dwight,
...No single person had the greatest influence in my life. Different people are important at different times, and you can't put them in order of importance. Probably the three most important were my mother, from age zero to twenty, Richard Feynman, from age twenty to thirty, and my wife, from age thirty to seventy-four. My mother gave me a splendid education, Feynman gave me my chance to do an important piece of science, and my wife gave me a big family, so I was three times lucky. Happy Christmas and New Year to you all.
Yours sincerely,
Freeman Dyson

Through audacity or oversight, two-and-a-half years later we asked Professor Dyson essentially the same question. He patiently answered us again, but this time partitioned his life, not into three eras, but into three roles:

1 May 2001
Dear Professor Dyson,
Once again as we near the semester's end, our Science, Technology, and Society class sends greetings to you and your family....
Who is (or was) the most influential person in your life?

3 May 2001
Dear Dwight, thank you for the May Day message and thanks to the students for their list of questions....
My life has been many-sided, and different people are most influential in the various sides of my life. In my life as a scientist, the Russian mathematician Abram Besicovitch, who

---

[34]First published in 1937.

set my style and my way of solving problems. In my life as a writer, the writer Herbert Wells, who wrote a first-rate history of mankind[35] as well as wonderful novels and a textbook of biology. In my life as a human being, my mother Mildred Dyson, who formed my tastes in literature and also in religion.

It will be noticed that, in responding to our essentially identical questions, Professor Dyson's mother Mildred appears in both partitionings of his life.

7 December 1999
Dear Professor Dyson,
On behalf of the Fall 99 "Science, Technology, and Society" class, we wish you and your family a joyous and meaningful Christmas Season. We hope you will all have a wonderful time together, including ample time to spend with your beautiful grandchildren.
...1. You have met many interesting people in your life. You have described what you learned from them. Flipping the coin, what is one thing you think these people have learned from you that influenced them significantly?
...2. Along with the science and technology, your book displays an intense passion for the humanities, especially literature, music, poetry, and philosophy. What led you to develop such broad interests? Do you view the humanities and sciences as separate disciplines, or as two complementary sides of the same coin? We hope you and all your loved ones are well. Best wishes and Season's Greetings.
Warm regards, Dwight

8 December 1999
Dear Dwight,
The questions from your students go immediately to the top of the pile of unanswered letters. The others can wait for a few days longer. Please give the students my greetings and thanks. Here are some off-the-cuff answers....
1. I can't answer this one. When I talk or write, I am the sower throwing seed into the wind. I never know where it lands or where it may be sprouting.
2. I emphatically agree with the statement that the humanities and sciences are complementary sides of the same coin. They are different ways of looking at the same world. I was always interested in literature and poetry, not so much in music and philosophy. My favorite teacher in high-school was a chemistry

---

[35]Professor Dyson may be referring to *A Short History of the World* (1922, Macmillan) by H.G. Wells.

teacher who read poetry aloud to his class. As he said, we didn't need to come to class to learn chemistry. And my parents were both humanists.

Since we share a lot of poetry and music in STS, we were glad to learn that a precedent exists which turned out well.

3 December 1998
Dear Professor Dyson,
...We might compare your life to a modern-day Benjamin Franklin, a Renaissance man who contributes to almost every important part of the culture. What are the most important lessons you have learned in your life?

5 December 1998
Dear Dwight,
...I have not learned any big lessons that can be expressed in words. To live well is an art and not a science. My life has been opportunistic, not making big plans but responding to opportunities wherever they arose. Perhaps the main lesson is, always be ready to jump at the next unexpected opportunity. The Sloan Foundation invitation to write a book was a good example. In the last twenty years I have learned more from my children's lives than from my own. They are all good at jumping at unexpected opportunities, and as a result they all have interesting lives.
... Happy Christmas and New Year to you all.
Yours sincerely,
Freeman Dyson

4 December 2000
Dear Professor Dyson,
Our Science, Society, and Technology class wishes you and your family a joyous Christmas season...
1. If you were beginning your scientific career today, and were in the process of choosing among the various sub-fields that are hot on the burners right now, to which one(s) would you choose to contribute your time and talents?
2. What is our most important duty as individual human beings?...

7 December 2000
...1. The problem I had with choosing a field of science to work in was that my interests were much broader than my talents. I have always been intensely interested in biology and medicine, but I couldn't do biology or medicine because I didn't have the

right skills. In choosing a profession, the first criterion has to be, do you have what it takes? I didn't have what it took to be a biologist. My only real talent was mathematics, so I became a mathematician. Then I found that with my mathematics I could also solve problems in physics, so I switched to physics. I became a theoretical physicist. In biology there was much less scope for mathematics.

Things are changing, and now it is possible to be a theoretical biologist, but real biologists who work in the laboratory do not have much respect for theoretical biologists. If I were young now, I might have become a theoretical biologist, studying the evolution of genomes and populations with mathematical tools.

We interrupt this letter to note that the first priority in Professor Dyson's choice of a profession places the love of the game ahead of probability for fame and fortune. His life suggests this advice: follow your talents and interests. Take care of quality and competence and the respect will take care of itself. The letter continues:

But I think it more likely that I would have stuck to mathematics and physics. Probably I would have tried my hand at string theory, the fashionable branch of theoretical physics that uses very sophisticated mathematics. String theory may not have much to do with the real world, but it is mathematically deep and beautiful. I am sure I could have enjoyed a happy life as a string-theorist. Whether or not string theory is useful, it provides the right sort of sand-box for a person with my talent to play in. And after making a reputation as a string-theorist, I could then have broadened my activities and written books about other things as I actually did.

2. I don't believe there is any duty that is most important for everybody. People have different circumstances, different opportunities and different talents. Therefore they have different duties. A duty is like a vocation. My daughter Mia had a vocation to be a Presbyterian minister. Now she has a church and it is her duty to help her parishioners by preaching and counseling and administering the church. That is for her the most important duty. But I don't have a duty to be a minister. My vocation, if I have one, is different. At present, after I have retired as a working scientist, my most important duty is to help my wife take care of children and grandchildren.

For your young students, there is a wide choice of vocations and a wide choice of duties. Some of you have a duty to be Martha and some have a duty to be Mary.

The story of Mary and Martha comes from the *Gospel According to Luke*:

As Jesus and his disciples were on their way, he came to a village where a woman named Martha opened her home to him. She had a sister called Mary, who sat at the Lord's feet listening to what he said. But Martha was distracted by all the preparations that had to be made. She came to him and asked, "Lord, don't you care that my sister has left me to do the work by myself? Tell her to help me!"
"Martha, Martha," the Lord answered, "you are worried and upset about many things, but few things are needed—or indeed only one. Mary has chosen what is better, and it will not be taken away from her."[36]

Returning to Professor Dyson's letter,

> *I always thought Jesus was unfair when he scolded Martha for being jealous of Mary. The world needs Martha just as much as it needs Mary. Mia knows this well, since she is also a mother with three children. As a mother she is Martha and as a minister she is Mary. She knows that, as Jesus said, her first duty is to be Mary. Her second duty is to be Martha and not to be jealous of Mary. The first sermon that she preached when she was ordained was on the story of Martha and Mary. She told us how she has to be Mary first and Martha second. At some point in your lives, you will all be faced with similar choices between conflicting duties. There is no easy way to decide which duty comes first.*

Our copy of the 1999 Dyson Family Chronicle, their New Year Letter that highlighted their experiences in 1998, carried above the typewritten text a handwritten note, "Happy New Year to you and your students, and thanks again for your friendly messages. Yours ever, Freeman." That issue of the Chronicle opened by describing Mia's dual roles as Mary and Martha:

1998 was Mia's year. She graduated from the Princeton Theological Seminary in May, gave birth to a son in July, moved with her family back to their home in Maine in August, and was ordained as minister of Saint Andrew's Presbyterian Church in Kennebunk in November. Her husband Kevin is working as a fund-raiser for the Casco Bay Conservation Society, an organization dedicated to preserving the wildlife in the waters around Portland. He loves

---

[36]Luke 10:38-42, New International Version.

Fig. 4.1   *The Dyson east coast grandchildren, 1998.* (photo courtesy of Freeman Dyson)

the work and has a strong incentive to do it well. As he says, if he does not do it well the results will be obvious. The picture shows our six East Coast grandchildren on the sofa at Mia's home in Maine when baby Liam was about six weeks old. From left to right, George, Donald, Tess, Bryn, Liam, Randall. Tess, Bryn and Liam are the Maine crowd. George, Donald and Randall are still living in Princeton. Too bad the West Coast contingent, Lauren (Bellingham) and Max (San Diego) could not be there.

The East-coasters reassembled in Maine for Halloween and All Saints' Day when Mia was ordained. On the day of the ordination, Mia was up early preparing her sermons, cooking breakfast pancakes for twelve, nursing Liam, and driving a car-load of kids and food to Kennebunk, before conducting the morning service. She preached two splendid sermons, a funny one for the kids and a serious one for the grown-ups. In the evening she was ordained, first taking her vows before the congregation in a ringing voice, then kneeling while the other ministers and elders laid their hands on her head. The congregation was friendly and welcoming. They had prepared a huge meal so that we could relax after the ceremony and get to know one another while the kids ran around. Mia's new life as a minister is off to a good start.

In his Templeton Prize speech of May 2000, Professor Dyson was ecumenical: "When I am in Maine I am a Presbyterian and when I am in England I am a Catholic." [Dyson(2000)] His daughter Mia is a Presbyterian minister and his sister Alice, in Winchester, converted to Catholicism.

In a denomination-sponsored faith-based institution such as our university, the task of career selection gets more complicated for some students than is typical for the wider population. Many of our students grew up in devout homes and have felt pressure to "find God's will" for their lives, as if the Creator of the Universe has a singular plan for their lives, which they have to figure out—and had better get it right. Some students, feeling pressured by parents or pastors to be a Mary when their passions call them to be a Martha, are made to feel selfish and guilty. Coming from such a background, I relate to their dilemma. They have been taught the story of Moses.[37] While the Hebrews were slaves in Egypt, Moses, the Hebrew adopted son of the pharaoh's daughter, struck and killed an Egyptian who was mistreating a slave. Moses became a fugitive and fled to wilderness, where he lived for forty years.

According to *Exodus*, one day God speaks audibly to Moses out of a bush that burns without being consumed. This bizarre sight grabs Moses' attention. God tells Moses out of the burning bush that He has heard the groanings of the Hebrews. He commands Moses to return to Egypt, confront the pharaoh and say "Let my people go." Moses understandably does not want to do this. He raises objections, but eventually he goes, and after several dramatic showdowns with the pharaoh that include loathsome plagues and the Angel of Death, the people are liberated.

Some of our students grew up hearing this story with the interpretation that if they follow their own interests then they could be ignoring the commands of the Almighty—how dare you selfishly pursue your little life while ignoring the divine Plan! I empathize with their bewilderment when they are having trouble determining whether it is God or Grandma calling them to a life of pious service.

However, even if we take the burning bush story at face value, it is important to recognize that Moses was a special case. As a Hebrew who grew up in the pharaoh's household, Moses was the only person who could empathize with the plight of the oppressed slaves *and* knew the personalities and power plays of court life. No one else had that combination of qualifications so necessary for the task of confronting the pharaoh about the Hebrews. So Moses was on the hook. What does the story of Moses have to do with students in the twentieth and twenty-first centuries? When advising my students who struggle to reconcile who they are with what others (divine or otherwise) want them to do, for whatever it's worth I advise

---

[37] *Exodus*, Chapter 3.

them as I advised my own children: In the absence of a burning bush experience, follow your passions. *They* are God's gift to you, so sharpen those tools. Get your personal Paggio and go after it. I believe that any Cosmic Mind worthy of respect cares more about what we *are* than what we *do* because, in every sphere of life, we need Marthas *and* Marys.

> *20 November 2012*
> *Dear Professor Dyson,*
> *...4. If you wanted to begin a non-science career now, what would it be, and why?*
> *5. What advice do you have for this generation of students?*
>
> *25 November 2012*
> *Dear Dwight,*
> *...4. If you wanted to begin in a non-science career now, what would it be, and why? The main requirement for a successful and useful career is a high level of skill. You must be highly skilled to do any job well. I have two basic skills, calculating and writing. So my choice of a career is either to do mathematical calculations or to do literary exercises. In practical terms, that means either science or journalism. If I would begin a non-science career now, it would be a writing career. I would begin with a job as a journalist or a teacher, with the hope of writing a best-seller and becoming independent. My daughter Esther began her professional career as a journalist, took a job with Forbes which is a business magazine, then decided that it would be more fun to be a player than a spectator, and ended by becoming a successful venture capitalist. If I were young and beginning a non-science career, I would start the same way as Esther did and look for unexpected opportunities.*
> *5. What advice do you have for this generation of students? I would say the same thing that my daughter Esther said when she was giving a commencement address to the graduating class at Carleton College. Worry about your fourth job, not your first. The first job is just to get your foot in the door. Don't expect to enjoy it. Use your first job as a training to find out what you can do. The first job also gives you a better bargaining position when you are looking for the second job. And so it goes on. If you are still unhappy with your fourth job, then you have a problem.*
> *I do not have much more to say. Each of you is different from the others and has different needs. Some like stability. Others like adventure. If you like stability, choose a safe career path as a teacher or a nurse or a police officer. If you like adventure, be ready to grab at any opportunity that comes by. My daughter Esther, who likes adventure, has a motto which appears at the*

end of her E-mail messages. "Always make fresh mistakes."
Do not do the same dumb thing twice. That is good advice for
all of you.
Happy Christmas and New Year to all of you.
Yours ever, Freeman Dyson

Two-and-a-half years later, the Spring 2015 class had a similar question:

22 April 2015
Dear Professor Dyson,
...What professions would you most recommend to twenty-somethings starting their careers today? Would you encourage them to lean towards technology-dependent professions, or to careers that require the maintenance of skills that cannot be done by automation?

His reply offered some more insight about security and adventure, held practical advice that cuts across all professions, and told us a little more about daughter Esther's experiences:

1 May 2015
Dear Dwight,
...I would advise young people to be prepared to switch from one job to another every few years. Concentrate on acquiring skills that remain useful in different jobs, such as writing clear English, understanding simple mathematics, managing financial accounts, organizing computer networks, running committees. There are of course exceptions. A few professions, for example, medical doctor, minister of a church, university professor, give a good chance of finding a secure and permanent job. But most jobs are not secure and not permanent. The disappearance of jobs is not predictable. It is not only caused by automation or by new technology. So the important thing is to be prepared to switch. I like to recommend my daughter Esther as a role model. She began working as a journalist for the business magazine Forbes, then switched to working as a technical analyst for the banking firm Oppenheimers, then switched to publishing her own business news-magazine, then switched to running her own venture-capital business, and now recently switched to running her own private health-care foundation. Her motto which is printed on every E-mail says, "Always make new mistakes." The thing to avoid is making the same mistake over and over again.

6 December 2005
Dear Professor Dyson,
We hope 2005 has been good to you and your family. During this fall semester of 2005, 44 more students have walked down the path of your experiences, and from your experiences have expanded their own....
If today you somehow fell into the Fountain of Youth and emerged as a 20-year-old, what would you pursue, and why?

6 December 2005
Dear Dwight,
Thanks to you and the students for another thought-provoking lot of questions. 2005 has indeed been a good year for us and our tribe of fourteen grandchildren. We have much to be thankful for....
I just spent four exciting days lecturing at St. John's College in Annapolis, a remarkable place (founded in 1696) where the students study a purely classical curriculum based on the Great Books. Those students asked me the same question. I told them I would still have the same problem that I had sixty years ago when I was a real twenty-year-old. My problem is that I have many interests—biology, medicine, astronomy, physics, literature, history, languages—but only one talent, mathematics. So I would do the same thing that I did sixty years ago, looking around for ways to use my talent to explore interesting problems in many different fields. Sixty years ago, the most interesting problems were in physics, and so physics was my first playground. Today the most interesting problems are in biology and I would probably concentrate my efforts on those, trying to understand the deep structure of cells and brains and genomes and their relationships with one another, using my mathematics to dig a little deeper into the mysteries.

As already mentioned, most STS students are in their early twenties. They have reached the place in life where, in addition to figuring out what they are going to do with themselves professionally, they are also questioning their childhood pieties and certainties. They are trying to form their own identity and philosophy of life. "Finding yourself" may be the most important task of one's life, and the most difficult. Professor Dyson closed his letter to us of 7 May 2005 by enclosing a poem written by one of his grandchildren:

In conclusion I send you a poem that came this week from my eleven-year-old grandson Donald in California.

I am Donald Reid
I wonder if my dreams will come true
I hear the bubbling acid
I see the chemicals
I want to work on laser transportation
I am trying to be smart.

I pretend nothing
I feel the glass bottles
I touch the pencil that will sign contracts
I worry about my grades
I cry when I'm sad
I am trying to get into a good college.

I understand it will be hard
I say I can do it
I dream of being a famous professor
I try to do things I can't
I hope my dreams will come true
I am Donald Reid.

With greetings and good wishes to you all from the Dyson family.

I see Donald's yearnings in my students. I see them also in myself, past and present. Thank you Donald Reid. We who were privileged to receive your birth announcement also say, because we have been there: you can do it, and you inspire us.[38]

Professor Dyson's candid recollection of going through the excruciating process of finding himself, as recorded in *Disturbing the Universe*, offers reassurance:

So I asked myself the age-old questions, why does God permit war, and why does God permit injustice, and I found no answers... Enlightenment came to me suddenly and unexpectedly one afternoon in March... And in a blinding flash of inner light I saw the answer to both of my problems, the problem of war and the problem of injustice. The answer was amazingly simple. I called it Cosmic Unity. Cosmic Unity said: There is only one of us. We are all the same person. I am you and I am Winston Churchill and Hitler and Gandhi and everybody. There is no problem of injustice because your sufferings are also mine. There will be no problem of war as soon as you understand that in killing me you are only killing yourself. [Dyson(1979a)][17]

---

[38] As of this writing, ten years after the above letter, we are happy to learn that Donald is a university student majoring in philosophy.

Referring to this passage about "the problem of injustice," the Fall 1998 class asked:

> *3 December 1998*
> *Dear Professor Dyson,*
> *... How do you define or describe "justice" (and therefore "injustice") in today's society?*

> *5 December 1998*
> *Dear Dwight,*
> *...In today's society the most important problem is social injustice, which means the division of the population into rich and poor with unequal opportunities. We have legal justice but not social justice. In many ways the new technologies of the internet make social injustice worse, because people with access to the internet have access to jobs and business opportunities and information, while people without access are left behind and become unemployable. Genetic manipulation could also make social injustice worse, if genetic therapies and treatments are only available to the rich. This is the main danger that I see arising from genetic manipulation. The rules governing genetic therapies must be written so that they are equally accessible to rich and poor.*
> *... Happy Christmas and New Year to you all.*
> *Yours sincerely,*
> *Freeman Dyson*

A similar concern, raised in a different context, was voiced by the Spring 2004 class:

> *May 6, 2004*
> *Dear Professor Dyson,*
> *The students in our spring 2004 semester section of our "Science, Technology, and Society" class have enjoyed reading "Disturbing the Universe" and discussing the issues it raises, reflecting over the "six faces of science," mulling over the timescales you calculated in "Physics and Biology in an Open Universe," seeing pictures of George's baidarka and tree house, and hearing portions of "The Canterbury Pilgrims" composed by your father. If you have a few moments to answer some questions, we would be much obliged....*
> *How has your experience in science influenced your perspective on human rights?*

> *6 May 2004*
> *Dear Dwight,*
> *Thanks to you and the class for a good set of questions. Our*

*son George is here for a week and also sends you his greetings.
It is a long time since he lived in the tree-house. Now he is
officially here as a historian writing a history of the Von Neumann computer project. He is also a single dad with a beautiful
and temperamental teenage daughter. As Shakespeare said, each
man in his time plays many parts.*

Here are some answers to your questions.

*...How has my experience in science influenced my perspective
on human rights? So far as I can remember, I don't see any
connection between science and human rights. I remember when
I was visiting Berkeley in California in 1957, there was a lecture on civil disobedience by a young man I had never heard of.
His name was Martin Luther King. I went to hear the talk and
wrote home to my mother: "This is a man I would be glad to
go to jail for." Later I heard him again in Washington when
he spoke at the Lincoln Memorial and said "I have a dream."
This had nothing to do with science. Some of the leaders in
the fight for human rights have been scientists, the most notable
being Andrei Sakharov, but others such as Gandhi and King
and Mandela were not. I think I would probably have been more
concerned with human rights if I had been a lawyer rather than
a scientist.*

In the speech called "The Power of Nonviolence" delevered at Berkeley on 4 June 1957, the young prophet named Martin Luther King Jr.,
from Montgomery, Alabama, told his listeners that from the beginning of
their civil disobedience in the cause of civil rights, "there was a philosophy
undergirding the Montgomery boycott,[39] the philosophy of nonviolent resistance.... [W]e had to get over the fact that the nonviolent resister does
not seek to humiliate or defeat the opponent but to win his friendship and
understanding." [King and Washington(1986)][12–15]

Every STS topic seems to converge on ethics. An overly broad question
about ethics as related to scientists and their work was asked by the class
of the spring 2011 semester:

29 April 2011
Dear Professor Dyson,
*We trust that 2011 so far has been a splendid year for you and
your extended family...*
Do you think that scientists are becoming more—or less—

---

[39]King refers to the Montgomery, Alabama, bus boycott triggered by the arrest of Rosa
Parks (1913–2005) on 1 December 1955 for refusing to surrender her seat to a white
passenger.

sensitive to ethical issues regarding their work than when you wrote "Disturbing the Universe" in 1979?

29 April 2011
Dear Dwight,...
...Your thoughtful letter and the students' questions arrive just as we are leaving for a week in England, and your deadline [the last day of the course] is the day after we get back... Humble apologies to the students.
... I do not see any big change in ethical sensitivity of scientists. The great majority of scientists have nothing to worry about because their work has no serious effect on human affairs. Those who work on nuclear weapons or medical trials have generally been sensitive to the ethical consequences. I do not know whether their sensitivity has increased since 1979. [emphasis added]

Even though he had to write this reply in haste, we appreciated that Professor Dyson took a moment for us as he headed out the door for England. In his note we noticed his significant distinction between what he *sees* and what he *knows*.

1 May 2000
Dear Professor Dyson,
Here once again, if we may impose on you for a few moments of your time, are selected questions from my Spring 2000 "Science, Technology, and Society" class...
..."I had a hard time wrapping my mind around the concept of Cosmic Unity and how it was significant in regard to ethics. Could you explain a little more how it was a firm foundation for ethics and how you came to realize this concept?" –Jennifer M.

1 May 2000
Dear Dwight,
Luckily I have a few short days left before your term ends....
Jennifer M. My idea about cosmic unity was very simple. You and I and Hitler and Stalin are the same person in different disguises. When you hurt another person you are hurting yourself. So this does make a firm foundation for ethics. Since each person you meet is you, it makes sense for you to treat them as you would like to be treated yourself. It makes no sense for you to treat them badly. In other words, the golden rule follows: "Love thy neighbor as thyself," or "Do as you would be done by."
I thought of cosmic unity first as a way to solve the problem

of injustice in the world. If we are all the same person, then there is no injustice, because we are all suffering equally. So injustice does not really exist and is not a problem. Then, after having invented cosmic unity to solve the problem of injustice, I realized that it also solves the problem of ethics. If you kill your enemy, you are killing yourself, so it follows that you should not kill.

Of course this all sounds much too simple to be true. When I was fourteen I believed it whole-heartedly. It helped me to deal with the tragic world of the nineteen-thirties in which I grew up. Now I think of cosmic unity as a hope rather than a fact. It still makes sense as a foundation for ethics. It is an ideal toward which we should strive.

Cosmic Unity as an ethical principle begins with personal unity, removing self from the center of the universe and entering the lives of others. Professor Dyson made this point when relating his mother's version of *Faust*, when Faust abandons self-interest and gives himself over to helping villagers desperately trying to plug a leaking dike: "Suddenly he [Faust] realizes that this is the blissful moment that he has been seeking all his life, the joy of working together with his fellow men in a common endeavor, the joy of being immersed in a cause larger than himself." [Dyson(1979a)][16]

At the end of Chapter Two of *Disturbing the Universe*, we overhear the teenage Freeman Dyson making one last effort to win a convert to the gospel of Comic Unity. He and his mother take another walk. The young Freeman expounds the new faith to his mother. When he finishes she replies, "Yes. I have believed something rather like that for a very long time." [Dyson(1979a)][18] The chapter ends there. Nothing more is said at this time about Cosmic Unity or Mildred's beliefs. But near the book's end Professor Dyson reveals a hint of what may have been on her mind. When Mildred was in her late eighties and could no longer walk the distances she once could, her outings were short and close to home.

Her favorite walk in those years was to a nearby graveyard which commands a fine view of the ancient city of Winchester and the encircling hills. Here I often walked with her and listened to her talk cheerfully of her approaching death....

Sometimes we talked about the nature of the human soul and about the Cosmic Unity of all souls that I had believed in so firmly when I was fifteen years old. My mother did not like the phrase Cosmic Unity. It was too pretentious. She preferred to call it a world soul. She imagined that she was herself a piece of

the world soul that had been given freedom to grow and develop independently
so long as she was alive. After death, she expected to merge back into the
world soul, losing her personal identity but preserving her memories and her
intelligence. Whatever knowledge and wisdom she had acquired during her life
would add to the world soul's store of knowledge and wisdom. "But how do you
know that the world soul will want you back?" I said.... "Don't worry about
that," my mother replied. "It may take a little while, but I'll find my way back.
The world soul can do with a bit more brains." [Dyson(1979a)][252–253]

Mildred Dyson merged back into the world soul at the age of ninety-four, in 1974. In February 2013 Alice passed from this life as well. In the Dyson Family Chronicle that was sent the previous month, Professor Dyson sadly reported about one family development in 2012:

This year, alas, Alice could not be at the [three choirs] festival. She is
declining physically and mentally and cannot leave the old people's home where
she lives in Winchester. This year Imme nobly made four visits to England to
take care of her. I only went twice. Alice is pathetically happy when we come,
and sad when we say goodbye.

Alice passed away on February 13, 2013, in Winchester, "the town where we spent our childhood and where she spent most of her life as a medical social worker," as told in the Dyson Family Chronicle of January 2014:

She was 92, and she had been declining physically and mentally for the last
year. Imme flew over to be with her for the last days. Imme was rubbing her
back to let her know that she was not alone when she died. In February Imme
and I flew over for the funeral at the Catholic church of St. Peter. A crowd of
about 200 filled the church. Alice had a multitude of friends in the town, and
family came from all over England. Three of our children, Esther, George and
Rebecca, flew over from America. In April, Imme flew over for the last time,
to scatter Alice's ashes in the Water Meadows where she loved to go walking
with her dog. Alice was my closest friend and a beloved aunt to our children.
For three years, Imme has been flying over frequently to take care of her, to
arrange for the sale of her house and for her move into the old people's home
where she spent her final months and quietly died.

Now Alice, too, has merged back into the world soul.

26 November 2014
Dear Professor Dyson,
On behalf of the Fall 2014 Science, Technology & Society class
I bring you warm greetings. Once again we have journeyed with
you through the landscapes and personalities and issues we find
in "Disturbing the Universe"...
We know that you and your sister Alice were very close. We
offer our condolences to you and to your family for her passing.
What would you like for us to know and remember about Alice?

3 December 2014
Dear Dwight and students,
I am back from our five-day trip to celebrate with daughter Mia
and her family in Maine. The high point [was] a performance
of "A Christmas Carol" in a local theater with twelve-year-old
grandson Aidan on stage....
Here are answers to your questions.... As usual, the questions
are more interesting than the answers. The most important part
of your education is to work out your own answers....
You ask about my sister Alice. The main thing that you might
find surprising about her is her religion. She grew up in the
Church of England, which is in England the church of the up-
per classes, especially the church of old families who have been
rich for several generations. In England the division of peo-
ple into classes is sharper than in America. When World War
II started, she became a professional social worker, taking care
of patients who were not upper-class. As a result, she rebelled
against her upbringing and became a Catholic. In England the
Catholic church mixes the classes. It includes a few old upper-
class families, with many more working-class families and es-
pecially Irish immigrants. The Catholic Church gave her much
better contact with her patients, and especially with the Irish
priests who helped her to take care of them. As a result of her
change of religion, she moved away from the snobbish narrow
circle of friends that we grew up with. She moved into a different
crowd that she found far more congenial, including policemen
and criminals and their girl-friends and children, people who
had difficult problems and really needed help.
My most vivid memories of Alice come from days when I drove
with her in her car doing house-calls. She specialized in unmar-
ried mums, who need two kinds of help, for the mother and for
the baby. She liked to take me with her on house-calls, so that
she could talk seriously with the mother while I played with the
baby. These were happy experiences for both of us. My other
vivid memory is of the Catholic church where I would go to
Sunday Mass with Alice and pretend to be a Catholic. At the

> *memorial Mass after she died, about two hundred of her friends*
> *and family came to the service.*
> *Thank you once more for a good set of questions....*
> *Happy Christmas to you and the class! Yours ever, Freeman.*

In the Mass the congregation stands for the reading of the Gospels, because they contain the words of Jesus. Jesus was criticized by the legalistic upper-class establishment of his society for breaking bread with the those who did not follow the rules, society's outcasts—tax collectors, prostitutes, criminals, lepers, pagans, the homeless, unmarried mums. Matthew's gospel tells us, "And when the Pharisees saw this, they said to his disciples, 'Why does your teacher eat with tax collectors and sinners?' But when he heard it, he said, 'Those who are well have no need of a physician, but those who are sick. Go and learn what this means.'"[40]

Alice went and learned what this means. She did not have to be scolded by Jesus to do it.

***

In our imagination let us take an early morning walk through Mildred's peaceful and beloved Winchester graveyard that overlooks the ancient city with its cathedral, the surrounding countryside, and Water Meadows where Alice loved to walk her dog. The grey morning mist mingles with the world soul's store of knowledge and wisdom. That store of knowledge and wisdom is now enhanced with the image of Alice offering street-level help—offering herself—to those outcast unmarried mums, while Freeman plays with their babies. This image joins another sweet memory in the world soul—Mildred Dyson softly reciting poetic lyrics over the sleepy figures of her children, young Alice and Freeman. As the children drift off to sleep, we are privileged to listen:[41]

> *'Tis gone, that bright and orb'ed blaze*
> *Fast fading from our wistful gaze;*
> *Yon mantling cloud has hid from sight*
> *The last faint pulse of quivering light.*
>
> *Sun of my soul, Thou Savior dear,*
> *It is not night if Thou be near;*
> *O may no earthborn cloud arise,*
> *To hide Thee from Thy servant's eyes.*

---

[40] *Matthew* 9:11-13a.
[41] No known verses are omitted. Young Alice and Freeman preferred the long version.

When the soft dews of kindly sleep
My wearied eyelids gently steep,
Be my last thought, how sweet to rest
Forever on my Savior's breast.

Abide with me from morn till eve,
For without Thee I cannot live;
Abide with me when night is nigh,
For without Thee I dare not die.

If some poor wandering child of Thine
Has spurned today the voice divine,
Now, Lord, the gracious work begin;
Let him no more lie down in sin.

Watch by the sick, enrich the poor
With blessings from Thy boundless store;
Be every mourner's sleep tonight,
Like infant's slumbers, pure and right.

Come near and bless us when we wake,
Ere through the world our way we take,
Till in the ocean of Thy love
We lose ourselves in Heaven above.[42]

---

[42]Lyrics by John Keble (1792–1866), published in *The Christian Year* (1827). Minor variations of lyrics exist among hymn-books.

5 Engines with Souls

Discussions about Our Machines

> *"See the USA*
> *in your Chevrolet..."*[43]

***

Cadavers in the Classroom

We glimpse the thoughts of a student settling down for another evening in STS class...

```
When we came into STS today the Beatles tune ''Drive My
Car'' was playing... The professor just announced that we
are going to the lab to conduct a hands-on exercise--did I
hear him correctly?--working in groups we are going to
dissect a cadaver! And now he is wheeling into our classroom
a hospital gurney. Under the sheet there's something shaped
ominously like a body! I don't know about this...
```

The classroom has become very quiet. The professor grabs the sheet draped over the gurney, about to pull it back. The students lean forward. The professor pauses, lets go of the sheet and says, "You don't mind getting your hands a bit dirty do you? We have rubber gloves in the lab if you want to use them." He grabs the sheet. Students lean forward again. He thinks of something else and turns around to say "This evening's exercise will take about an hour and a half. We will meet back here at 6:30." He turns to the sheet again. Someone yells "Pull it back!" This time he lifts a corner of the sheet and reaches under it with both hands. He brings out...a lawn mower motor. "This," he says, "is the cadaver you are going to dissect today. Unlike the biologists, you will put your cadaver back together." Relief sweeps across some faces in the room. New fears appear in the faces of others. Sheridan S. wrote in a letter, "When my professor walked into the room with what we thought was a cadaver, I had a small moment of panic. Then my moment of panic continued when I heard we would be taking apart a lawn mower motor."

---

[43]Theme song sung by Dinah Shore in the "Dinah Shore Chevy Show," a variety show aired on the NBC television network from October 1956 to June 1963.

Fig. 5.1 *Engine cadaver lab.* (author photo)

Due to Oklahoma City's urban sprawl, limited sidewalks, few bike paths and lack of widespread public transportation, our students who commute or have off-campus jobs depend on cars. When asked for a show of hands, few students perform any mechanical work on their own car or know what goes on inside their car's engine. Being content with zero understanding of a technology on which one relies leaves one in a vulnerable situation.

Everyone migrates down the hall to the physics lab where a dozen 3.75 horsepower, 1-cylinder lawn mower motors await on tables with an array of hand tools. For ninety minutes, each group disassembles enough of their engine to see the crankshaft, piston, connecting rod, camshaft, timing gears, valves, flywheel, and magneto. Each student has a worksheet for identifying various parts and processes, and for making analogies between systems in the engine and the human body. The engine's electrical system is analogous to a nervous system, the air-fuel and exhaust systems resemble a respiratory and digestive system, and so on.[44]

In each group's interview that takes place while professor and students stand over the exposed innards of the engine, the four strokes of its operating cycle are discussed: intake, compression, power, exhaust. We examine strategies, realized in precision parts, for converting the explosion-driven linear motion of the piston into rotary motion of the crankshaft. We discuss the importance and the means for controlling this air-cooled engine's

---

[44]Although it's not asked about on the worksheet, one wag said that "A machinist is an engine's reproductive system."

temperature and keeping its moving parts lubricated. The systems are examined that mix air and fuel into a vapor and deliver it to the cylinder; that generate the spark to ignite the fuel at the critical moment; that carry exhaust gases away. We discuss the difference between gasoline and diesel motors, and between four-stroke and two-stroke engines. Lauren G. wrote in her next weekly letter,

```
    It was so interesting to actually see the inner workings of
a technological device that I use on a daily basis.  I am so
dependent on my vehicle, yet I get in the car every day,
trusting that it will start and take me to my destination
without ever knowing how it works.  When I stop to think how
many different things I use in this manner it is
mind-boggling.  I have no idea how even a simple thing like
my electric toothbrush works.  For that matter, I don't even
understand how my own body works...  I am left wondering if I
am so ignorant of those things, am I really properly and
respectfully using them?...  I hope to better learn how to be
a good steward of the items that I use on a daily basis.
```

Aubrey J. found a new appreciation for the people who take care of these machines:

```
    I gained a new respect for mechanics...  I had never
thought of automobile work as a skill comparable to that of a
doctor, but now I do!  The motor is just the patient
instead!...  I wonder how people might live differently if
they knew their technology on a more personal level.  I am
now catching myself looking at different objects as art,
which is something that I have never done...
```

Taking proper care of any machine requires the right attitudes. Attitudes are difficult to change. Practice the right ones on what you already have. Pirsig's son Chris asked if he could have a motorcycle when he grows up. Robert said yes, if Chris would take care of it. Chris asked, "Is it hard?" Robert replied, "Not if you have the right attitudes. It's having the right attitudes that's hard." [Pirsig(1999)][411] I know from ample experience that even a high-mileage old car, if treated with care and respect, will respond with many more years of faithful service. It may even grow into a good mechanical friend.

Nathaniel S. reflected, "How can I abuse or break something that I myself have no idea how to make? I would venture to say that just about everything that I own or use is something that I do not know how to make myself." Crucially, Natalie F. extended this notion beyond machines: "I believe that when we begin to see the things around us and observe how they work then we should want to take better care of what we have. I think about what would happen if we really took this appreciation and applied it to everything. Then maybe we would not be so quick to get rid of things or we would try to conserve the earth or even our bodies." Lessons with a humble lawn mower motor are highly transferable.

Cars and Appreciation

The second half of the class session resumes back in our usual classroom. The students re-gather to the sound of "Little Deuce Coupe" by the Beach Boys blasting out of the CD player. The image on the screen bears the title "Cars: Appreciation and Awareness" alongside a photograph of a bright red 1961 Ferrari Berlinetta powered by a V-12 engine. For the rest of this evening, says the professor, we will indulge in the first of a two-part presentation about cars. Next week we will think about Awareness. This evening is devoted to Appreciation. With the assistance of historical images and photographs of lovingly preserved antique machines, highlights of automotive history are reviewed.

In 1900 4,212 cars were produced in the USA. Of these 936 were gasoline-powered, 1,585 were electric, and 1,691 were steam-powered. [Clymer(1953)], [Car History 4U(2015)][45] At that time it was not clear which paradigm would dominate. Automotive design was a rapid evolution by conscious selection. When Professor Dyson's father George was a young man he toured Europe on a motorcycle:

Sixty years before Robert Pirsig, he learned to appreciate the art of motorcycle maintenance and the virtue of a technology based upon respect for quality. He sometimes came to villages where no motorcycle had been before. In those days every rider was his own repairman. Riders and manufacturers

---

[45] Early cars, motorcycles and airplanes owe much to bicycles. Bicycle technology gave us ball bearings, wire-spoke wheels, pneumatic tires, sprocket-and-chain drive. The Wright brothers, it will be recalled, were bicycle mechanics. Wright *Flyer 1* (1903) features bicycle sprockets and chains connecting the engine to the propellers.

Fig. 5.2   *The author's father (right) and uncle Paul on the running board of Grandpa's 1929 Dodge, ca. 1933 in Grinnell, Kansas. Quoth Grandpa: "Thirty-five miles an hour is a pretty good speed. If you drive thirty-five miles an hour all day, you won't walk home for supper."* (photo courtesy of the author's father)

were together engaged in trying out a huge variety of different models, learning by trial and error which designs were rugged and practical and which were not. [Dyson(1979a)][105]

The first-generation cars (1890s–early 1900s) were mostly toys for the rich, driven in the jaunty spirit seen today in pilots of motorized hang gliders and speedboats. With the introduction of mass production, interchangable parts, the self-starter,[46] installment car payments, and after a vast used car market emerged, automobiles became available in industrialized nations to almost anyone who held a steady job. By 1930, the surviving manufacturers had all gone to gasoline or diesel power, and the main features of the automobile's gross anatomy were in place. If you can drive a modern car with a manual transmission, you can drive a 1929 Dodge like the one in the accompanying photo.

When Freeman decided to switch from pure mathematics to theoretical physics after World War Two, he was advised by G.I. Taylor at the Cavendish Laboratory to speak with Rudolf Peierls at Birmingham. The historian of quantum electrodynamics, Silvan Schweber, tells how "On the appointed day Dyson traveled on his motorcycle to Birmingham to confer with Peierls to help him decide where he should study in the United States." The young motorcyclist made the trip in a cold rain–"[I] could barely see anything through my goggles." [Schweber(1994)][492]

---

[46]Introduced on the 1912 Cadillac.

When motorcyclists approach one another on the highway they usually exchange a wave of greeting. Professor Dyson's riding days prompted a motorcyclist's wave from the STS professor:

> *13 November 2003*
> *Dear Professor Dyson,*
> *...Schweber's book mentions that you rode about England on a motorcycle. Also you mention in "Disturbing the Universe" that your father rode a motorcycle. As a motorcyclist myself since high school, I find this delightful. I sometimes say that it's hereditary: In 1952 my father was part owner with an Air Force buddy of an early-40s model Indian motorcycle.... His father as a young man rode an Indian with a sidecar, back in the 1920s.*[47] *So I am wondering if you rode a Norton or BSA or Triumph during your rides in England, and if you rode when you came to America. -DEN*

The risk analysis skills that Professor Dyson brought to Bomber Command during World War Two, he also applied to motorcycling:

> *18 November 2003*
> *Dear Dwight,*
> *Thank you for the long letter and the package of papers...*
> *Yes, the motorbike I rode in England was a Triumph.... I sold it when I came to America and never rode again. In America I soon had a wife and kids and staying alive became more important.... I remember in my motorbike years I collected statistics of my motorbike friends and the average expectation of life was about two years. Of course we were then young and reckless and nobody thought of wearing helmets.*[48]
> *... Warm greetings as always to the students, yours ever, Freeman.*

Sports cars, treasured antiques and hand-built street rods are not appliances for carrying people from point A to point B. With the outpouring of craftsmanship that goes into their construction, restoration, and preservation, they are works of art, built, driven, and cared for with passion. Technology engages the emotions as well as the intellect. Enzo Ferrari spoke fondly of "the song of the 12." [Fitzgerald and Merritt(1968)][13][49]

---

[47] Great-grandmother, addressing my paternal grandfather when, as a young man, he set out one day on his Indian motorcycle, ca. 1925: "Eugene, don't you go splittin' the breeze."

[48] Emergency room nurses call motorcyclists without helmets "future organ donors."

[49] Enzo Ferrari speaks of the 12-cylinder overhead-cam engine that is the iconic powerplant of most Ferraris. The Ferrari history cited begins "A Ferrari is, above all, an engine."

But one does not have to own a Ferrari to appreciate them. After looking at pictures of such cars, Amanda A. wrote, "Prof. N made a statement this week about cars that stuck in my mind... He said, 'You don't have to own it to appreciate it.' ...What I like most about this statement is that I think it can be applied to just about anything in life.... Anything and everything can and should be appreciated."

In June 1997, I received a pleasant surprise: a complimentary copy of *Darwin Among the Machines: The Evolution of Global Intelligence* by George Dyson, this George being Professor Dyson's son. On June 23 I wrote to Professor Dyson, "Thank you for thinking of me and sending George's book. When I read the preface, I knew I was going to like it." The preface began "I have attempted...to reconcile a love of nature with an affection for machines..." As one who gets attached to his cars and motorcycles, I share George's dilemma.

When he was 19, George built a tree house 95 feet up in a Douglas fir. The house had cedar paneling, a fireplace and glazed windows. George wintered in the tree house—"In winter I consumed books and firewood.... During those tree house winters I had a lot of time to think.... At odd, unpredictable moments, I found myself wondering whether trees could think. Not thinking the way we think, but thinking the way trees think; say, two or three hundred years to form the slow trace of an idea." In the summers, George worked as a crewman on various boats.

When you live within a boat its engine leaves an imprint, deeper than mind, on neural circuits first trained to identify the acoustic signature of the human heart. As I had sometimes drifted off to sleep in the forest canopy, boats passing in the distance, and wondered whether trees might think, so I sat in the engine-room companionway in the small hours of the morning, with the dark, forested islands passing by, and wondered whether engines might have souls.

...We are brothers and sisters of our machines. Minds and tools have been sharpened against each other ever since a scavenger's stone fractured cleanly and the first cutting edge was held in a hunter's hand. [Dyson(1997b)][ix–x]

After much discussion we still do not know what a "soul" really is. Like Quality, you can't define it. But when someone uses the word you know what they mean.

In *Disturbing the Universe*, Professor Dyson describes two classes of technology that he calls "gray" and "green." Boat engines are gray technologies, a Douglas fir tree is green technology. After George's preface about engines having souls was read to the June 2001 summer school class (which met four hours a day for two weeks), we sent to Professor Dyson the following letter:

> *4 June 2001*
> *Dear Professor Dyson,*
> *...Do you believe that a gray technology that has an awareness of itself could have a sort of soulishness, or in other words, an ability to create relationships with entities around it?*

His response threw light, not only on machines, but on *us*:

> *10 June 2001*
> *Dear Dwight, congratulations for having survived the two weeks of hard labor. That must have been a strenuous, as well as a rewarding, exercise. In my privileged life I never had to teach as much as four hours a day. And still, an average high-school teacher would consider that a light teaching load. It is amazing that so many good people are still teaching in high-schools.*
> *I have a quiet day alone while Imme is in San Diego celebrating our daughter Emily's fortieth birthday. I didn't go for the birthday because I was there two weeks earlier on my way to Jet Propulsion Laboratory. As I may have told you before, Emily has a new son Marcus, born on May 8. His brothers aged 4 and 2 seem to be tolerating him well. Emily inherited some good motherhood genes from Imme.*
> *Now for the students' questions....*
> *The question whether a machine can have a soul is one of the fundamental questions that lie at the root of our understanding of our own nature. Of course nobody knows the answer. We are, after all, machines of a different kind. Does God look for the DNA each time he hands out a soul? Or does he count the neurons and synapses? When my son George writes about trees thinking, and a ship's engine having a soul, he is writing poetry and not science. I do not believe literally that a tree can think or a ship's engine dream. But I find these poetic images full of meaning. There is another world out there, the world of trees and ships, and that other world may well have a mind of its own, or at least the capacity to grow a mind when it gets the chance.*
> *I have a theory about the human soul, which says that the essential feature of our brain that allows the soul to exist is randomness. In every human brain there are about a hundred trillion synapses, connections between neurons, which grow with a high degree of randomness during our first two years. It is the ran-*

domness of the synapses that gives us the chance to be creative, to be different from one another, to be individual souls. When God hands out the soul, he looks for that creative randomness. The machines that we build today, whether they are ships engines or supercomputers, do not have this quality of randomness. Therefore they do not have souls. When machines are built by us or by one another, with randomness equal to ours built into their structure, I would not be surprised to find that they also have souls. Our grey technology today is very far from being able to build such machines. But it is possible, as my son George has said, that the world-wide community of machines that we call the internet will develop into a kind of organism with enough randomness to grow a soul. That is a possibility that we should all take seriously. It is not the individual machine that threatens our dignity as human beings, but the world-wide community of machines. We rely on the machines to organize our lives, and we are growing increasingly dependent on them. When they develop a mind of their own, we may be in trouble.[50]

To those who care about their machines, engines having souls is a meaningful phrase. After getting to know the machine intimately from extended hands-on care, and collecting with it a store of memories, the machine acquires a personality. Robert Pirsig explains:

But over the miles... you pick up certain feelings about an individual machine that are unique for that one individual machine and no other....
I suppose you could call that a personality. Each machine has its own, unique personality which probably could be defined as the intuitive sum total of everything you know and feel about it.... it is this personality that is the real object of motorcycle maintenance. [Pirsig(1999)][49–50]

Pirsig's riding companions, John and Sylvia, love green technology but loathe the gray. They resent being reminded that they are using gray technology to escape to the green. John refuses to work on his motorcycle himself, but takes it to a dealer.

I disagree with them about cycle maintenance, but not because I am out of sympathy with their feelings about technology. I just think that their flight from the hatred of technology is self-defeating. The Buddha, the Godhead,

---

[50]Professor Dyson's discussion of randomness become especially poignant when we realize he discovered a relation between zeroes of the Riemann zeta function and eigenvalues of random matrices.

resides quite as comfortably in the circuits of a digital computer or the gears of a cycle transmission as he does at the top of a mountain or in the petals of a flower. [Pirsig(1999)][26]

Cars and Awareness

The week after our class discussion on automotive appreciation, the topic remains on cars, but the emphasis shifts to awareness.

Cars have changed the surface of this planet more than any other single technology. At the end of World War II, when driving across America one traveled on two-lane highways that went through the center of the towns, with all their stop signs and farm trucks hauling hay. Between towns a good highway cruising speed was about 55 miles per hour. It was not unusual for travelers to camp by the side of the road at night. When Freeman Dyson hopped a ride from Ithaca, New York to Albuquerque, New Mexico in Richard Feynman's Oldsmobile, there were no interstate highways. For better and for worse, every café and hotel you stopped in was unique.

America emerged from World War II with a roaring economy, feelings of superiority and unbounded optimism. Gasoline prices were low, and remained around 20 cents per gallon into the early 1970s. President Dwight Eisenhower signed the Interstate Highway Act in 1956.[51] Beginning in the 1950s the demand for houses and cars exploded, leading to suburbia and urban sprawl. World War II gave us atomic physics, rockets and jet aircraft, which found expression in popular culture through the 1950s in tail fins on cars and Googie signage and architecture. The brightly-colored fast food restaurants that originated on the wide boulevards of postwar Los Angeles swept the country.

With their big beautiful cars, inexpensive gas and interstate highways, Americans hit the road. Banking on the selling point of predictable conformity and economies of scale, the McDonaldization of America exploded in the 1960s and has accelerated ever since. Roads provide access for the ubiquitous franchising that has transformed the appearance and layout of cities and towns. Outside of the pre-war red brick historic downtown districts that managed to survive, the vast post-1960 sections of American cities all

---

[51]The Interstate system was one of Eisenhower's priorities. [Volti(2006)] In 1918 he led a motor vechicle convoy across the USA's muddy roads to test the effectiveness of truck transport for the Army, and in World War Two he became familiar with the German *Autobahn*.

look pretty much the same—the same restaurants, the same gas stations, the same big-box stores, the same motels,[52] the same tire and lube shops, ubiquitous look-alike car dealerships festooned with balloons. Convenient, accessible, congested, and utterly forgettable.

Each individual car is a marvelous machine that deserves care and respect. But the sheer number of them extracts a stiff price. In the United States today there are about 250 million registered motor vehicles, and about 1.2 billion in the world. [Sousanis(2011)] Millions more engines also power aircraft, boats, lawn mowers, farm and construction equipment. The large population of engines greatly contributes to the growing abundance of carbon dioxide, a "greenhouse gas" that accelerates climate change. What does my car contribute to this process? For every gallon of gasoline burned, how many pounds of carbon dioxide are released into the atmosphere?

As questions go, this one is fairly simple. It's not a matter of opinion, but a matter of calculation using measured observables. Octane (C_8H_{18}) is the dominant molecule in gasoline. In combustion the atoms rearrange in the chemical reaction

$$C_8H_{18} + 12.5O_2 \rightarrow 8CO_2 + 9H_2O.$$

In units where the mass of the hydrogen atom is 1, the mass of the carbon atom is about 12 and the oxygen atom about 16. Thus the mass ratio of eight carbon dioxide molecules to the original octane molecule is about 3 to 1. A gallon of gasoline weighs about six pounds; therefore, each gallon of gasoline burned produces about 18 pounds of carbon dioxide.[53] That means if my pickup truck gets 18 miles per gallon, it emits one pound of carbon dioxide with every mile driven. In 100,000 miles that's 50 tons! But one cannot haul sheets of plywood in a Smart Car or pull a horse trailer with a Prius.

Professor Dyson has long expressed skepticism about the more dire predictions regarding climate change. A 29 March 2009 *New York Times* biographical article labeled him a "heretic" on the topic. [Dawidoff(2009)] His

---

[52] "Motel" is a contraction of "motor hotel."

[53] Existing cars can be adapted to run on compressed or liquefied natural gas. Consider methane, CH_4. The combustion reaction is $CH_4 + 2O_2 \rightarrow CO_2 + 2H_2O$. The carbon dioxide molecule weighs 44 units against 16 for methane, a ratio of 2.75, slightly less than the 3-to-1 ratio for octane. But methane's energy density is about ten percent greater than gasoline, about 55 kJ/kg to 44 kJ/kg. Methane and other lightweight hydrocarbon fuels are touted as "clean energy" because they have fewer byproducts (e.g., sulpher) found in petroleum and coal.

biographer, Phil Schewe, reports on Professor Dyson's views about climate change:

> He does not deny that atmospheric carbon dioxide is increasing; he does not deny that human industrial activity is largely to blame; he does not deny that the ensuing climate change will bring some bad effects such as sea level rise or intensified regional drought. He does argue, however, that the climate problem isn't as grim as we are being led to believe by climate modelers. For one thing, those long-term climate models aren't accurate enough to justify a trillion-dollar retrofit of existing power plants. For another thing, some climate-change consequences will be beneficial, such as longer growing seasons. Finally, Dyson says, there are problems more pressing requiring action: improving hygiene and health care, enlarging literacy, and reducing poverty. [Phua *et al.*(2014)][301]

In a letter of 20 November 2012, the STS class asked Professor Dyson about climate change.

> *25 November 2012*
> *Dear Dwight,*
> *...What is the solution to climate change, for this century and in the long run? Answer, climate has always been changing and always will be changing. We do not understand why climate changes and we cannot predict it. So the best we can do is to adapt to the change as it happens. There is no ideal solution to the problem. One place where climate change is most extreme is Illulisat, a place in Greenland where Al Gore goes to take his spectacular pictures of melting glaciers and disintegrating icebergs.*
> *I also went to Illulisat and saw everywhere the evidence of rapid warming. I talked with the people who live there and they love the warming. They hope it continues. It makes their lives much easier. In the old days when it was colder, they lived by fishing in the ocean, and one third of all their young men died at sea. Now they stay on the land and grow vegetables and build hotels for all the tourists who come to take pictures of the melting ice. The fishing boats are now taking tourists for trips to the neighboring islands. Tourists pay much better than fish. There is no doubt that climate change is good for Illulisat.*
> *The big unanswered question is whether climate change is natural or caused by human activities. Many people believe that it is mainly caused by human activities. I believe it is mainly natural. It will take a long time before we know who is right. In the meantime, China and India will continue to burn large quantities of coal in order to become prosperous modern societies.*

> *Coal-burning is certainly bad for the environment. Fortunately, we recently discovered ways to drill for shale gas which is a much cleaner substitute for coal. There are big reserves of shale gas well distributed over the earth, in China, in India, in the USA and in Europe. In the USA, shale gas is already replacing coal. I would say, for this century the continued development of shale gas will counteract the bad effects of coal burning. Then, after a hundred or two years, when the shale gas runs out, we will probably have cheap and efficient ways of using solar energy. But to spend big money now, subsidizing expensive ways of using solar energy, makes no sense.*

Among some questions sent to Professor Dyson on 4 June 2001, we asked "Has your career ever been in conflict with your convictions?" It was an intentionally broad question; we were not thinking of any particular position he has taken or work he has done. But since climate change issues have caused him some controversy, he responded on that subject:

> *10 June 2001*
> *Dear Dwight,*
> *...At the moment I have some conflict arising from my work on climate. I am not really an expert on climate, but I worked on climate at the Oak Ridge National Laboratory for a while and I think I understand the problems quite well. The conflict is the following. The official climate experts have a very dogmatic party line which says that Global Warming is a real and important danger and that we understand it well enough to take action against it. My conviction is that the official experts are wrong, that they rely on unreliable computer models instead of on observations of the real world, and that we should put far more effort into observations before deciding what to do.[54] So my conviction goes directly against the politically correct party line. This is for me a problem. Should I shout or should I keep quiet? On the whole I think it is wise to keep quiet, because I am not a certified expert and any shouting that I do is likely to be ineffective. But I have a bad conscience keeping quiet, because I kept quiet about the bombing campaign during World War Two for similar reasons.*
> *...Yours ever, Freeman.*

---

[54]This letter was written in 2001. By 2007, NASA had 17 missions collecting climate data, and today climate data is collected and shared between the US Department of Defense, National Oceanic and Atmospheric Administration, and various groups operating European, Japanese, and Russian weather satellites. [*http : //climate.nasa.gov/nasa_role*]

Whether or not one agrees with Professor Dyson's prognosis for the climate, one must respect him for speaking his conscience when it would be easier to keep quiet. We will hear more about the bombing campaign of World War Two that left him with a life-long regret for not speaking out.

According to the petroleum geologists, about eight billion barrels of oil lie beneath the Arctic National Wildlife Refuge in northern Alaska. For many years the question of whether to drill for this oil has been a political football. Some proponents of drilling speak of ANWR oil contributing to American energy independence. Let us do another small calculation. How long does it take for the USA to consume eight billion barrels of oil? The USA consumes about 20 million barrels of oil every day.[55] At that rate of consumption a reserve of eight billion barrels will last 400 days, about 13 months. The suggestion that the ANWR reserve will result in energy independence for the USA is laughable.

In the debate about whether to drill in the ANWR, let us at least be honest about motives. When oil prices are $100 per barrel, the ANWR reserve represents 800 billion dollars moving through the economy. But once that oil is gone, it's gone forever, and the landscape will not be the same for many generations. On the last point, one wonders what part of "Wildlife Refuge" needs explanation.

At a 1956 meeting of the American Petroleum Institute, M. King Hubbert presented a seminal paper on the lifetime of oil reserves.[Hubbert(1956)], [Hubbert(1993)], [Hubbert(1971)] From projected demand and supply data he predicted that US domestic oil production would peak about 1970. The world turned, 1970 came and went, and, looking back, the data shows that US oil production peaked about 1970 as Hubbert predicted. Hubbert's calculation, when applied to data on global demand and reserves, predicts that global oil production will peak sometime around 2020. [Sorrell *et al.*(2010)Sorrell, Miller, Bentley and Speirs] With more sophisticated extraction techniques (such as "fracking"), oil and natural gas can be squeezed out after the "easy" resources are depleted. This broadens Hubbert's peak and moves it slightly forward in time, but the essential point remains: the consumption of any finite, non-recyclable resource increases, reaches a peak, then declines asymptotically to zero.

Ever since the 1920s gasoline and diesel have dominated the market because these liquid hydrocarbon fuels pack much more energy density than batteries (about 44 kJ/kg for gasoline compared to about 0.2 to 2 kJ/kg for

---

[55]Actual US consumption as of this writing is closer to 21 million barrels per day. For class discussion I round it down to 20 MB/day.

various kinds of batteries). With our present network of ubiquitous filling stations, gasoline is always nearby. You can refill your tank in five minutes and be on your way for another two hundred miles or more. To go as far with an all-electric car you must recharge the batteries from two hours to overnight, depending on the battery. For driving 600 miles in a day, with present technologies gasoline or diesel are the ways to go. However, most driving is short urban trips. An electric car with a daily range approaching a hundred miles would meet the routine needs of most urban drivers. Thus alternative engine technologies are slowly being revisited, including gasoline-electric hybrids, electric cars with plug-in rechargeable batteries, cars propelled by compressed air or spinning flywheels. Newer technologies include hydrogen burned directly in engines or used in fuel cells.[56]

Do these technologies solve the emission problem, or merely shift it elsewhere? Hybrids still burn fossil fuels. The energy to recharge batteries, compress air or spin flywheels must come from electrical power plants, most of which burn either coal or natural gas. Other sources of electricity include nuclear power plants, hydroelectric plants, wind turbines and solar collectors. Each has its advantages and problems. We move to rapid and unsettling rhythms.

Technologies that hold some promise for automobiles, which did not exist in the early days of motoring, include hydrogen fuel and solar power. Hydrogen gas can be mixed with oxygen and burned in an adapted conventional engine. Alternatively, hydrogen can be reacted with oxygen in a fuel cell, making current to drive an electric motor. In both cases the reaction products are energy and water.[57] The hydrogen is produced by dissociating the water molecule into oxygen and hydrogen, but this takes a greater input of electrical energy than the energy released in combusting the hydrogen.

Since 1990, the Sunrayce has been held, an annual cross-country race for solar-powered cars. Some of them occasionally reach speeds of 70 mph. However, to keep weight and wind resistance within the capabilities of the solar-powered electric motors, the car's payload can carry only the reclining driver. But the entries demonstrate that solar-powered cars are possible in

---

[56] A compressed-air car was exhibited at a London show in 1888. [Clymer(1953)] Although not currently in automobile production, steam has not been entirely forgotten. A British team recently built a car to break the land speed record for steam-powered vehicles. In 2009 they succeeded with a speed of 149 mph. The previous record of 127.66 mph was set by the Stanley Steamer "Rocket" driven by Fred Marriott in 1906. [Woodbury(1950)][231]

[57] The chemical reaction is $2H_2 + O_2 \rightarrow 2H_2O$; no carbon dioxide is produced.

principle. As of this writing the first around-the-world flight by a solar-powered aircraft, the *Solar Impulse 2*, is underway. Although its typical speed is about 30 mph, it is a marvel of solar panels, battery and electric motor technology, 3-D printing, technical redundancy, and strong but lightweight materials. While solar-powered passenger airliners are a long way off, *Solar Impulse 2* makes a statement. When the wood-and-canvas Wright *Flyer* first flew in 1903, nobody envisioned the Boeing 707 jetliner appearing fifty-one years later. [Irving(1993)][58]

4 December 2013
Dear Professor Dyson,
...This semester we looked at the various options for automotive power, such as gasoline and diesel, electric cars, hybrids, steam cars, cars that run on compressed air or flywheels, and even solar powered cars (e.g., entries in the annual Sunrayce). Your experience on Project Orion [see Ch. 10] suggests that you would take seriously proposals for unconventional propulsion systems intended for everyday ground transportation. If the USA were going to launch an ambitious organized program (e.g., with federal funding) to develop alternative energy sources for ground transportation, what recommendations would you make for prioritizing our investment?

6 December 2013
Dear Dwight,
Thanks to you and the students for the questions....
In general I do not think government programs to develop new kinds of cars or trains are a good idea. What we need is small risky ventures that can be allowed to fail, and government is not good at taking risks. Private ventures do the job better. Government programs are needed when the job is too big for a private venture, and then there is a danger that it becomes too big to fail, and it is kept alive for political reasons when it is really a loser. I see only one good candidate for a government program in this area, and that is the fast train project of Gerard O'Neill. He called it VSE for Velocity, Silence, Efficiency. The project died when O'Neill died in 1992. I believe Elon Musk has been promoting a similar project quite recently.
The idea of VSE is that any new ground transportation system must beat the existing system by a factor of ten to capture the market. So VSE is designed to beat the roads and airlines by a factor ten in velocity, a factor ten in silence, and a factor ten

---

[58]The 707 prototype, dubbed the Dash-80, was rolled out in 1954.

*in efficiency. The fast trains are not really trains but little cap-
sules traveling independently, each carrying six passengers with
luggage through steel tubes. The tubes are standard gas pipe-line
tubes with 8-foot diameter and are quite cheap. Inside the tube
is almost a vacuum, with just enough air to conduct heat but
not enough to create drag. The essential idea that makes the
system efficient is that every trip is non-stop. There are no big
stations like airports to delay travelers. There is a small station
underneath every shopping-mall parking-lot. You park the car
and get into the capsule and punch in your destination, and off
she goes, maximum coast-to-coast travel time 50 minutes. The
whole system operates like a telephone network, with a network
of pipes and capsules programmed to avoid collisions. That was
O'Neill's dream. When he was dying of leukemia, he gave me
his model of the system to take to Washington. I had a meeting
with the high-up people at the Department of Energy and showed
them the model and explained how it would work. Of course we
all knew that the project could not survive without O'Neill's
driving force to push it along. When he died, the project died
too. Perhaps, within your lifetimes, it could be resurrected.*

Between 1904 and 1947 the Oklahoma Railway Company operated an
electric interurban railway line that served Oklahoma City and several surrounding towns. The Interurban made a stop in front of our campus. But
no more. In 1947 the company switched to buses (which sparsely serve
the metropolitan area today, none stop at our campus). This scenario was
repeated across the United States in the mid-twentieth century, making
the commitment to cars and trucks dominant. Today the Interstates are
crowded with heavy 18-wheeler trucks, and commuters are overly dependent on cars, most carrying one person. Fortunately, some push-back is
occurring slowly and sporadically, in the form of bike paths, a return of
sidewalks, and construction of a few miles of commuter rail systems in
cities that did not have them before. But we have yet to see every city with
a commercial airport also served by passenger trains, and the US still has
no high-speed trains like those in Europe and Japan.

When my wife and I returned from Rome, our son looked at our photos
of the narrow streets and tiny cars and perceptively observed, "In Rome,
cars are designed for the city." In American cities like Dallas and Denver
and Phoenix and Oklahoma City that have unbridled urban sprawl and
abundant SUVs, the cities are designed for the cars.

The blessings of car culture are considerable and numerous. These machines stand ready to be of service whenever and wherever we want to go. Cars and their supporting infrastructures provide millions of jobs. Some people find driving to be fun, like skiing—the car becomes an extension of the driver as you choose your line through a curve. Cars deserve being celebrated for their own sake, as the abundance of car clubs and car shows illustrate. Appreciation!

On the other hand, what are the costs? To keep the oil flowing we support corrupt dictators, start wars on false pretenses and tolerate catastrophic oil spills. We accept urban sprawl and congested traffic and the homogenizing of America, adopting as normal its frenetic drive-through culture and stressful commuter congestion, cookie-cutter suburbs and highway fatalities. We pay a stiff price in pollution,[59] in the destruction of landscapes and wildlife habitat and historic sites. Car culture in its present form is clearly not sustainable. After a 1200-mile spring break trip by car on the Interstate, Kristeen C. wrote, "As I was traveling this week, I couldn't help but notice the wonderful landscape that surrounded the roads... However, I also noticed the overbearing, paved roads that seemed to slice the landscape creating an odd puzzle of nature. I was quite upset that this beautiful scenery...was all of a sudden disrupted by the highways of speeding cars... Lastly, I could see the numerous dead animals which this overpowering interstate was not so nice to..."

Throughout my life I have tried to balance my love of nature with my love of cars and motorcycles. The point of driving an interesting car or riding a motorcycle is not merely to arrive at a destination, but to enjoy the journey. As Robert Pirsig said, on a motorcycle trip you want to make good time. But the emphasis is on "good" rather than "time." [Pirsig(1999)][13]

In 1950, after refurbishing a 1917 Stanley Steamer and touring the eastern states with it, George Woodbury took a backward glance at motoring in the mid-twentieth century. His comments six decades ago uncannily anticipated our own time:

Civilization, as evidenced by its machinery, seems to have moved perceptibly in the past generation.... Furthermore the direction seems to be away from simplicity and towards complexity...

---

[59]Traffic before automobiles also had abundant pollution. "As for air pollution, it was then, as it is now, especially irksome in the cities. [In 1900], New York blossomed under 2.5 million pounds of horse manure and 60,000 gallons of urine deposited on its streets every day. Dead horses littered the streets at the rate of 15,000 carcasses per year. Clearly, horsepower had its drawbacks." [Mandel(1982)][16]

I like my Stanley Steamer.... Something in the spirit, independence, and inge-
nuity of the men who made it clings to the old machine....
Mounted on the towering quarterdeck of this venerable Rip van Winkle, we
steam silently along, admiring the beautiful countryside..., feeling we have
gained perspective on a number of other things too, which we never could have
seen had we scooted in a streamlined goldfish bowl. [Woodbury(1950)][217,
221]

6   Steered from Afar

Conversations about Identity and Conformity

"The stored-program computer, as conceived by Alan Turing and delivered by John von Neumann, broke the distinction between numbers that mean things and numbers that do things. Our universe would never be the same."
–George Dyson[60]

***

One afternoon my family was sitting in the Oklahoma City airport waiting to board a flight to Portland, Oregon. Boarding was about to begin. We began to wonder if we had turned off the electric oven in the kitchen. "Did you check it?" "No, did you?" "No." My wife picked up her cell phone and called friends who had a key to our house. Very well, they sighed, they would drive out and check it. A way to remotely check and control our oven would have come in handy that day. Every time we have left house since then, we double-check everything. From our airport experience we got the benefit of some education. Incidentally, our friends called later to say the oven was off.

A recent television ad mocks hapless old-fashioned homeowners who still set the household thermostat by hand. The ad bellows "Your house is dumb!" and offers to rescue us from the crushing burden of manually locking our doors and turning off our lights. Merely purchase a contract for the company's programmable controls, and—bingo!—from anywhere on Earth with your smart phone you control your doors and thermostat and coffee maker. Thus empowered, the ad proclaims triumphantly "Now your house is smart!" That these systems work is an impressive technical accomplishment of sensors, electronics, and computer programming.

John von Neumann came to the Institute for Advanced Study to incorporate programmable software into electronic computers. His team was hard at it when Professor Dyson began his permanent tenure there in 1953.

"Hello, Johnny," said [his friend Gleb] Wataghin. "I suppose you are not interested in mathematics any more. I hear you are now thinking about nothing but bombs." "That is quite wrong," said von Neumann. "I am thinking

---
[60][Dyson(2012)][ix].

103

about something much more important than bombs. I am thinking about computers." [Dyson(1979a)][194]

Today computers run just about everything. Most of us use them all day on the job. We have them in our cars, clothes, cameras and phones; they are in our kitchens, exercise equipment and strapped to our wrists. They fly commercial airplanes and keep track of every keystroke of our on-line shopping; when you swipe your debit card a computer across the continent records the transaction and deducts the amount from another computer in your bank. Numbers *do* things.

The ad shouting at you to make you house "smart" tells only one side of the story. Unlike the sellers of pharmaceuticals, automation hawkers are not required to describe side effects. With a "smart house" it will be easier to leave the house with careless inattention. With your home's electrical appliances networked into the regional utility, social engineering will become easier for bureaucrats. Inevitably hackers will figure out how to remotely unlock your doors and disable your security cameras. With this outsourcing of personal responsibility, as the houses get smarter will the people inside them get dumber? Timara S. warned in a weekly letter, "The problem with technology is that we are letting a machine—a lifeless object—take the place of our own brain." What a step down from the gumption-building attitude of any three-year-old who, when offered help, haughtily declares "I can do it *myself!*"

Idiot Park

Cars and eighteen-wheeler trucks are being developed that drive themselves. I have been in enough traffic jams to appreciate how hundreds of vehicles organizing themselves into platoons and moving collectively like a train could, if all went well, move everyone along. In addition, those who can no longer drive, such as the disabled, would still be able to travel by private autonomous cars. But one wonders why we would turn cars into trains when six decades ago we got rid of passenger trains to promote the use of cars. For the mass of commuters, why not bring back real trains? Why not restore high school driver education courses? Why do we automatically reach for even more layers of technology to get us out of the problems produced by technology, while simultaneously buying into our own deskilling?

Home Depot and Wal-Mart do not steer you to the self-checkout line to save *your* time, but to reduce *their* payroll. Consider what is being so nonchalantly discarded. The texture of life is enriched by little moments of informal personal interactions, including small talk at the check-out-line and bank teller window. Because my wife and I still go into our bank in person, the tellers and officers there have come to be our friends through a history of brief face-to-face interactions, repeated three or four times a month across several years. "Both as workers and as consumers, we feel we move in channels that have been projected from afar by vast impersonal forces..." [Crawford(2009)][7]

26 November 2014
Dear Professor Dyson,
On behalf of the Fall 2014 Science, Technology & Society class I bring you warm greetings....
Are we becoming too dependent on automation? A reference we have used on this topic is the new book by Nicholas Carr, "The Glass Cage: Automation and Us." Carr begins by describing a January 2013 FAA Safety Alert for Operators.... When the automation fails, the pilots suddenly find they have forgotten how to fly the airplane by themselves. Now we see the same trend—towards turning our skills and responsibilities over to software—being relentlessly advocated to all of us, such as autonomous cars, networked appliances in households, and so on. In addition to the deskilling, our relationship with our machines gets drastically changed. Carr writes, "Pilots have always defined themselves by their relationship to their craft. Wilbur Wright, in a 1900 letter... said of the pilot's role, 'What is chiefly needed is skill rather than machinery.'" Carr continues, "As we begin to live our lives inside of glass cockpits, we seem fated to discover what pilots already know: a glass cockpit can also be a glass cage." This reminds us of "The Magic City"—once we wish for machinery we are stuck with it. But it seems now that we are stuck with it even if we do not wish for it; it is foisted upon us even when we do not ask for it. What are your thoughts on automation and what it does to our abilities to be self-reliant?

3 December 2014
Dear Dwight and students,
I am back from our five-day trip to celebrate with daughter Mia and her family in Maine.... Here are answers to your questions.... As usual, the questions are more interesting than the answers. The most important part of your education is to work out your own answers....
I have not read the Nicholas Carr book, but I agree with your re-

marks about it. I recommend that you read another book, "The Human Use of Human Beings," published by Norbert Wiener in 1950, an amazingly far-sighted view of the problems that would arise from automation. Wiener was writing before electronic computers existed, but he was expert in mechanical control systems, and he foresaw the dangers that would come from the combination of electronics and control systems. His most famous prediction was made on page 189 of the book:[61] "The automatic machine is the precise economic equivalent of slave labor. Any labor which competes with slave labor must accept the economic conditions of slave labor. It is perfectly clear that this will produce an unemployment situation, in comparison with which the present recession and even the depression of the thirties will seem a pleasant joke." This is a different problem from the loss of skills and loss of self-reliance discussed by Carr, but the loss of skilled blue-collar and white-collar jobs goes together with a loss of self-reliance. This is a permanent loss, and will make any lasting economic recovery impossible so long as our politicians believe that market economics will solve our problems.

In my opinion, any lasting recovery will require that we abandon market economics applied to human labor. We must take human labor out of the market-place. Let workers be paid according to their need, even when machines can do the job more cheaply. This makes sense, even though Karl Marx said it. Other parts of Marx, such as the dictatorship of the proletariat and the public ownership of the means of production, do not make sense. Unfortunately the disasters caused by Marxist nonsense have discredited the Marxist ideas that make sense.

Fortunately, there are two human enterprises that will always depend on human skills and keep highly skilled people productively employed. The two skill-driven enterprises are art and science. In the future, as machines take over more and more of the routine work required by a modern society, more and more of our young people will be artists and scientists. In the future, as in the past, the great civilizations will be those that give art and science sustained and generous support.

Thank you once more for a good set of questions....

Happy Christmas to you and the class! Yours ever, Freeman.

The next time you are in the checkout line at Wal-Mart or Home Depot, and there are four self-checkout stands for every human cashier, think about Weiner's remarks, echoed by Professor Dyson, that those human checkers are being treated, economically, as slave labor. Are you OK with that?

---

[61]Professor Dyson was evidently referring to another printing; the quote is found on p. 162 of the 1954 reprint cited in the bibliography.

The 1950 book that Professor Dyson recommends—*The Human Use of Human Beings* [Wiener(1950)] by Norbert Wiener (1894–1964)—was written to make available to the wider public the ideas of a technical book on the same subject that Wiener published in 1948. The technical book was called *Cybernetics*, a name Wiener derived from the Greek word *kibernëtës*, or "steersman." [Wiener(1948)]

Checking one's own oil while filling the gasoline tank was a habit familiar to generations of drivers. But many newer cars do not have a dipstick. Instead of pulling out the dipstick to check the oil level yourself, you have to take your over-sophisticated car to a dealer who will hook up a computer and charge you a hundred dollars an hour for labor, merely to tell you what owners of earlier models can learn for themselves, for free, in about thirty seconds, in their driveway. How is the no-dipstick paradigm an improvement? Whose interest does it serve? A simple, reliable, low-tech measurement has been replaced with engineered dependency. One feels like a hooked fish on a line. In *Shop Class as Soulcraft* Matthew Crawford laments the loss of replacing hand-on engagement with black boxes.

We often hear of the need for an "upskilling" of the workforce, to keep up with technological change. I find the more pertinent issue to be: What sort of personality does one need to have, as a twenty-first century mechanic, to tolerate the layers of electronic bullshit that get piled on top of machines? [Crawford(2009)][7]

Joey C. wonders, "Is our ever-increasing dependence on this technology healthy?... the legitimate concerns of our techno-savvy lives seemed to be hushed by the moguls of the microchip." The new cars today are loaded with electronic gadgets galore that make the power windows and signal-seeking radio of a 1956 Cadillac seem quaint. One has to respect the ability of engineers to take silicon and metal and put them together with sensors and mathematics programmed into a million lines of code that enable cars to parallel-park themselves, carry GPS navigation systems and voice-activated messaging, anti-skid control, blind-spot sensors and radar coupled to the steering and brakes. Most of these features contribute to safety. Their virtues, which are real and significant, are justifiably touted by those who sell them.

But our machines now do so much of the thinking for us that our skills are allowed to atrophy. At a social level the automation marketed as making our lives easier also represents the institutionalization of infantile dependency and outsourced responsibility. The most important safety feature in any car is the driver. In the television ads selling cars with radar and blind spot sensors, the drivers are shown being distracted and the technology swoops in to save the day at the last split second, heroically preventing an accident. No one is against preventing accidents. But one cannot help but notice these messages imply that, had the driver paid attention to driving, all this marvelous technology would not be necessary. Attentive, minds-on driving needs no gadgetry.

How ironic it is that, while we are learning the hard way about the downsides of what automation has done to the flying of commercial airliners, proponents of automation are trying to convince us to do the same thing with millions of cars and 18-wheeler trucks. Some people find driving boring. Fair enough; but since driving requires active engagement with the outside world, it cannot be nearly as boring as watching the computer screens that will surround you in the glass cage.

A set of sensors coupled to the steering and brakes responds to what is *already* happening around the car, whereas an engaged driver actively looks several cars ahead and all around, anticipating what *might* happen. Matthew Carr summarizes,

> Google and other software companies are, of course, in the business of making our lives easier... But as their programs become adept at doing our thinking for us, we naturally come to rely more on the software and less on our own smarts.... When that happens, we end up learning less and knowing less. We also become less capable. [Carr(2014)][80]

Musician and STS student Elliott T. observes this happening in his field:

> Our parents had to do many things manually that we don't
> have to today, but that built character and discipline....
> This reminds me of my quandary over most modern music. It is
> so over-produced, meaning it's digitally altered to sound
> more aesthetically pleasing to the masses.... It's becoming
> easier to make an album, because the need for talent is
> declining. Most of the artists today wouldn't have made it
> in their time, because you had to be good enough without
> these new technologies.

By trying to "help" us with software that completes words and sentences and architectural drawings for us, the software may be cutting off chances for critical and creative thinking. Are you comfortable with the computer completing your doctor's sentences in your medical record, thereby closing off deeper thinking that lies outside the software's algorithm? [Carr(2014)][122–123]

There have always been drivers who found parallel-parking to be difficult. You had to practice until you got it. Now drivers who can't parallel-park won't have to. Parking incompetence has been transformed into a technological status symbol. When oil pressure gauges, temperature gauges and ammeters on automobile dashboards were replaced with warning lights in the mid-1950s, everyone called them "idiot lights." Should the system that enables a car to parallel-park itself be called "idiot park?"

McCulture

Thanks to technology and economics, society is relentlessly steered towards homogenization and conformity and the loss of diversity. The McDonaldization of society cuts across all varieties of franchised retailing, from fast food to hotel chains, from auto care to home furnishings, from lasik eye surgery to hospitals and mortuaries. Its strategies rely on efficiency, economies of scale, calculability, conformity, predictability, and the control of people. [Ritzer(2011)], [Schlosser(2012)] Globally the food economy becomes dominated by giant corporations, and locally the computerized technology enables the fast food chains to rely upon a low-paid unskilled workforce who are taught little more than which buttons to push. Morale is low and turnover rates are high, but there are more where they came from. Many independent businesses do not survive, and the world's quality of interestingness declines.[62]

On the other hand, McDonalds indoor playgrounds offer a well-designed, reasonably safe, clean and fun place for children to play. On a car trip with small children, or during an afternoon of babysitting when there are papers that must be graded, safety and predictability can trump interestingness.

---

[62]My young grandchildren love to get a McDonalds Happy Meal. It's name "Happy" suggests the child psychologist consultants have done their homework. It comes in a colorful box with a toy inside, a polymerized representation of a character in the latest release from the Disney movie empire. At home it's hard to find anything in the child's toy box, closet or bedding that does not bear the image of a Disney character. On the other hand, the Disney movies, while following a predictable story line template, are quality products and offer wholesome electronic entertainment for children. Nevertheless, the reflective parent or grandparent feels pushed towards the world described so well in the 2008 computer-animated Disney movie "Wall-E."

McDonalds and its clones offer predictable mediocrity, but their restaurants are not "greasy spoons." How ironic that today we go out of our way to find one-of-a-kind restaurants that still have unique ambience.

Biological diversity is necessary for the survival of life on this planet. Cultural diversity is necessary for life with interestingness. The McDonalization and Disneyfication result when mass marketing is the goal and technological efficiencies are the means. The price is the loss of diversity in biology and culture. Does the First Commandment apply to the God of Efficiency? Professor Dyson wrote, "It is likely that in the future our survival and our further development will depend in an equally crucial way on the maintenance of cultural and biological diversity." [Dyson(1979a)][220–221]

Bombed from Afar

An Air Force officer sits inside a windowless bunker east of Colorado Springs, surrounded by another glass cage of computer and television screens. Across the world, a drone aircraft armed with air-to-surface missiles responds at the speed of light to his satellite-relayed commands, literally steered from afar.

In the summer of 2014, Professor Dyson received a message from a translator in Madrid who had converted *The Magic City* into Spanish. In his reply to the translator, Professor Dyson graciously copied us:

> *July 13, 2014*
> *Dear N. R.,*
> *Thank you for your friendly message. I am delighted to hear that you translated "The Magic City" and understood the deeper meaning of the story.*
> *Now we have a new example of the same story. My grandchildren are playing with a beautiful new toy, a radio-controlled helicopter with four propellers that they can control accurately with two little switches. The toy is amazingly cheap (30 US dollars) including an electric charger to recharge the engines. It is light and rugged and safe for children to play with. It keeps them happily playing either outside or inside the house. The propellers are so light that a child can grab them with bare fingers and will not be hurt.*
> *Unfortunately somebody had the clever idea of using the same design of radio-controlled helicopter to kill people. All you have to do is make the machine bigger and put an accurately-controlled missile on board, and you have a killer drone airplane. And now these killer drones are killing people in Pakistan and*

*many other places. My grandchildren's beautiful new toy has
become a permanent part of modern weaponry.
Thank you for your work as a translator. Translators are making a big contribution to the world community, helping us all to
understand one another.
Yours sincerely,
Freeman Dyson.*

The next December, a newspaper article describing the high demand at Christmas-time for toy drone aircraft included a statement by Bill Sulzman, director of the Colorado Spring-based Citizens for Peace in Space. Citing near-misses with other aircraft, Sulzman argued that drone regulations are needed. He also saw a moral dimension: "In the military realm they're a new weapon that I see as sinister because they're so secretive and so outside the moral code—they don't have any jeopardy on the side of those using them and have changed the definition of what is an act of war." [Kelly(2014)][63] Every technology is more than a tool. It can change the user's moral code.

The 2013 disclosures by Edward Snowden of warrantless spying on US citizens by the National Security Administration was a major story in the news. At the same time, in the ongoing war in Afghanistan, armed drone aircraft were hunting terrorists. In US cities, speed limits are increasingly enforced by automated cameras that photograph a car's license plate and sends a computer-generated ticket to its owner. Cookies on our computers track every website we visit, surveillance cameras are everywhere, including the Google Glass wearer walking towards you who might be surreptitiously photographing. There is nothing on Facebook or Twitter or e-mail that ever goes away, whether or not you gave consent to be photographed or quoted. While these technologies are marvelous and we appreciate what they can accomplish, where does one go to be left alone? While these technologies can be liberating, they can be a tight leash. These developments inspired one of our questions for Professor Dyson in the fall of 2013:

*4 December 2013
Dear Professor Dyson,..
Recent disclosures about data being collected by the National
Security Administration, along with the growing use of surveil-
lance cameras, data mining, and drone aircraft, raises inter-
esting dilemmas in the interactions of technology with society.*

---

[63]Debby Kelley, "Drones Create a Buzz at Store," Colorado Springs *Gazette*, 21 December 2014, pp. A1, A4.

What moral principles, translated into policies and laws, should guide our decisions on these issues?

6 December 2013
Dear Dwight,
There are two separate issues here. One is the collection of personal information about people. The other is the use of drones to kill people. Both are serious problems. The use of drones to kill people is a more urgent problem. It blurs the distinction between war and peace. If we persist in killing people this way, we will never have any real peace. The only solution that I can see to this problem is to stop killing people by executive action, to go back to the old rule of law, that you kill people only by legal process with a fair and open trial.
The collection of information is a more complicated problem. There are many good reasons to collect information. The problem now is that it is cheaper to store information than to destroy it, so huge amounts of information are stored and little is destroyed. The problem is to avoid the abuse of this information by vindictive people and governments. In my opinion the most urgent need is to get rid of secrecy as far as possible.
The worst abuses happen when information is kept secret. Most of the secrecy is harmful and unnecessary. To me, anyone who breaks the rule of secrecy and brings the abuses out into the open is a hero. To punish whistle-blowers is a clear sign of tyrannical government.

A large attractive poster bearing the caption "Quantum Information" hangs in the hallway outside my office. It says, "Through massive parallel processing, quantum computers are expected to easily crack popular encryption schemes and offer faster ways of searching vast databases."[64] In a society already relentlessly data-mined and hacked, are we supposed to be happy about taking it to another level? Life will go on, but should we be concerned?

6 May 2005
Dear Professor Dyson,...
Do you see quantum computing having a major impact on modern life?

---

[64] "Quantum Information" poster produced by the Joint Quantum Institute of the University of Maryland, the American Physical Society, and the National Institute for Standards and Technology.

7 May 2005
Dear Dwight,...
Quantum computing is an exciting scientific problem. By exploring the possibilities of quantum computing, we are reaching a deeper understanding of quantum mechanics. Where that deeper understanding will lead is impossible to say. It is much too soon now to begin designing quantum computers or to predict what they may do. My own guess is that we will not have quantum computers standing alone, but quantum subroutines incorporated inside ordinary computers for doing special jobs. I do not see any major impact on the lives of people who are not computer experts. But I could well be wrong. It all depends on what kind of jobs the quantum processors may do. Your guess is as good as mine.

After John von Neumann became a US citizen in 1937, his involvement with the military increased over the next two decades. George Dyson's history of early electronic computers recalls Stan Ulam's observation that von Neumann "...seemed to admire generals and admirals and got along well with them... [This] fascination with the military...was due more generally to his admiration for people who had power." [Dyson(2012)][56] This is interesting because Professor Dyson identified subversion of authority as one of the beautiful faces of science. In the closing episode of *The Ascent of Man*, Jacob Bronowski returns to this "age-old conflict between intellectual leadership and civic authority..."

The man who personifies these issues for me is John von Neumann.... He became more and more engaged in work for private firms, for industry, for government.... Johnny von Neumann was in love with the aristocracy of the intellect.... If we are anything, we must be a democracy of the intellect. We must not perish by the distance between people and government, between people and power... And that distance can only be conflated, can only be closed, if knowledge sits in the homes and heads of people with no ambition to control others, and not up in the isolated seats of power." [Bronowski(1973)][429–435]

4 December 2000
Dear Professor Dyson,
Our Science, Society, and Technology class at SNU wishes you and your family a joyous Christmas season.
Another book we read this semester was "The Ascent of Man" by Jacob Bronowski. In his final chapter, "The Long Childhood," Bronowski describes his disappointment with John von Neumann ("the cleverest man I ever knew"), who (in Bronowski's

*view) "was in love with the aristocracy of intellect." Bronowski
went on to say that we must be a "democracy of the intellect."
Since you probably knew John von Neumann at the Institute,
would you care to critique Bronowski's comment on von Neumann, and of the danger of a too-close relationship between
science and the high seats of government and power?*

Here again Professor Dyson looked at this situation from another perspective:

*7 December 2000
Dear Dwight,...
I didn't know Von Neumann well and never talked with him
about his philosophy of life. During the time I knew him, he
was working hard against great obstacles to get the first modern
computer operating here at the Institute for Advanced Study.
The computer was being used for three main purposes, (1) simulations of hydrogen bombs about which I knew nothing, (2) simulations of weather aimed at improved weather-prediction, (3)
simulations of evolution of living organisms in an artificial universe. There was a lively group of young meteorologists working
on problem (2). Most of them came from Norway, which has
always been a great country for meteorology since it has atro-
cious weather and depends on fishing to stay alive. I enjoyed
talking with them and hearing their stories. They all had a great
respect for Von Neumann.
...I knew Bronowski well, better than I knew Von Neumann.
They struck me as being very similar. Both of them amus-
ing, both brilliant, both arrogant prima donnas, both "in love
with the aristocracy of intellect." The main difference is that
Von Neumann's love of power took him to Washington, while
Bronowski's love of power took him to Hollywood. Both of them
were fundamentally decent people trying to do good for humanity, but Von Neumann was corrupted by Washington just as
Bronowski was corrupted by Hollywood. Both kinds of corrup-
tion are dangerous, but I think both men preserved a basic integrity in spite of the temptations of fame and power.
I happen to agree with Von Neumann that it is not wrong, and
it is often part of our duty to society, for scientists to talk with
generals and admirals. Generals and admirals are isolated from
the real world, and we should talk with them whenever we get
the chance, just as Jesus talked with publicans and sinners.... If
Von Neumann and Bronowski were running for president (what
a delightful prospect that would be!), Bronowski would probably
win, but I would vote for Von Neumann.*

Professor Dyson has been talking to generals and admirals for a long time, doing his part to keep them from being isolated. He does not always tell the generals and admirals what they want to hear. His letter reminds us that the digital computer and the hydrogen bomb grew up together. The hydrogen bomb, that used nuclear fusion, was preceded by the atomic bomb, that used nuclear fission. The day after Hiroshima was destroyed with a uranium fission bomb, Freeman Dyson recalled that "...on August 7, the News-Chronicle arrived at my breakfast table in London with the giant headline 'New Force of Nature Harnessed.'..." [Dyson(1979a)][44] The world had, once again, thanks to technology and its coupling to human values, abruptly changed.

7 The Swamp Angel

Letters on Ends and Means

> *"It is well that war is so terrible–we should grow too fond of it."*
> –General Robert E. Lee to General James Longstreet, Fredrickburg, Virginia, December 13, 1862[65]

***

The igniting of the American Civil War occurred in Charleston, South Carolina, when the Confederates fired on Fort Sumter on April 12, 1861. Two years later, the Federals attempted to retake the fort. In the summer of 1863 the Union army under General Quincy Gillmore built a "cunningly engineered" heavy gun emplacement on Morris Island, a stretch of sand parallel to the Charleston harbor entrance. Gillmore's gun, an eight-inch rifled cannon that fired a 200-pound shell, was dubbed the Swamp Angel by Union soldiers. It was aimed not at Fort Sumter but at the city. General Gillmore warned that unless Fort Sumter was immediately evacuated the Swamp Angel would bombard Charleston. The ultimatum was ignored, and the Swamp Angel opened fire.

The gunners used a new type of incendiary shell, hoping to set the city ablaze. Under a white flag of truce Confederate General P. G. T. Beauregard sent a message of protest, outraged at this firing into a city "filled with sleeping women and children." It was Beauregard's turn to be ignored, and the firing continued. Fortunately for the sleeping women and children, the incendiary shells were ineffective and no firestorm swept across Charleston. After thirty-six firings the Swamp Angel exploded. Although its impact on the outcome of the Civil War was negligible, the Swamp Angel was a portent of things to come. Civil War historian Bruce Catton noted its significance:

> It would hardly be worth mentioning, except that it showed how war had hardened men's emotions, so that things that would have been horrifying in ordinary times horrified no longer. The idea of throwing Greek fire into homes where women and children slept did not seem dreadful at all. Good men even

---

[65][Catton(1965)][13]

rejoiced in it...

When good men could talk so they consented to terror. A later generation might be able to make incendiaries that would really work. [Catton(1965)][224–226]

On 6 July 1945, a uranium-fission bomb called Little Boy detonated 2000 feet over the Japanese city of Hiroshima. Little Boy's yield was the equivalent of about 12 thousand tons of dynamite. In the nine seconds it took the shock wave and fireball to sweep across the city, some 70,000 to 80,000 people were killed. Thousands more would later die in agony from burns and radiation sickness. Three days after Hiroshima, a plutonium-fission bomb called "Fat Man," with a yield of 22 kilotons, exploded over Nagasaki. Estimates of immediate deaths range from 40,000 to 80,000.

As these bombings were being planned, someone might have argued on moral grounds against using these weapons on civilians. But by the summer of 1945 it was too late for bomber commands to be smitten with morality. Such arguments should have been voiced years earlier. In Chapter 4 of *Disturbing the Universe* Professor Dyson recalls,

Two factors made it almost inevitable that [Secretary of War] Stimson, and President Truman following Stimson's advice, would decide to use the bombs. First was the fact that the whole apparatus for delivering the bombs...already existed.... The second factor prejudicing Stimson's decision was the fact that indiscriminate fire bombing of Japanese cities had already occurred and was widely approved... The ground on which Stimson might have been able to make a moral stand was already surrendered... [Dyson(1979a)][43]

Let us review the events that prejudiced Stimson's decision. Five months before the atomic bombings, on the night of March 9–10, 1945, waves of American B-29 bombers dropped thousands of incendiary bombs on Tokyo, making in two great swaths a giant X of fire. A strong wind and the wooden Japanese houses did the rest, and a hundred thousand people burned to death.

A month earlier the British firebombed Dresden in Germany. Dresden was a center of art and architecture with no weapons factories, few bomb shelters, 26,000 Allied prisoners and swollen with refugees fleeing Soviet advances from the east. The raid destroyed the historic city center and left at least a documented 24,000 dead.

In July 1943, the British raised a firestorm in Hamburg that killed 45,000. Thousands of German civilians suffocated in underground shelters deprived of oxygen, or were swept into the flames by the tornadic winds feeding the firestorms, or became trapped in the melted asphalt of the streets as they fled burning buildings. [Rhodes(1986)][471–474.]

In August 1942, General von Richtofen's air raids reduced most of Stalingrad (now Volgograd) to rubble, leaving 40,000 civilians dead at the outset. The Battle of Stalingrad would eventually claim two million casualties and be the war's turning point in the eastern front. [Beevor(1999)]

World War Two started on September 1, 1939 with the German invasion of Poland. The *Luftwaffe* leveled Warsaw, subjugated Poland, then invaded France through the Low Countries, flattening Rotterdam on the way. When the *Wehrmacht* got to the English Channel, London was next. Thus began the Blitz of the Battle of Britain, which continued throughout the fall of 1940. Hermann Goering, as head of the *Luftwaffe*, boasted that German air power would quickly bring the British to their knees. Before the Blitz, before Warsaw, there was Guernica.

"No, you did."

The first modern firebombing of a city by aircraft happened on April 26, 1937, to the Basque town of Guernica, Spain. The Spanish Civil War was underway, as the Nationalists under General Francisco Franco tried to overthrow the Popular Front Republican government of President Manuel Diaz. The Republicans received Soviet aid in the form of advisers and equipment. Franco appealed to Fascist countries for assistance. Goering urged intervention, "firstly, to prevent the spread of communism; secondly, to test my young *Luftwaffe* in this or that technical aspect." [Jablonski(1971)][15] For the Nazis, the Spanish Civil War was practice. On April 26, 1937, Heinkel 111 and Junkers 52 aircraft, ostensibly passenger planes but designed to be easily converted into bombers,[66] swooped in over Guernica, dropping incendiary bombs. In this town of 7,000, on that day 1,654 people were killed and 889 wounded. [Jablonski(1971)][16–17]

The day after Guernica's bombing, protests of outrage erupted around the world. The Spanish artist Pablo Picasso (1881–1973) was living in Paris at the time. He expressed his outrage by painting *Guernica*, which he completed in June. Picasso used abstract art to express his outrage at the firebombing. No attempt at realism could do justice to the atrocity. The distorted black-and-white figures suggest the horror. Your imagination does the rest. The mother cradling her dead infant. The dismembered soldier

---

[66]Germany was forbidden by the 1918 Treaty of Versailles from having an air force.

with a broken sword. The horse gored by the bull. The man engulfed in flames. Daggers for tongues in the mouths of the screaming victims. A Gestapo officer searching Picasso's apartment during the occupation saw *Guernica* and asked Picasso, "Did you do that?" Picasso replied, "No. You did." [Regan(1992)][25][67] From the moment it was first displayed, *Guernica* transcended the story of its namesake to symbolize the murderous brutality of all war. The foreshadowing of the Swamp Angel was coming to pass.

When Goering arrived at the English Channel and looked with greedy eyes towards the white cliffs of Dover, the British prepared for the worst. Because of his mathematical abilities, Freeman Dyson was recruited by the Ministry of Aircraft Production, and given the job of analyzing bombing strategies and their results. He worked at Bomber Command headquarters, Operations Research Section, in the town of High Wycombe between London and Oxford. [Schewe(2013)]

From the Swamp Angel to Little Boy and Fat Man, one rationalization for bombing cities has always been to destroy citizen morale. Rather than destroying morale, shared hardship in desperate times brings people together and hardens resolve.

Making Evil Anonymous

"The more technical the world imposed on us by the war, the more dangerous was this indifference of the technician to the direct consequences of his anonymous activities." – Albert Speer[68]

In 1939, with the outbreak of World War Two imminent, a British government and military command center began operations within a complex of rooms deep underground, across the street from Parliament. Any moral argument against the bombing of civilians should have been made here, in the Map Room and the Cabinet Room, now preserved as the Churchill War Rooms. The British *Most Secret Operation Order No. 173* included morale destruction as a justification for "de-housing" (Churchill's euphemism) the citizens of enemy nations.

The total destruction of this city would achieve immeasurable results in reducing the industrial capacity of the enemy's war machine. This, to-

---

[67] With Franco in power Picasso never returned to Spain. He would not allow *Guernica* to be sent to Spain until democracy and personal liberty were restored there. From Paris, the painting went New York. It finally came home to Spain in 1981.

[68] Albert Speer [Speer(1970)][253]

gether with the effect on German morale, which would be felt throughout the country, would play a very important part in shortening and in winning the war. [Rhodes(1986)][471]

The latter point was the same reason Goering used three years earlier for pounding London in the Blitz. But those months solidified rather than destroyed the morale of the Brits. Why the British and American planners thought the residents of Hamburg would respond differently is anyone's guess. The British bombed Germany by night, the Americans by day. The commanders saw hope for their strategy in July 1943 with the Hamburg firestorm. When I visited the Churchill War Rooms in 2011 and looked at the conference tables and wall maps, the words of Freeman Dyson ran through my head:

The ground on which [US Secretary of War Henry] Stimson might have been able to make a moral stand was already surrendered when the fire bombing [of Tokyo] started in March [1945]. Long before that, in England and in America independently, the moral issues had been effectively prejudged when the decisions were made to build strategic bomber forces and to wage war with them against civilian populations. Hiroshima was only an afterthought. [Dyson(1979a)][43]

Strategic bombing killed hundreds of thousands of families on both sides, and reduced to ashes venerable cities that housed some of humanity's finest art and architecture. Despite all that, the bombings spectacularly failed to destroy morale. Professor Dyson recalls after the war, while riding across the USA with Richard Feynman, who had worked on the atomic bomb, Feynman "had an absolute confidence in the ability of ordinary people to survive the crimes and follies of their rulers... He knew how tough ordinary people are, how death and destruction often brings out the best in us." [Dyson(1979a)][61]

The German capital of Berlin was the ultimate Allied European target. From the data he analyzed, Freeman Dyson knew by January 1944 that the optimistic hope expressed by Bomber Command's slogan "Victory through Air Power" was an illusion. The Berlin defenses got better and the scatter in Allied bombings got worse.

The boys who flew in the Lancasters were told that this battle of Berlin was one of the decisive battles of the war and that they were winning it. I did

not know how many of them believed what they were told. I knew only that
what they were told was untrue. [Dyson(1979a)][19–21]

Besides having access to data that showed the disparity between the
campaign's ambitions and its cost in lives and Lancasters, Freeman was also
haunted by a sense of guilt for working in a snug office while thousands of
young men his age—the "boys"—risked violent death with every mission.
The 2001 summer session class asked Professor Dyson about inner struggles
he faced in writing about his experiences at Bomber Command.

> *4 June 2001*
> *Dear Professor Dyson,*
> *...What kinds of emotions did you have to overcome to write*
> *about the "Childrens Crusade?"*

> *10 June 2001*
> *Dear Dwight,*
> *...The conflict that I had to overcome when writing the Chil-*
> *dren's Crusade was the conflict between truth and loyalty. I*
> *felt an intense loyalty to the young boys who flew in the bombers*
> *and died in thousands in the belief that they were winning the*
> *war against Hitler. And I felt an intense shame for having*
> *failed to speak the truth during the war, the painful truth that*
> *the sacrifice of these young lives was in vain, that our losses*
> *were out of proportion to the military damage we were doing to*
> *Germany. It took me twenty-five years to resolve the conflict.*
> *The first time I wrote about the bombing campaign was in 1970,*
> *in a piece called "The Sell-Out" published in the New Yorker*
> *(February 21, 1970) and afterwards reprinted as chapter 10 in*
> *my book "Weapons and Hope" in 1984.*

We interrupt this letter for a look into chapter 10 of *Weapons and Hope*:

I was sickened by what I knew. Many times I decided I had a moral obli-
gation to run out into the streets and tell the British people what stupidities
were being done in their name. But I never had the courage to do it....
After the war ended, I read reports of the trials of men who had been high up in
the Eichmann organization. They had sat in their offices, writing memoranda
and calculating how to murder people efficiently, just like me. The main dif-
ference was that they were sent to jail or hanged as war criminals, while I went
free. I felt a certain sympathy for these men. Probably many of them loathed
the SS as much as I loathed Bomber Command, but they, too, had not had the
courage to speak out. Probably many of them, like me, lived through the whole
six years of war without ever seeing a dead human being." [Dyson(1984)][120]

Returning to the letter of June 10, Professor Dyson continues,

> *The "Children's Crusade" chapter that you read covers the same*
> *ground in a different way. The resolution of the conflict was to*
> *speak truth, even if it was twenty-five years too late, and even*
> *if it wounded the surviving bomber-pilots deeply. So I wrote the*
> *piece and published it, at the invitation of William Shawn who*
> *was then the editor of the New Yorker. It was no accident that*
> *this happened in 1970, at the same time that a similar conflict of*
> *loyalties was raging, between those who had fought and suffered*
> *in Vietnam and those who proclaimed that the war in Vietnam*
> *was pointless. The number of British who died in the bombing*
> *campaign was roughly equal to the number of Americans who*
> *died in the war in Vietnam, and the anguish of those who sur-*
> *vived the war was also similar.*
>
> *After the piece was published, I received a number of bitter, an-*
> *gry and tragic letters from old bomber-pilots, just as I expected.*
> *Those letters ought to be published some time, after we are all*
> *dead. They are eloquent, passionate, denouncing me for insult-*
> *ing the dead. Those bomber-pilots, who saw so many of their*
> *friends and comrades shot down in flames, can never believe*
> *that they died in vain. To say that they died in vain insults*
> *their memory. And who are you, a privileged young kid who*
> *sat out the war in comfort at Command Headquarters, to pass*
> *judgment on those who fought and died?*
>
> *I answered those angry letters as best I could, explaining that*
> *I was not insulting the dead when I told the truth about the*
> *way they died. But of course none of the old bomber-pilots for-*
> *gave me. As long as they live they will revile me as a traitor,*
> *a smart-aleck who saved his own skin and then slandered the*
> *memory of those who did not save theirs.*

Professional soldiers are also caught in this machine that someone
wished for; now we are all stuck with it. In a May 12, 1962 commencement
address at the United States Military Academy at West Point, General
Douglas MacArthur admonished the graduating cadets that they were not
to be warmongers:

> ...your mission remains fixed, determined, inviolable—it is to win our wars....
> This does not mean that you are war mongers. On the contrary, the soldier,
> above all other people, prays for peace, for they must suffer and bear the
> deepest wounds and scars of war. [Krist(1987)][109–112]

Nevertheless, from trebuchets and gunpowder to bombers and guided
missiles, technology has unrelentingly made mass murder more efficient.

Strategic bombing neither deterred the war nor won it... In spite of the clear evidence of history, the strategic bombing doctrine flourished in Bomber Command throughout the Second World War. And it flourishes still, in bigger countries, with bigger bombs.

Bomber Command was an early example of the new evil that science and technology have added to the old evils of soldiering. Technology has made evil anonymous. Through science and technology, evil is organized bureaucratically so that no individual is responsible for what happens. [Dyson(1979a)][29–30]

Upon reading this passage, psychology major Casey S. remarked,

One area I did not learn about in my classes is the psychology of killing. A couple of summers ago I read a book called *On Killing*[69] and it really opened my eyes to...the darker side of human nature. The research presented in the book was conducted by a military psychologist seeking to make the military more efficient. He talks a lot about the need to make people seem as detached as possible. Essentially, if we can teach a soldier that the enemy is as unlike himself as possible, then it will be easier to kill.... It is all about putting distance between you and the enemy.

Dyson hits on a similar point when he talks about the advancement of technology. He says that ''technology has made the evil anonymous.'' I really think that he is right. There is no personal responsibility involved in shooting at a target on a radar screen or dropping a bomb over people which whom you will never make eye-to-eye contact....

I've often wondered how far technology will separate people. Among my friends I've noticed an increasing trend of only communicating over the phone, e-mail, or instant messaging.... Technology is great most of the time, but I think that there are certain things we must strive to keep. Being able to look others in the eye is one of those things.

In the "Children's Crusade" chapter of *Disturbing the Universe*, as in chapter 10 of *Weapons and Hope*, Professor Dyson bitterly criticizes him-

---

[69]Casey refers to *On Killing: The Psychological Cost of Learning to Kill in War and Society* by Lt. Col. David Grossman (Little, Brown, and Co., 2009). Grossman discusses how the military trains soldiers to overcome their instinctual loathing to kill other human beings.

self for becoming part of the war machine. He describes how, at the beginning of the war he was committed to nonviolence, a follower of Gandhi. As the war expanded he was drawn into accepting that which was previously unacceptable. By the war's end he sadly concluded, "I had surrendered one moral principle after another, and in the end it was all for nothing." [Dyson(1979a)][31] But perhaps it was not all for nothing. Sixty years later, his reflections gave a student named Alex D. the courage to make a change of direction:

> In my first semester of college I was in the Navy Reserve
> Officer Training Corps... to live out my childhood dreams of
> being an airplane pilot. After three months... I found
> that, for a reason I could not explain, I could not sign away
> the next 20 years of my life to the Navy, even though that
> meant abandoning my dreams. My father and my grandfather
> [were] happy that I was going into the military, so...they
> had some serious questions for me that I had no answers
> to.... Chapter 3 of *Disturbing the Universe* described what I
> had unconsciously gathered about the military.... The main
> problem is summed up when Dyson says ''I had surrendered one
> moral principle after another...''

When Alex began reflecting on what happens after Navy pilots release their missiles, to keep his dream alive he found himself surrendering his personal moral principles. Professor Dyson's experience helped Alex live divided no more.

In the spring of 1999, the US and its allies intervened to stop "ethnic cleansing" in the war between the Serbs and Croats of the former Yugoslavia. Much was made of NATO air power. Few troops, it was optimistically claimed, would be needed on the ground. As students of "The Children's Crusade," we were skeptical.

> *6 April 1999*
> *Dear Professor Dyson,*
> *Would you care to comment on the events of the past two weeks between NATO and Yugoslavia, in view of your experiences at Bomber Command?*
>
> *10 April 1999*
> *Dear Dwight, thanks for your message, and thanks to the class for their good questions. It is a wet Saturday in Minnesota,*

*with rain blowing horizontally all day long, a good day for stay-
ing indoors and answering letters....*
*Bombing of Yugoslavia. In my opinion this cannot possibly do
any good. In the history of bombing there is only one clear case
in which bombing succeeded. That was Japan in 1945, and it
only succeeded because the bombing was totally destructive and
ruthless. I hope the world today will not allow us to bomb Yugoslavia in that style. Even if we could do it, it would probably
not succeed. In my opinion, Serbia has already won the war.
This fact has nothing to do with right and wrong. No matter
how right our objectives may be, bombing will not achieve them.
On the other hand, putting an army into Yugoslavia would be
even worse than bombing. The worst danger is that the failure
of the air-force will cause the army to believe that they could do
it better.*

Two years later came the terrorist attacks of September 11, 2001. Three
thousand people were murdered when two dozen young men, armed with
nothing more than box cutter knives and determination beyond the pale,
slit the throats of the flight deck crews on four airliners and turned the
airplanes, heavily laden with jet fuel and passengers, into flying bombs.
Within a few months Afghanistan was invaded because the sponsors of
the 9/11 hijackers had sanctuary there. Most of the world understood US
motives for entering Afghanistan. Less understandable were noises coming
from President George W. Bush's administration about invading Iraq on
the grounds that Sadaam Hussein's regime was building nuclear weapons.
The evidence for these weapons' existence was unconvincing. Some of us
signed a "No War in Iraq" petition. In the spring of 2003, President Bush
ordered US forces to invade Iraq, a mission touted as "cutting off the head
of the snake." Instigators of wars almost always assume the conflict will be
over quickly. Almost always they are wrong.

Democracies are not supposed to launch preemptive invasions of other
nations. Democracies are supposed to go to war only when they are at-
tacked first. In May 2003, the STS class asked Professor Dyson his opinion
on President Bush's preemptive invasion of Iraq.

8 May 2003
Dear Professor Dyson,
I hope you and your family are well...
*In light of "The Ethics of Defense," we would appreciate your
comments on the USA strike against Saddam's regime in Iraq.*

21 May 2003
Dear Dwight,...
Of course I am strongly opposed to the war in Iraq, both for ethical and political reasons. It goes totally against all the principles I have been preaching, using offensive weapons aggressively against a defenseless adversary. If we were serious about defending ourselves against terrorism, the highest priority would be civil defense at home, and improving our lousy public health system. The war in Iraq has nothing to do with the war on terrorism. I am particularly disgusted with the dishonesty of the Bush regime, telling the American people lies about non-existent weapons of mass destruction in Iraq. I am proud to belong to our local Coalition for Peace Action in Princeton, a group of citizens led by a splendid young Baptist minister called Bob Moore. The Coalition has done a lot of marching and lobbying in the last few months, and we have had some success. Five of the New Jersey representatives in Washington voted against giving Bush the power to make war in Iraq.

On the day when the invasion of Iraq started, I happened to be in Costa Rica with a few students and colleagues. We had gone there over spring break for the field study component of an astrobiology course. When the attack began, late afternoon was turning into evening in Central America. We were in San José to be near the airport for our flight home the next morning. The public square in downtown San José boasted a jumbotron television. While we enjoyed ice cream cones and listened to street musicians, the giant screen announced the attack and showed images of US fighter jets circling over Bagdhad. The faces of the Costa Ricans were incredulous. We thought gloomily, "It's easier to get into situations than to get out of them," and "Whether or not Iraq was a terrorist state before this, it will become one now."

The war's public relations campaign told us that "smart bombs" were being widely used to minimize "collateral damage." We wondered what Professor Dyson thought about "smart bombs:"

8 May 2003
Dear Professor Dyson,...
...Has the development of precision guided bombs changed the situation in regard to air power, as described in "The Children's Crusade?'

21 May 2003
Dear Dwight,
Good to hear from you again....

The development of precision guided bombs has increased the effectiveness of air power to some extent, but not as much as the public is led to believe. It remains true, as it was true in World War Two, that precision bombing works well when there is no serious defense and not otherwise. In the final months of World War Two, the RAF worked out a splendidly effective way of doing precision bombing at night, and we destroyed all the remaining oil refineries in Germany in a few nights. The method was to have a "Master Bomber" flying low over the target in a small Mosquito airplane and laying flares precisely on the target. While the heavy bombers overhead were dropping their bombs on the flares, the master bomber continued to broadcast instructions in plain language, telling them precisely where to aim. With this system, very few bombs were wasted. But it could only work after the German defenses had collapsed. The same situation holds today, as we saw in Iraq. If the Iraqi defenses had been serious, the bomber airplanes could not have loitered over Iraq, the GPS guidance system would have been jammed, and we would have soon run out of cruise missiles. Unfortunately the American public has been led to believe that what worked so well in Iraq would also work in other places. If we get into a fight with a country that has serious defenses, as we did in Vietnam, none of these systems of precision bombing will work. The Vietnamese had good surface-to-air missiles supplied by Russia, and they shot down enough B-52 bombers to stop us from bombing precisely. Pray God Mr. Bush will not lead us into another Vietnam.

Aviation historian Edward Jablonski notes that for centuries, although civilians have been killed in wars, most of the time it was because they happened to be in the way:

...no one deliberately set out to kill him. The introduction of the doctrine of strategic bombardment changed all that.... Curiously, the idea of strategic bombardment was nurtured in the peace-loving democracies, England and, to a greater extent, the United States. [Jablonski(1971)][xii]

Turning Good Causes into Bad Ones

Frank Thompson was an older classmate of Freeman Dyson at Winchester College. Thompson was a brash adventurer with a gift for languages and a deep love of poetry. We meet Frank in *Disturbing the Universe*, Chapter 4, "The Blood of a Poet:" "Poetry was man's best effort down the ages to distill some wisdom from the inarticulate depths of his soul. Frank could no more live without poetry than I could live without mathematics...." [Dyson(1979a)][35]

> *8 December 2003*
> *Dear Professor Dyson,*
> *Thank you once again for your patient willingness to consider our questions....Who is your favorite poet?*
>
> *9 December 2003*
> *Dear Dwight and students,*
> *My favorite poet is still William Blake. I won't try to explain why I like Blake so much. Poetry is like music. You feel it but you can't explain it. Blake had strong words to say, usually rebellious, about many different subjects. In "Disturbing the Universe" there is only one quote from Blake, "Drive your cart and your plow over the bones of the dead" (page 157), which came into my head after Dover Sharp was murdered. In another of my books, "Infinite in All Directions," there is more about Blake and several longer quotes (pages 131–134). There I explain why I find Blake to be a kindred spirit. The quotes come mainly from his poem, "America, a Prophecy," written in 1793.*

We will return later to Professor Dyson's quote of Blake. In the meantime, Frank Thompson left Winchester in 1938 and Freeman saw him no more. Frank went to Oxford and joined the Communist Party. When the war began in 1939 he enlisted and was sent to Libya, Egypt, Palestine and Persia, "occasionally fighting and always adding to his stock of friends and languages. In January 1944 he parachuted into German-occupied Yugoslavia. His mission was to serve as British liaison officer with the underground resistance movement in Bulgaria." [Dyson(1979a)][37]

Frank and some comrades were captured, held for ten days in a show trial, and executed. At the trial Thompson answered questions in correct and idiomatic Bulgarian. When asked why he was in Bulgaria he said "I came because this war is something very much deeper than a struggle of nation against nation.... I am ready to die for freedom. And I am proud to die with Bulgarian patriots as companions..." The condemned men were led out with Frank Thompson in the lead, giving the defiant salute of the underground Fatherland Front, the salute of freedom. They all died raising this salute, the scene "one of the most moving in all Bulgarian history." [Dyson(1979a)][37–38]

In the war of Frank Thompson, the poet's war, death was faced fearlessly and with dignity, towards a lofty end. In the war of Bomber Command, the technician's war, death was delivered at the industrial scale, becoming an end in itself.

I knew that if any hope of salvation for mankind was to emerge from the wreckage of World War II, that hope could come only from the poet's war that Frank fought, not from the technician's war that I was engaged in....
What lasting lesson can we learn from these experiences? For me, at least the main lesson is clear. A good cause can become bad if we fight for it with means that are indiscriminately murderous. A bad cause can become good if enough people fight for it in a spirit of comradeship and self-sacrifice. In the end it is how you fight, as much as why you fight, that makes your cause good or bad. And the more technological the war becomes, the more disastrously a bad choice of means will change a good cause into evil. [Dyson(1979a)][40–41]

In a letter of 7 May 2002, anticipating the first anniversary of the 9/11 attacks, we quoted back to Professor Dyson this passage about good causes becoming bad, and asked, "In light of this truth, would you care to comment on the events of September 11 and its aftermath, and/or the current Israeli/Palestinian tensions?" Our question reached Professor Dyson while he was in the middle of a trip. However, he has never brushed us off:

> *7 May 2002*
> *Dear Dwight, just to let you know I can't answer your questions just now as I am on the road (at JPL in California) and will not be back home till May 16. These are good questions and cannot be answered in a hurry.... apologies to the students. Yours ever, Freeman.*

> *7 May 2002*
> *Dear Professor Dyson,*
> *No problem.... I am glad you feel free to not try and people-please us. Thanks to email I can keep in touch with students..., so enjoy your trip & don't worry about our questions...*

The delay was worth the wait. His answer contained more than we could have imagined. Professor Dyson brought news of his family first. Then he turned to our question.

20 May 2002

Dear Dwight and students,

I am back from my travels and ready to answer your questions. On May 12 which happened to be Mothers' Day, we heard the joyful news from our daughter Mia the Presbyterian minister that we have another grandson. She timed it so cleverly that he was born just after midnight. According to the rules of managed-care bureaucracy, that gave her three nights in the hospital instead of two. Mother and child are both doing well.

What do I think about the September 11 events and the Israeli-Palestinian fighting? I think it is too soon to tell whether the cause for which the September 11 hijackers were willing to die, to get the United States military forces out of Saudi Arabia, was good or evil. In my judgment the cause for which the Palestinian suicide bombers were willing to die, to get the Israeli military forces out of their homeland, was good. In both cases, the fact that the fighters killed so many innocent civilians did harm to their cause. By fighting in such a ruthless way they turned a good cause into evil.

In this connection I would like to tell you about a vivid and uncomfortable memory from my own younger days. I am sixteen years old, an angry kid lying in bed in London in September 1940. Although I have been brought up as a privileged child in England, I am violently hostile to the British Empire and everything it stands for. I hate London, the citadel of oppression, with its huge buildings sucking the wealth from every corner of the world. Overhead the German bombers are droning. I lie in bed listening to the bombs exploding and the buildings crumbling.

Fig. 7.1   *Collapse of the facade of the premises of John Wood & Sons, Cigar & Tobacco Importers, 23 & 25 Queen Victoria Street, in the City of London, 11 May 1941. The night raid of May 10 was the most severe attack London had sustained throughout the Blitz. Police Constables Arthur Cross and Fred Tibbs took this photograph after the area had been given the "all clear" on the assumption it was reasonably safe to approach.* (photo and caption courtesy of the Museum of London)

What joy to hear, after each explosion, the delicious crunch of buildings falling down, the great British Empire audibly crumbling. The joy far outweighs any fear that my own home might be hit, or any pity for the people dying in the burning buildings. When I see now on television the pictures of the World Trade Center buildings collapsing, I think, how many angry sixteen-year-olds all over the world are feeling the same joy that I felt in 1940. I find it easy to imagine the state of mind of the young men who so resolutely smashed those planes into the buildings. Almost, I could have been one of them myself.

The only wisdom that I can extract from this memory is that the problem of terrorism is not a military problem. It is a problem of people's hearts and minds. Attempts to solve it by military means will only make it worse. I don't pretend to know how to solve it. A good way to start would be for our country to stop telling the rest of the world how to behave. We must learn to live with the world as it is, not as we want it to be. We must treat our enemies with respect, so that we do not appear to be trampling on their cultures and traditions. The ultimate goal must always be, not to destroy our enemies but to convert them into friends.

As the war continued and the Londoners daily put out fires and spent the nights huddled together using the Tube as a bomb shelter, young Freeman Dyson's attitudes toward the Blitz grew more nuanced:

My ethical doctrines grew more and more complicated as I was increasingly torn between my theoretical repudiation of national loyalties and my practical involvement in the life of a country fighting with considerable courage and good humor for its survival. For my father the issues were simple. He did not need to argue with me.... When things were going badly in 1940, he said, "All we have to do is to behave halfway decently, and we shall soon have the whole world on our side." When he spoke of the whole world, he was probably thinking especially of the United States of America and of his own son. [Dyson(1979a)][87]

In response to this passage a student named Michael reflected,

```
This week I have been affected by Freeman Dyson's
Disturbing the Universe.  In the book his father says, ''All
we have to do is to behave halfway decently, and we shall
soon have the whole world on our side,''...  I agree
entirely...  If everyone would only just act ''halfway
```

decent'' then there would not be war, hunger, or poverty.
Halfway decent people do not kill others over greed and
power; halfway decent people do not let someone starve to
death; halfway decent people chip in a few bucks for someone
to lead a decent life. Right now I am going to work on being
halfway decent. Later, I will worry about being an idealist
that changes the world.

On April 19, 1995, the residents of Oklahoma City were victims of a
bombing, delivered by a rental truck loaded with ammonium nitrate and
parked in front the Alfred P. Murrah Federal Building. One hundred and
sixty-nine people lost their lives, including nineteen infants and toddlers
in the second-floor day care center. When the bomb went off we felt the
shock wave on our campus seven miles away. After April 19 we could better
appreciate what it must have been like to have such events occurring in our
city every day, as the residents of London had to endure for thirty-seven
weeks, starting in September 1940 during the Blitz. A few days after the
Murrah bombing, when our class sent questions to Professor Dyson, we
attached an extra letter:

> *25 April 1995*
> *Dear Professor Dyson,*
> *...Update from downtown Oklahoma City: The city still mourns
> as the grim work goes on. Even now the rescue workers are ap-
> proaching the ruins of the day care center, buried under tons of
> rubble, containing the little ones and others.... But this is a city
> filled with grace. Whatever is needed by the victims, families,
> and rescue workers, when the word is put out the community re-
> sponds instantly and generously. The cowardly and evil actions
> of the few are no match for the outpouring of love and grace of
> the many. "Set like a seal upon thy heart, Love is stronger than
> Death."*[70]

Our letter about ongoing events in Oklahoma City reminded Professor
Dyson of the other side of his sixteen-year-old response to the Blitz:

> *26 April 1995*
> *Dear Dwight Neuenschwander,*
> *Thank you for your moving report from Oklahoma City, and for
> the questions from the students. What you say about Oklahoma*

---

[70] *Song of Solomon* 8:6, deliberately modified in the letter. The original in the King
James Version reads, "Set me as a seal upon thine heart, as a seal upon thine arm: for
love is as strong as death."

City brings back memories of the London blitz. The spirit of community and strength and brotherly love was exactly as you describe it. We had the additional advantage that there was little hate for the German boys in the sky who were also risking their lives. We knew that we and the boys overhead were all in it together.

This prompted a follow-up letter to Professor Dyson:

May 16, 1995
Dear Professor Dyson,
...Thank you for your gracious words about the "spirit of community and strength and brotherly love" that have come out of the tragedy in Oklahoma City. Your words in "Disturbing the Universe" were so appropriate to the events of the past few weeks.... For instance, "In the end it is how you fight, as much as why you fight, that makes your cause good or bad." Evidently the bombers of the Murrah Building thought of themselves as waging war on the federal government. To use tactics that include truck-bombing to oblivion 168 innocent people, including 19 pre-school children, reminds us again that the ends do not justify the means....
I don't believe there is a single family in Oklahoma City and the surrounding area that was not personally involved. If you didn't know someone who was lost or injured in the building, you quickly found someone in your second tier of contacts—friend of a friend, relative of a co-worker, etc. Many of the students in the class volunteered for service in the days after the bombing, distributing supplies to rescuers, or counseling, or working in the downtown convention center that was converted into a hotel for the rescuers from other cities. From donating time and supplies, to hastily organizing a substitute birthday party for a small boy whose parents were suddenly called downtown to identify an aunt's body, everyone was directly involved. The way the community pulled together, and put their arms around the victims and their families, is the finest redeeming grace in all of this. Indeed, it touched the entire country. Not only did my own children's classes write letters to the rescuers, but children all over the country wrote letters to Oklahoma City children.... The fury of the bombers is no match for such a spirit. Perhaps those of us who did not experience the Blitz or Dresden or Hiroshima ourselves can now better appreciate, at least in some approximate way, what values and principles are tapped by those on the receiving end of such disasters....

The spring 2004 semester class visited again the important question of harmonizing ends and means:

> *May 6, 2004*
> *Dear Professor Dyson,*
> *...You demonstrated how "a good cause can become bad if we fight for it with means that are indiscriminately murderous...."*
> *The attacks of September 11, 2001, were unquestionably bad, but what was the good cause whose fate it was to be made bad by those attacks? In other words, what was the message that we should be listening to from responsible people in the Arab world? Has our fighting back by taking the war to them turned a good cause into a bad one?*

> *6 May 2004*
> *Dear Dwight,*
> *...This is a difficult question. We still do not know exactly what the September 11 gang had in mind. Perhaps we will never know. We know that Osama Bin Laden resents the existence of American military bases and commercial operations in Saudi Arabia, and is trying to foment violence so as to drive the Americans out of the Arab world. I do not consider this to be a noble cause, but it is understandable. Certainly we played into his hands by invading Iraq. The invasion of Iraq turned a local squabble into a full-scale war and turned our good cause into a bad one. The message from moderate Arabs that we ought to have listened to was: "Give the Palestinians some support in their fight for independence, and stop your unconditional support of Israel."*

On the Friday morning of November 2012 when Professor Dyson attended the meeting in Orlando along with six hundred enthusiastic physics students, I had the privilege of a few moments in conversation with him. After asking him about his family (a grandson had just started medical school), I wanted to ask him a question that had not surfaced among the student's questions. Recalling "it's how you fight as well as why you fight that makes your cause good or bad" I mentioned that, in the weeks following the 9/11 attacks, little if anything was said in public about what we should have learned from the hijackers. Although their cause was turned into a bad one by such indiscriminate killing, no one in the USA, as I recalled, asked publicly *why* the hijackers hated us so much. Professor Dyson's thoughts on this point surprised me. "I disagree," he said. "They did not do it because they hated us. They did it because they loved each other." He went on to describe how, in the waning days of World War Two,

the Japanese kamikaze airplanes held two flyers. Whatever they thought
of the war or the Emperor, when two young men climbed into their plane
and took off for their no-return flight, they went as comrades. Duty and
coercion put them in the plane, but loyalty to each other kept them in it
as they swooped into their final dive together.

In the spring 2009 semester Philip M. raised questions about motives in
one of his weekly letters,

```
...those described as ''terrorists'' [in a magazine
article] are pigeon-holed as closed-minded.  The reader is
told people should discuss instead of attack, listening
before reacting, but is simultaneously informed that we are
fighting villains, and that our side is the right side in
this international upheaval.  But I ask, why are we right?
Why is the other party wrong?  An answer I have often been
given is that these terrorists attacked us, unprovoked.
''But why did they attack us?''  I ask.  ''Because they hate
us,'' is the response I am given.  The reason for their
hatred is undefined, as though it is part of the definition of
being a terrorist.  Terrorists hate people; that is simply
what they do.  This seems to fly in the face of my
understanding of human rationality.
It seems to me that no matter who started the fight, we have
had some part in continuing it.  ''We will not negotiate with
terrorists'' is the common line...But why will we not hear
them out?...  The ability of a ''terrorist'' to listen to
reason is non-existent from this perspective; I suggest that
so is our own.
```

The "Arab Spring" of 2011 offered another opportunity for an STS
class to consider means versus ends. We were especially interested in these
developments because of the pivotal role played by students in the affected
countries.

> *29 April 2011*
> *Dear Professor Dyson,*
> *We trust that 2011 so far has been a splendid year for you and
> your extended family....*
> *In view of your observation that it is "how you fight, as well
> as why you fight, that makes your cause good or bad," what are
> your thoughts on recent events in Tunisia, Egypt, Libya, and*

Syria? (We proudly notice that students were leading the way in many of these protests.)

29 April 2011
Dear Dwight,...
...Your thoughtful letter and the students' questions arrive just as we are leaving for a week in England, and your deadline is the day after we get back.... I will give quick and superficial answers to the questions.... Humble apologies to the students.
...Recent events in the Middle East are too recent for me to pass any judgments. The effects of good or bad ways of fighting only become clear after a few years. My own judgment is that for students, to engage in passive resistance to governments is likely to be successful, and to engage in rioting and bloodshed is likely to be unsuccessful. But it will take time to find out whether that is true. In the meantime we can only admire the courage of those who passively resist. I happen to think it is very unwise for us to start a civil war as we are doing in Libya.

We admire the courage of the students who started the "Arab Spring," but subsequent events have shown that Professor Dyson was wise to withhold judgment on how it will turn out. A class recently asked about the new threat that has emerged out of the chaos that resulted from the civil war in Syria, the unraveling of Lybia and the unrest in surrounding nations.

22 April 2015
Dear Professor Dyson,
What should the USA, NATO, and other concerned countries do about ISIS? You wrote in a previous letter that terrorism is ultimately a problem about people's hearts and minds, and thus military action alone will not solve it. If the atrocities and excessive certitude of ISIS could not pull diverse nations from the US to Iran together in common cause, its hard to know what could.

1 May 2015
Dear Dwight,
...I do not claim to know anything about ISIS or how to deal with ISIS. My guess is that the present policy of trying to suppress ISIS by military force will not succeed. If I were in charge, which fortunately I am not, I would leave ISIS alone for a few years and see what happens. I would also make friends with Iran, which seems to me to be the most stable and civilized country in the Middle East. I would also not get excited if Iran decides

to build some nuclear weapons. It was stupid for us to get so deeply involved in the Middle East in the first place.
...With all my good wishes and thanks to all of you, yours ever,
Freeman Dyson

Students have always been the first to protest injustice. They have passion, energy, and a future in front of them that they want to see improved. The Arab Spring was started by students. The Tiananmen Square protests of 1989 were led by students. Alexander Solzhenitsyn recalled how, early in the era of Joseph Stalin's iron rule of the Soviet Union, in the universities "The non-Party students at this time sought 'autonomy for higher educational institutions,' the right of assembly, and the removal from the curriculum of excessive political indoctrination. Arrests were the answer." [Solzhenitsyn(1973)][38] Professor Dyson was present at Dr. Martin Luther King's immortal "I Have a Dream" speech, delivered at the Lincoln Memorial in Washington D.C. on 28 August 1963. As he marched with the demonstrators towards the Memorial, Freeman Dyson noticed that "The people from the deep South were very young, hardly more than children.... From the toughest places only the young people came." [Dyson(1979a)][141] Sometimes I wonder what it would take for the students in our little prairie university to become sufficiently aroused to take to the streets in determined protest. To their credit, many of them quietly work behind the scenes as volunteers with community groups that operate soup kitchens and halfway houses and clean up tornado debris. They are doing what they can to improve the world one task, one life at a time. As we repeatedly say in class discussions, "You and I are not called to change the world. But we *are* called to do what we can, where we are, with what we have."

Young people are always attracted to social and technological challenges. When World War Two began and the atomic bomb had a sudden urgency, many young people—some still students—helped work on it. The average age of the builders of the first nuclear weapons was twenty-nine. [Else(1981)]

8 Rapid Rupture

Letters about Nuclear Weapons

"It is a profound and necessary truth that the deep things in science are not found because they are useful; they are found because it was possible to find them." –J. Robert Oppenheimer[71]

***

Any student seeking a university education after 1945 should understand that a nuclear bomb is not just another weapon. It is a club too big to swing.

While telling the story of the Swamp Angel firing on Charleston, Civil War historian Bruce Catton tracked the "insane chains of war-time logic in which men step from one undeniable truth to another and so come at last to a land of crippling nonsense. The logic that brought the war to Morris Island was above reproach." [Catton(1965)][217] Each step in the logic that delivered atomic bombs to Hiroshima and Nagasaki was above reproach. That logic led in turn to the strategic policy of the Cold War, where decent people found themselves holding hostage the populations of entire nations.

Nuclear physics began in 1911 when Ernest Rutherford and his students in Manchester, England, discovered the atomic nucleus by studying the deflections of positively-charged alpha particles[72] directed at a thin gold foil only a few atoms thick. Thirty years later, the growth of nuclear physics and the rise of Fascism in Europe occurred coincidentally in a way that we easily forget now. In particular, the neutron was discovered by James Chadwick at Cambridge in May 1932. In January 1933, Adolf Hitler was appointed Chancellor of Germany. In 1934, Enrico Fermi in Rome used the neutron as a keen knife for probing the nucleus. Using Fermi's techniques, nuclear fission was discovered in December 1938 when Otto Hahn and Fritz Strassman in Berlin gathered the data, and their former colleague Lise Meitner in Sweden found the interpretation. World War Two started in September 1939. Atomic bombs were dropped on Japan in August 1945.

---

[71][Rhodes(1986)][11]

[72]An alpha particle is a nucleus of helium-4, two neutrons and two protons bound together. Three modes of radioactive decay were discovered early on: alpha decay, where a heavy nucleus emits an alpha particle; beta decay, where a neutron turns into a proton or *vice versa*; and gamma decay, where the nucleus emits a high-energy photon.

Let us fill in a few details, to glimpse how this work was done, since the microscopic objects of interest are too small to see—their existence and properties had to be inferred indirectly. Between 1911 and 1932, the nucleus presented curious puzzles, such as how nuclei with more than two protons could hold together despite the proton's electric repulsion, and why atoms of an element could have different weights. A "neutral proton" had been suggested, and Chadwick teased out the neutron by using radioactive radium, which decays by emitting alpha particles. Chadwick directed the alpha particles onto a sample of the lightweight metal beryllium. The alpha particle (with 2 protons) embeds itself into the beryllium nucleus (with 4 protons), producing a nucleus of carbon and kicking out a neutron. The neutron was identified by the reactions it produced in subsequent collisions. Chadwick's neutron-generating scenario would soon have consequences far beyond Cambridge.

It was immediately realized that by carrying no electric charge, neutrons offered a keen knife for probing the nucleus. The year after Chadwick's discovery, Fermi and his students started bombarding various elements with neutrons to see what would happen. Fermi's techniques were taken up by others, including Lise Meitner, Otto Hahn and Fritz Strassmann in Berlin. Shortly after the *Anschluss* in 1938, Meitner, being Jewish, fled Germany for Sweden. Through letters, Hahn kept Meitner apprised of experimental progress back in Berlin. As the 1938 Christmas holiday approached, Hahn and Strassman bombarded uranium with neutrons and separated the products through chemistry. They were astonished to find among the products relatively lightweight elements such as barium. Upon being hit by a neutron, what improbable chain of alpha and beta decays would quickly turn heavy uranium, with 92 protons, into barium with 56 protons? Hahn wrote to Meitner, "You can see that you will be performing a good deed if you find an alternative [explanation]." [Rhodes(1986)][254] Meitner's physicist nephew Otto Frisch came from Bohr's institute in Copenhagen to join her for the 1938 Christmas holiday. While discussing the mystery, Meitner envisioned the incoming neutron's collision with the nucleus drastically distorting the latter, like a peturbed liquid drop, into a dumbbell shape. The two proton-laden sides joined by the neck could repel each other, rupturing the nucleus. The energy released by the electric repulsion would, atom for atom, be about twenty million times greater than chemical reactions, about the same as the energy released in the reactions observed by Hahn and Strassman.

Seeking further evidence for uranium splitting into pieces that included barium, the energy released as calculated from $E = mc^2$ was the same as in the electric repulsion scenario. In February 1939, Meitner and Frisch published their interpretation of the Hahn-Strassmann discovery. [Meitner and Frisch(1939)] Borrowing a term from the biology of cell division, they called it "fission."

When one particular isotope of uranium nuclei breaks apart, two or more neutrons emerge from the debris.[73] These secondary neutrons create the possibility of a chain reaction. Should each secondary neutron strike two nearby unfissioned uranium nuclei, two more fissions result, releasing four neutrons. With further fissions, the four neutrons become eight, then 16, 32, 64, 128, 256, 512, and so on, with about one hundredth of one millionth of a second between fissions. To fission a pound of fissile material (about $10^{23} \approx 2^{80}$ nuclei) requires about a hundred doublings, and thus a millionth of a second. The total energy released by fissioning a few pounds of fissile material would be equivalent to exploding several thousand tons of dynamite.

Otto Frisch returned to Copenhagen after the 1938 Christmas, and soon thereafter, Bohr sailed from Copenhagen to New York. As he was boarding the ship, Otto Frisch handed him a note with Lise Meitner's and his conclusions. For Bohr and his colleague Léon Rosenfeld, it was to be a working voyage. Their ship docked in New York on January 16. One of the physicists who met Bohr upon his arrival was John Wheeler of Princeton University. Bohr had come to visit Princeton for a few weeks of collaboration, but would linger briefly in New York. Rosenfeld went on to Princeton with Wheeler. [Rhodes(1986)]]264–265]

In the spring semester of 1939, an undergraduate physics major named Richard Stoner was taking a course from John Wheeler at Princeton. Four decades later, I was one of Professor Stoner's graduate student teaching assistants. He told me about the day in January 1939 when Wheeler walked excitedly into the classroom and said "I just met Niels Bohr and Léon Rosenfeld as they got off the ship in New York, and I heard some astonishing news." Picking up a piece of chalk and thinking out loud before the physics majors, he began telling them what he had just heard about fission, musing over the physics of the chain reaction. Bohr later came to Princeton and he and Wheeler hammered out the theoretical details of the fission mechanism.

---

[73]On the average, about 2.3 neutrons per fission are emitted in a chain reaction of uranium-235 or plutonium-239. Uranium-238, while more abundant than U-235, will fission but does not chain-react, because it emits too few secondary neutrons.

The following September they published in *Physical Review* a paper entitled "The Mechanism of Nuclear Fission," [Bohr and Wheeler(1939)] spelling out in quantitative detail the criteria for neutron-induced "liquid drop" fission to occur.

The paper bore the publication date of September 1, 1939, the same day that Hitler's *blitzkrieg* invaded Poland. Although no one could know it at the time, how ironic that on the day World War Two started, a paper was quietly published in a scholarly journal that foreshadowed how the war would end! Professor Stoner finished his Bohr and Wheeler story by telling me that after September 1, 1939, "the whole fission business went underground and nothing more about it was said."

Sixty Christmases after fission was discovered, we asked Professor Dyson an open-ended question about science's mistakes.

> *3 December 1998*
> *Dear Professor Dyson,*
> *...What do you consider to be science's biggest mistake?*

> *5 December 1998*
> *Dear Dwight,*
> *...Science's biggest mistake happened in 1939 after nuclear fission was discovered, before the beginning of World War Two. The physicists could have organized an international meeting of experts to discuss the problem of nuclear weapons, as the biologists did in 1975 when the sudden discovery of recombinant DNA technology made genetic engineering possible. The biologists agreed on a set of rules to ban dangerous experiments, and the rules have been effective ever since. The physicists could have done something similar in 1939, and there was a good chance that nuclear weapons would never have been built. But the chance was missed. Once World War Two had begun in September 1939, it was too late, because the scientists in different countries could no longer communicate.*
> *...Happy Christmas and New Year to you all.*
> *Yours sincerely, Freeman Dyson*

Building the Gadget

In August 1939, Albert Einstein sent his famous letter informing President Roosevelt of nuclear fission. There were reasons to believe the Germans were attempting to build an atomic bomb. The Japanese attack on Pearl Harbor on 7 December 1941 gave the atomic bomb a sudden urgency. The project to build it, code-named the Manhattan District, got underway with General Leslie Groves appointed the liaison between project scientists and the government.[74] General Groves selected J. Robert Oppenheimer to direct the scientific side of the Manhattan Project. The code name for Oppenheimer's new job was Coordinator of Rapid Rupture.[75]

Enrico Fermi escaped with his family from Fascist Italy in 1938. Columbia University in New York City gave him a place to land, and Fermi was one of the physicists who met Bohr upon his arrival on 16 January 1939. Soon thereafter Fermi was offered a permanent postition at the University of Chicago. There he led the experiment that produced the first nuclear chain reaction. It took place on 2 December 1942 in the squash court under the football stadium grandstands. Within a huge matrix of graphite bricks, Fermi's chain reaction was controlled by neutron-absorbing cadmium-coated rods interspersed among containers of uranium oxide. The demonstration began with the rods fully inserted, absorbing all secondary neutrons. The rods were slowly withdrawn until half the neutrons were absorbed. Each fission then produced only one surviving neutron to drive one more fission, a self-sustaining but not a runaway chain reaction. [Fermi(2009)] This principle forms the basis of commercial nuclear reactors. The heat released is used to boil water into superheated steam, which spins a turbine that turns a generator to make alternating voltage.[76]

Other refugees who helped build the first nuclear bombs include Hans Bethe from Germany who, after the war, became Freeman Dyson's mentor at Cornell. Edward Teller from Hungary ended up at the University of Chicago, and mathematician Stanislaw Ulam from Poland landed at the University of Wisconsin.

The Manhattan Project started in widely scattered university laboratories, but Oppenheimer knew a remote site would be needed where the researchers could talk freely among themselves while maintaining security. The Los Alamos Boy's School in northern New Mexico was requisitioned by the Army. The students moved out, and the physicists, chemists, mathe-

---

[74]General Groves had recently led the construction of the Pentagon, which under his leadership was completed on time and under budget.

[75][Else(1981)] Coincidentally with the Bohr and Wheeler paper on nuclear fission, R. Oppenheimer and his student H. Snyder published a paper, in the same issue of *Physical Review*, that predicted from Einstein's general theory of relativity the gravitational collapse that later generations would call "black holes." [Oppenheimer and Snyder(1939)]

[76]The 1986 explosion at the Chernobyl reactor in Ukraine, and the 2011 meltdown of the Fukushima reactor in Japan, were not nuclear detonations. Chernobyl was the explosion of high-pressure superheated steam that ruptured the reactor containment building, spewing vast quantities of potent radioactive materials across the countryside. Fukushima was caused by catastrophic leakage of the reactors after tsunami damage.

maticians, machinists and their families moved in, making an instant boom town of Quonset huts and wooden barracks surrounded by barbed wire and an army camp.

The Manhattan Project brought together a concentrated assembly of talent and resources on a scale never seen before. The professors recruited their best students. Imagine yourself a graduate student studying nuclear physics in the spring of 1943. Your thesis advisor disappears. A month later you receive a telegram from your advisor asking you come to New Mexico to join a project that would be described after you arrive. Once inside the Los Alamos laboratory, you present yourself to Robert Serber, one of Oppenheimer's former graduate students. Serber sits you and other new arrivals down for a seminar, to bring you up to speed on the Los Alamos mission: "The object of the project is to produce a practical military weapon in the form of a bomb," Serber began, " in which the energy is released by a fast neutron chain reaction in one or more of the materials known to show nuclear fission." [Serber(1992)][4] For security reasons the word "bomb" was quickly replaced with "gadget."

The uranium isotope U-238 [77] will fission when hit by a fast neutron, but does not chain-react because it produces too few secondary neutrons. The lighter uranium isotope U-235 fissions with fast or slow incoming neutrons, and produces enough secondary neutrons to chain-react. However, out of every 140 uranium nuclei, only one is U-235; the others are are U-238. Since U-235 and U-238 are chemically identical, their tiny mass difference offers the only leverage for separating them. In the 1940s, the most efficient of the few inefficient separation methods was gaseous diffusion, which required a facility the size and complexity of an automobile factory, that was built in Oak Ridge, Tennessee.[78]

Plutonium-239 fissions twice as readily as U-235, with either fast or slow neutrons, and it enthusiastically chain-reacts.[79] Plutonium does not appear in minerals because its radioactive half-life of only 24,000 years means that any produced naturally decays on a timescale short compared to geologic processes. Pu-239 can be synthesized by firing a slow neutron into a U-238

---

[77]U-238 = 92 protons +146 neutrons; U-235 = 92 protons + 143 neutrons; Pu-239 = 94 protons + 147 neutrons.

[78]Today centrifuges are the preferred method to "enrich" uranium with a preponderance of U-235. They were considered in 1943 but the materials available at the time were not up to the necessary stresses.

[79]"Fissions twice as readily" means that the fission "cross-section," the area centered on the target nucleus within which the incoming neutron must hit in order to score a fission, is about twice as large for Pu-239 as for U-235.

nucleus, turning it into slightly unstable U-239. After two beta decays the nucleus becomes plutonium-239.[80] To produce Pu-239 and separate it from uranium cost another car factory in Hanford, Washington. At the outset of the Manhattan Project it was not clear whether uranium or plutonium would work best as bomb fuels, so development moved full speed ahead on both; cost was no object. The government could always sell more War Bonds.

The work that nuclear weapons do is very crude. But the machines themselves are marvels of deep science, elegant engineering and precision machine shop work. Major engineering problems facing the bomb designers included (a) preventing the first fissions from blowing the remaining unfissioned active material beyond the reach of the secondary neutrons, to result in a fizzle; and (b) introducing the initial neutron when and only when the bomb was to be detonated. Problem (a) was solved by surrounding the active material with a massive jacket of steel or U-238.[81] The inertia of this "tamper" held the fissile material together against the rapidly growing pressure for the necessary microsecond. Problem (b) was solved by designing an "initiator," a walnut-size layered assembly with a core of a alpha-emitting radium, an outer layer of beryllium, the two separated by alpha-absorbing nickel. Crush the walnut, the radium and beryllium mix to produce neutrons in the same reaction that Chadwick used to demonstrate the neutron's existence.

A bomb's "critical mass" is the minimum amount of fissile material necessary for an explosive chain reaction. To avoid pre-detonation, the fissile material is initially dispersed sub-critically, then the pieces are brought together to form a super-critical mass at the moment of detonation. Because Pu-239 fissions twice as readily as U-235, the gun barrel Little Boy design, that made a super-critical mass by firing a sub-critical U-235 bullet into U-235 rings, was too slow an assembly mechanism for plutonium. However, squeezing the volume down by a factor of two reduces the critical mass by a factor of four.[82] The active material for the plutonium bomb was a sphere whose mass was about five kilograms. The design called for the sphere

---

[80]While the uranium sample is bombarded by neutrons, some nuclei absorb a second neutron, yielding plutonium-240. Pu-240 was a headache for the bomb designers because it is a potent radioactive emitter of alpha particles, and an alpha particle striking another nucleus could kick out a neutron and start the chain reaction prematurely.

[81]Robert Serber describes in *Los Alamos Primer* how gold was temporarily considered for use as tamper. Gold was cheap compared to a few kilograms of U-235 or Pu-239. In a commercial nuclear reactor the fissile material is untampered.

[82]The critical mass is inversely proportional to the mass density squared.

to be rapidly crushed symmetrically from all sides, making the five kilograms go from sub-critical to super-critical. This was cleverly arranged by surrounding the plutonium sphere and its tamper with conventional explosives, Baratol and Composition B. Buring more slowly than Composition B, Baratol was shaped as lenses embedded in the Composition B. The wave of rapid burning propagating from the bomb's surface detonators was thereby focused to slam onto the plutonium core simultaneously from all sides—an implosion.

The spherical plutonium core was about the size of a grapefruit. Slice the grapefruit in half, and hollow out a small cavity in each of the two halves, like the pit of a peach. Within this pit sits the walnut-size initiator. The implosion that crushes the plutonium core to super-critical density also breaks open the initiator to start the chain reaction and the nuclear explosion—all in a millionth of a second.

In a nuclear explosion the detonation site reaches a temperature similar to the core of the sun, about 15 million degrees Celsius. The air temperature within a mile of the detonation site, or hypocenter, rises to over a thousand degrees Fahrenheit (550 C). A shock wave propagates at supersonic speed from the hypocenter. In wartime use the bombs would be detonated about two thousand feet above the ground. Before it hits the ground the spherical shock wave moves radially in all directions from the hypocenter. Ground zero, the point on the ground directly below the hypocenter, receives the shock wave first. Upon hitting the ground the shock wave reflects back up. The reflected shock wave passes through air warmed by the passage of the original shock wave, and thus moves faster than the unreflected shock wave, and, at ground level, overtakes it. These combined shock waves form at ground level a cylindrical wall of shock moving from ground zero initially faster than the speed of sound—you don't hear it coming.[83] Swept along with it comes a hurricane of supersonic debris. Armageddon comes from a device that would fit in the bomb bay of a B-29.[84] No one intended all of this when Fermi and his students started bombarding nuclei with neutrons.

When Otto Hahn stumbled upon the discovery of nuclear fission in 1938 he had no inkling of nuclear weapons, no premonition that he was treading

---

[83]This mechanism was explained to me and my undergraduate classmates by one of our physics professors, Dean McCowan. He was one of the young people who worked on the Manhattan Project during WWII, in his case, shock wave physics.

[84]The two B-29s that delivered the atomic bombs—*Enola Gay* that delivered Little Boy to Hiroshima, and *Bock's Car* that delivered Fat Man to Nagasaki, had to be modified so the bombs would fit.

*on dangerous ground. When the news of Hiroshima came to him seven years
later, he was so overcome with grief that his friends were afraid he would kill
himself.* [Dyson(1979a)][7]

I have learned that most students come to university knowing essentially
nothing about nuclear weapons and their history, or the people who built
them. Ryan M. wrote, "I have never been taught about the atomic bomb,
let along the people who were behind it." Janislynn I. added, "If it weren't
for the discussion we had in class, I wouldn't have known the broad scope
of everything behind this massive piece of destruction. One of the facts
about the atomic bomb that really interested me was the core of it...was a
small sphere that weighed only about 10 pounds. It is unfathomable to me
to think about how something that small could produce a chain reaction to
cause that much destruction."

In STS class the students are asked: If you had been invited to join
the Manhattan Project, knowing only what one could have known at that
time, what would you have done? Megan C. responded,

```
What a loaded question!...To be honest, when this question
was posed, I thought it required an obvious answer, therefore
I assumed it was rhetorical; however, soon to find out, it
was not. So I began to think... At the beginning of class,
my answer was a strong NO WAY--I would never help bring so
much destruction to the world; however, upon further
reflection I began to realize that the answer is not so easy.
I began to walk a mile in the scientists' lab coats, so to
speak. I put myself in their position and started to
consider all the benefits of working on such a historically
scientific contribution.... This job provided great
scientific connections,...job offers, ...research,...[and] a
legacy. It would not only effect the present, but also future
generations. How could such young people be equipped to make
such a life-altering decision?...
It is funny how this class is making me reevaluate every
ethical dilemma I was once so certain about...
```

Many factors weighed on one's decision. While you are sitting in Robert
Serber's seminar, your classmates from high school and college are carrying
machine guns in Italy or flamethrowers on Iwo Jima. If your training in

physics could help end the war sooner, wouldn't you feel obliged to give it your best? Was making nuclear weapons less moral than making bullets or bombers? The nightmare of those who joined the Manhattan Project was fear that the Nazis would get the atomic bomb first. Sooner or later someone was going to build it, and wouldn't it be better if a democracy rather than a brutal criminal police state got it first? Besides, it would be a tremendous opportunity to work shoulder-to-shoulder, in a cause that seemed just, with the very people who created nuclear physics.

While discussing these issues, our class views the 1981 Jon Else documentary *The Day After Trinity.* [Else(1981)] It tells the story of Robert Oppenheimer and the Manhattan Project and its aftermath. Interviewed on camera are Hans Bethe, Haakon Chavalier, Freeman Dyson, Dorothy McKibbin, Frank Oppenheimer, Isaac Rabi, Robert Serber, Stan and François Ulam, Robert and Jane Wilson, and others. Before starting the movie I ask the class to describe how they picture the personalities of the people who built the first atomic bombs. The students have a few moments to discuss the question among themselves, then the floor opens for suggestions which are recorded on the white board. Intelligent. Focused. Patriotic. Driven. Nerdy. Cold. Anti-social. After making our list we watch the documentary. How did the students do in predicting the personalities of the authors of the first nuclear weapons? Holly W. weighed in:

At first, I thought these people were war addicts, manipulating, hateful, angry, stubborn people. Who would want to create something so powerfully destructive? Then I was shown these people. Families with loved ones all around the world who have a love for science. Wait, love science, love people? That sounds too much like myself. I want to become an educator to create life-long learners in my students. These men and women who created nuclear bombs were those types of people.... I was overwhelmed with their loyalty to the project. It was another perspective to this time of history that has now affected me in the present.... Before I jump to conclusions about people's motives and characteristics based on stereotypes...I must look at the people's stories....

Emily B. added,

I wondered how they could do something like that--invent
something that would kill so many innocent people. I always
thought that, in that situation, I would've stood up and
rallied against such violence. However, I've been
considering this and I realized that, in their position, I
would've done the same thing. Nearly everyone in this time
period felt strongly nationalistic pride...If I wasn't
qualified to do the actual fighting, but could use my
intellect and skill set to create something we could fight
with, I probably would have.

    From Sierra P.:

It was interesting...to see the people behind this work,
and to realize that they were normal people, with normal
lives. The only difference between me & them were our
passions & talents. They loved & laughed, but also happened
to be insanely brilliant and interested in science.... They
were qualified to take on this task, yet in my mind they
weren't the right fit. The war and bombings require dark,
villainous figures, who are cold and indifferent.... When we
saw their reactions to the bombing and heard their thoughts,
all of a sudden I realized that they are *people*.... I'm very
interested in the questions of ethics and morals when it
pertains to science.... I don't want to look back and feel
remorse & guilt over my accomplishments because of what they
ended up doing to others.

Robin H. applied these meditations to her own real life: "Many scientists, then and now, walk a very fine line between curiosity and ethics....
This is something that I, as a blooming scientist, find a little scary... who
is to say there are not 'Manhattan projects' in my future?" Most STS
students report that, had they been invited to join the Manhattan Project,
their first inclination was to say No. But the more they thought about
it, the more inclined they were to say Yes. Nancy W. wrote in one of her
weekly letters:

I'm not sure exactly what I thought this class would be
about, but so far it is definitely much different than what I

imagined. Some of the things I find myself thinking about
are things I have never given any thought to before. What if
I were given the opportunity to work on the first nuclear
bomb? (Let's also pretend I'm smart enough for that.) Would
I do it? My immediate reaction, no way. Why would I work on
something that would kill, injure, and destroy innocent
people? But after watching ''The Day After Trinity'' in
class, I thought a bit more about it & saw this question in a
different way.
If I had the opportunity to work on something that had never
been done before & that I was interested in & passionate about,
chances are I'm going for it. While at first I thought of
those who worked on a nuclear bomb as military-minded people,
I realize that was not the case. These were brilliant
scientists doing what they love & trying to help. They knew
that something this destructive would be discovered with or
without them being the first to make it happen. They saw it
necessary to protect & defend their country.... these people
were maybe not so different from me as I first thought (except
maybe IQ score). The second thing that has really been on my
mind is the aftermath of the nuclear bombs. I can't imagine
the inner conflict & mixed emotions they must have experienced.
I sympathize for them in a way I had NEVER thought about.

Did anyone walk away from the Manhattan Project before it was finished? Frank Oppenheimer recalled that after Germany surrendered, "Nobody said, 'Oh well, it doesn't matter now.' We wanted to see this thing go. It's amazing how the technology traps one." [Else(1981)]

We know of one person who walked away, for reasons of conscience, from the Manhattan Project. His name was Joseph Rotblat.[85] He lost his motivation for the whole business when it became clear that the Germans had not come close to building an atomic bomb. Furthermore, one evening in March 1944 at a dinner in James Chadwick's home, Rotblat heard General Groves say that the bomb's real purpose was to intimidate the Soviets. [Abrams(1995)] That's not what this was supposed to be about,

---

[85]In 1955 Rotblat was the youngest signer of the famous Russell–Einstein Manifesto that called on world leaders to eschew hydrogen bombs. He became a founder and Secretary General of the Pugwash Conferences on Science and World Affairs, bringing East and West scientists together.

thought Rotblat, so he asked for and was granted permission to leave. At the end of the Fall 2001 semester our class asked Professor Dyson what he would have done in 1944:

> *5 December 2001*
> *Dear Professor Dyson,*
> *I hope you and your family are looking forward to a wonderful time together over the holidays. The events of the past several months have caused us all to remember what is truly important....*
> *Would you have walked away from Los Alamos [during the Manhattan Project]?*
>
> *8 December 2001*
> *Dear Dwight,*
> *...Would I have walked away from Los Alamos if I had been there during World War Two? Answer, definitely no, since I did not walk away from RAF Bomber Command, and Bomber Command was at least as evil as Los Alamos. In fact I had better reasons to walk away from Bomber Command than Rotblat had to walk away from Los Alamos. The evil that Bomber Command was doing, killing thousands of our own young men as well as thousands of enemy civilians every month, was much clearer than the evil that Los Alamos promised to do later. I am sure that if I had been at Los Alamos I would have worked on the project enthusiastically just as everyone else did, with the exception of Rotblat, right up to the end. And even now, although I admire and respect Rotblat enormously, I do not altogether agree with him.*
> *...Happy Christmas and New Year to you all, Yours ever, Freeman.*

Little Boy was never tested to the extent of an explosion; they knew it would work. Because of its complexity, the Fat Man design was tested despite its billion-dollar price tag. The test took place in the New Mexico desert, between Socorro and Alamogordo at a site Robert Oppenheimer code-named Trinity. The Trinity site desert was known to locals by its Spanish name, *Jornada del Muerto*, the Journey of Death. The countdown ended at 5:30 A.M. on July 16, 1945. Shortly after the test Kenneth Bainbridge, the test director, walked up to Oppenheimer, shook his hand, and said "Oppie, now we're all sons of bitches." [Goodchild(1981)][162]

On the Question of Use

"It does bring home to one just how powerful this is—to treat human beings as matter." –Isaac I. Rabi[86]

On July 17, 1945, two months after the German surrender and the day after the Trinity test, President Truman, Prime Minister Churchill, and Premier Stalin met in Potsdam, a suburb of Berlin, for the first day of a two-week conference. They were to decide how to finish the Pacific war and discuss postwar plans. Extrapolating from bitter experience in battles across the Pacific, the casualties on both sides of an invasion of the Japanese homeland were expected to be astronomical. On that July morning, President Truman learned he had another option.

Shortly after he became President upon Franklin Roosevelt's death in the spring of 1945, Truman formed an Interim Committee, chaired by Secretary of War Henry Stimson, to advise him on the bomb's use.

Henry Stimson and his advisers were not insensitive to the moral issues with which they were confronted. The record of their deliberations leaves no doubt that they agonized long and hard over the decision to use the bombs. [Dyson(1979a)][42]

The Interim Committee sought the advice of a subcommittee of prominent scientists who led in building the bomb, including Enrico Fermi, Arthur Compton, Ernest Lawrence, and Robert Oppenheimer. They in turn solicited the opinions of their colleagues.

Another question put to the STS students asks if they would have ordered the atomic bomb to be used on Japan had they been in President Truman's place in the summer of 1945. Sarah W. responded,

```
What a question!  Initially I thought NO! There is no way I
could possibly be responsible for taking that many
lives...but then I started thinking about it more.  Perhaps a
better question would be, ''Could I have not dropped the
bomb?''  In the same way that I wonder if I could take so
many lives in one moment, could I allow the taking of lives
to continue over a drawn-out period?  With no guaranteed end
in sight, could I allow a war to continue, to take lives all
over the world, the lives of the very people I had sworn to
```

----
[86][Else(1981)]

protect? There is nothing simple about this question. As
quickly as I could condemn President Truman for dropping the
bomb, I could easily condemn him just as quickly if he had not
dropped it...

What were the arguments in 1945 for dropping nuclear bombs on
Japanese cities? First, by being so devastating the atomic bomb offered
hope of ending the war quickly, making an invasion of Japan unnecessary.
In that event the atomic bomb could save more lives than it destroyed.

Second, Japan and the Allies were at an impasse. The Allied leaders
called for "unconditional surrender." The Japanese high command was divided. The hard-line military commanders saw death as more honorable
than surrender and insisted on "fighting to the bitter end." The civilian
leaders saw defeat as inevitable and wanted to salvage as much of their nation as possible. [Giovannitti and Freed(1965)] In the end the Allies granted
one condition to the Japanese—the Emperor could be retained. As the only
authority which all Japanese would obey, maintaining the Emperor in his
role and treating him with respect prevented World War Two from degen-
erating into a long guerilla war fought with well-armed and still-undefeated
Japanese forces scattered across Asia and the Pacific. [Rhodes(1986)][745]

Third, by the summer of 1945, the moral high ground from which one
might have argued against using the atomic bomb had long since been
compromised.

Fourth, it was not clear that a benign demonstration of the bomb would
convince the Japanese commanders to surrender. As the narrator grimly
noted in *The Day After Trinity*, "With a million civilians dead and Tokyo
in ruins, the Japanese fought on." [Else(1981)][87]

Fifth, the Manhattan Project cost, in inflation-adjusted dollars, approximately what the USA spent on the space program of the 1960s. To not
use the result of that investment would have been difficult to justify. When
news of the Trinity test reached Potsdam, Secretary Stimson said to his
assistant, "I have been responsible for spending two billions of dollars on
this atomic venture. Now that it is successful I shall not be sent to prison
in Fort Leavenworth." [Rhodes(1986)][686]

Sixth, by the time of the Potsdam conference the Soviets were eager
to join in the invasion of Japan. But Truman and Churchill did not want
Stalin's dictatorship to control any part of Japan. That would have led to

---

[87]Nor did they surrender between the atomic bombings of Hiroshima and Nagasaki. The
devestation of the atomic bomb made reliable communication with Hiroshima difficult.

its partitioning, which the Allied leaders could see was going to happen in Europe. The Soviets declared war on Japan the same day the plutonium bomb was dropped on Nagasaki. But the Japanese surrendered before Soviets troops could enter Japan.

Seventh, no love was lost between the American public and ethnic Japanese. The Bill of Rights notwithstanding, the US government held American citizens of Japanese ethnicity in internment camps. Most of them lost homes and businesses. The third director of Los Alamos, Harold Agnew, who was aboard the instrument plane *Great Artiste* that flew next to the *Enola Gay* over Hiroshima, sadly reflected on the 40th anniversary of the bombings, "Without Pearl Harbor, there would not have been a Hiroshima." [Agnew(1985)]

Eighth, we must remember *who* an American President is sworn to defend. After the atomic bomb became available, could anyone realistically expect the President of the United States to sacrifice thousands more American lives in a massive invasion of Japan in order to spare the lives of Japanese citizens? In the summer of 1945, President Truman had no good options.

> *1 May 2000*
> *Dear Professor Dyson,*
> *Here once again, if we may impose on you for a few moments of your time, are selected questions from the Spring 2000 "Science, Technology, and Society" class.*
> *...In your opinion, did President Truman make the right decision to drop the atomic bomb on Hiroshima and Nagasaki?*

> *1 May 2000*
> *Dear Dwight,*
> *...Yes, I think Truman made the right decision. So long as World War Two continued, we were killing more people every month than we killed at Hiroshima and Nagasaki. So the dropping of the bombs was saving lives, if it shortened the war only by a couple of months. We can never know whether or not Japan would have surrendered in a couple of months if the bombs had not been dropped. The best evidence on this question was collected by Robert Butow in his book "Japan's Decision to Surrender."[88] Butow interviewed the Japanese wartime leaders while their memories were still fresh and asked them the question "Would Japan have surrendered without the dropping of the bombs?" The Japanese leaders themselves did not know the*

---

[88]Robert J. C. Butow, *Japan's Decision to Surrender*, Stanford University Press (1954).

answer. Therefore we cannot know the answer, and certainly Truman could not know the answer. It is quite possible that if the bombs had not been dropped the Japanese armies would have fought to the last man as they did in Okinawa in the spring of 1945, with millions more dead before the war ended. Nobody can know whether or not this would have happened. So I say, Truman made the right decision.

Another question is, whether Truman in fact could have made a decision not to drop the bombs and made the decision stick. Perhaps he had no choice. A decision not to drop the bombs would have been violently opposed by the army generals and their friends in Congress, and Truman was in a weak position to impose his will on Congress, having only recently become President. Certainly Truman could only have prevailed over Congress if he had overwhelmingly strong reasons not to drop the bombs. And I am sure he did not see any strong reason not to take this chance to end the war. I thought at the time that he was right, and I still think so.

Wendy R. reflected,

The discussions about Hiroshima and WWII... brought up issues I had never given much thought. It was interesting to hear about the struggles of the Los Alamos scientists and to try to place myself in their shoes when it came down to moral issues.... I have benefited the most from these discussions because they made me decide where I stand on issues that involve human life...

From Julie D., who wants to teach history:

I enjoyed the week of class when we discussed the atomic bomb and the people who worked on that project. I found it interesting & helpful to me because I am a history major. [We] touched more on the people & life of Los Alamos than what I have learned in my history classes. This information will help me when I begin to teach on this period of time & what the scientists were like & [what they] went through, instead of just a military outlook. I will be more personal and maybe more understandable to the kids.

Chapter 4 of *Disturbing the Universe* closes with this somber reflection:

Those fellows who had built the atomic bomb obviously knew their stuff. They must be an outstandingly competent bunch of people. The thought occurred to me that I might one day get to meet them.... It was easy...to forget the agony of the people still slowly dying of burns and radiation sickness in Hiroshima. Later, much later, I would remember these things. [Dyson(1979a)][44]

Requiem for My Friend

"Doctor," a patient commented to Michihiko Hachiya a few days later, "a human being who has been roasted becomes quite small, doesn't he?" –Hiroshima Diary[89]

The classroom lights go out. Music begins. It is a Mass, the Lacrimosa section of "Requiem for My Friend" by Zbigniew Preisner. *Lacrimosa* is the Latin word for "weeping." Four minutes, three seconds. The first measures, subdued and haunting, are played by cellos. On the screen we see the mushroom cloud over Hiroshima; four measures later, the second mushroom cloud over Nagasaki. The music builds, the images move in: debris of flattened houses, burned to ashes, desolate. The music pauses, then a vocalist begins....

Lacrimosa dies illa,	*Ah! that day of tears and mourning!*
Qua resurget ex favilla	*From the dust of earth returning,*
Judicandus homo reus....	*Man for judgment must prepare him...*

Images closer in... individual victims. A chorus joins the vocalist. *Lacrimosa, Lacrimosa...* Flash burns, shapes barely recognizable as human beings, a pile of skulls... *Lacrimosa, Lacrimosa...* The last image shows two survivors, a bewildered Japanese mother with her child. Surrounded by smoke, they look vacantly into the camera. The music builds and builds to a climax–*La-cri-mo-sa...* and abruptly ends. Requiem for my friend.

The screen goes black. The reverberation of the last chord dies down slowly in the darkened room, then... silence.[90]

---

[89][Hachiya and Wells(1955)][92]

[90]"Requiem for My Friend" (Lacrimosa) by Zbigniew Preisner, performed by Sinfonia Varsovia and the Varsov Chamber Choir, conducted by Jacek Kaspszyk, soloist Elzbieta Towarnicka. Warner music (2000). On the day following this presentation, I have to play "Requiem for my Friend" again, multiple times, to not let the Preisner's sublime Mass be uniquely associated in my mind with images of the bombings.

After the reverberations from "Requiem for my Friend" fade, we linger several moments in dark silence. Then the next image on the screen appears, white letters on a black background, that simply says "Postwar Developments."

The Beginning or the End

"The release of atomic energy has not created a new problem. It has merely made more urgent the necessity of solving an existing one." –Albert Einstein[91]

In a 1965 interview a journalist asked Robert Oppenheimer what he thought of Senator Robert Kennedy's suggestion that President Johnson initiate talks with the Soviets to limit nuclear weapons. Oppenheimer answered with resignation, "It's twenty years too late. It should have been done the day after Trinity." [Else(1981)] From the moment the Trinity bomb went off, Oppenheimer tried to convince those in power to put nuclear weapons under international control. He stopped only when the United States government let it be known that it no longer wanted his counsel, by revoking his security clearance in 1954.

On 24 July 1945, eight days after the Trinity test and one week into the two-week Potsdam conference, Secretary of War Henry Stimson and Secretary of State James Brynes joined President Harry Truman for lunch. They had a delicate situation to discuss. Their chronically suspicious wartime ally Joseph Stalin needed to be told about the new atomic bomb, and they feared Stalin would resent having been kept out of the loop. Nor did they want to give much away. If Stalin realized the power of the bomb, he might order the Red Army to invade Japan at once. Trying to make a big deal seem like a small one, Truman tried the offhand approach.

"I casually mentioned to Stalin that we had a new weapon of unusual destructive force. The Russian Premier showed no special interest. All he said was that he was glad to hear it and hoped would make 'good use of it against the Japanese.' " "That," concludes Robert Oppenheimer dryly, knowing how much at that moment the world lost, "was carrying casualness rather far." [Rhodes(1986)][689–690]

---

[91][Einstein(1956)][185]

Truman did not know that, thanks to spies, Stalin already knew about the atomic bomb's existence. With Stalin not told forthrightly about the bomb, and with him knowing he was not being told, one can argue that the Cold War began at that instant.

In July 1946 the USA conducted new nuclear weapons tests, Operation Crossroads, which tested two fission bombs on the Bikini Islands in the Pacific. [Shurcliff(1947)] The spoken reason given for the tests was to measure the effects of atomic bombs on shipping. One cannot help but wonder if the unspoken reason for conducting two tests at that time was to make a statement: The US had more of these bombs. "Sending mixed signals," Operation Crossroads took place "while experts tried to devise a system for the international control." [Rhodes(2005)][478] The world was at a crossroads indeed.

The 1946 Bikini tests were not the only time the USA talked of international weapons control while developing new weapons for itself. Forty years later, starting in 1997 the US began stockpiling the B61-11 earth penetrating nuclear weapon, the so-called "bunker buster," while scolding North Korea and Iran for pursuing nuclear weapons programs. The B61-11 missile flies vertically into the ground so fast that it buries itself deep before its warhead explodes. Illustrating semantics engineering, when introduced the B61-11 was touted as "weapons modernization." This prompted an article in *The Bulletin of Atomic Scientists* to ask,

According to government officials, the United States is no longer developing new nuclear weapons. But what is a new weapon? Those connected with the B61-11 program say it is not new because its "physics package" remains unchanged from an earlier model of the B61, the B61-7.
Indeed, the physics package has apparently not been changed. But an undisclosed number of B61-7s have been transformed, adding greatly enhanced capabilities against underground targets. Does that make it a "new" or an "old" weapon? [Mello(1997)]

These developments caused a bewildered Cody H. to ask, "Is it all right for our country to create nuclear weapons, and tell others they can't? What makes us any different?"

In the second half of World War Two, it became clear that Stalin's Soviet Union intended to maintain control of a set of buffer states—Poland, Czechoslovakia, Albania, Hungary, Bulgaria, Romania, East Germany— that the Red Army occupied when it pushed the Germans back into Germany. At a speech at Westminster College in Fulton, Missouri on 5 March 1946, Winston Churchill introduced the term "iron curtain" into public vernacular:[92] "From Stettin in the Baltic to Trieste in the Adriatic an iron curtain has descended across the Continent...." [Rhodes(2005)][237] It is interesting to hear how Churchill's iron curtain speech was received in the Soviet Union. Stalin's successor, Nikita Khrushchev, who tried to undo some of Stalin's excesses, later recalled it in his memoirs:

> Our postwar relations with the capitalist countries were damaged severely by that arsonist and militarist Churchill. His famous speech urging the imperialist forces of the world to mobilize against the Soviet Union served as a signal for the start of the Cold War.... it was extremely significant that, of all the times and places he could have given that speech, he chose to give it during a visit to America. We knew that if there were to be another war, we would find ourselves confronted with a coalition of Western countries led by the United States. [Khrushchev and Talbott(1974)][355]

Wasting no time, the Soviets detonated their first fission bomb on August 29, 1949. Two decades separated World War Two from World War One. With the Cold War following on the heels of the Second World War, everyone dreaded World War Three fought in the 1960s with nuclear weapons. This palpable fear was never out of public consciousness. Posters advertising a 1946 movie, "The Beginning or the End," show two couples clinging together and looking fearfully into the distance as behind them looms an ominous mushroom cloud. The movie poster says the characters "face the atomic future with resolution, though they seem a bit confused about which direction the menace is coming from."[93] The December 18, 1950 issue of *Life* magazine described a plan to construct eight-lane highway "life belts" around major US cities, to provide escape routes with camps and Quonset hut hospitals for the survivors of the coming nuclear war. Bomb shelters were real estate selling points; duck-and-cover procedures were rehearsed in schools; sturdy public buildings with deep basements were designated as civil defense shelters.

The Cold War stakes were raised with the advent of the hydrogen bomb.

---

[92] Churchill attended the Westminster College commencement to receive an honorary degree.

[93] Starring Robert Walker, Audrey Trotter, Tom Drake, Beverly Tyler. General Groves served as a consultant.

"An Evil Thing"

Nuclear fusion reactions power the stars. In the Sun's core, through a sequence of collisions, four protons build up a nucleus of helium-4. This reaction sequence yields about six times more energy per particle than does fission.[94] To make a nuclear fusion bomb one must create in a small space, for a millionth of a second, conditions similar to a stellar core.

During the Manhattan Project Edward Teller strongly advocated the development of the hydrogen bomb. Oppenheimer let Teller's group see what could be learned about fusion. After the successful Soviet fission bomb test in 1949, fear that the Soviets might already be working on a fusion weapon gave the hydrogen bomb a sudden urgency. A General Advisory Committee (GAC) to the Atomic Energy Commission was formed, chaired by Robert Oppenheimer, to advise the government on the hydrogen bomb. Other members included senior physicists who led the fission bomb development. At its seventh meeting held at the end of October 1949, enough data had been collected to suggest its estimated yield would be thousands of times greater than a fission bomb. The proposed bomb was accordingly nicknamed the "Super."

The GAC firmly and unanimously recommended that the United States *not* build this hellish weapon: "No member of the Committee was willing to endorse this proposal." [Oppenheimer *et al.*(1949)], [Rhodes(2005)][396–403] They argued that developing the hydrogen bomb would be wrong militarily, wrong politically, and wrong morally.

The hydrogen bomb was wrong militarily: The "extreme dangers to mankind inherent in the proposal wholly outweigh any military advantage that could come from this development." Given the possibility that the Soviets might develop the weapon, the Committee retorted "Should they use the weapon against us, reprisals by our large stock of atomic bombs would be comparably effective to the use of a super."

The hydrogen bomb was wrong politically because it would turn the USA into a hostage-taker, with "far-reaching effects on world opinion; reasonable people the world over would realize that the existence of a weapon of this type whose power of destruction is essentially unlimited represents a threat to the future of the human race which is intolerable..." By *not*

---

[94]Fission of heavy elements, and fusion of lightweight ones, both yield energy because the products are nearer the middle of the periodic table of the elements, whose nuclei are more stable. The most stable nucleus is iron-56.

producing it, even though it could, the United States could show unprecedented leadership:

...In determining not to proceed to develop the super bomb, we see a unique opportunity of providing by example some limitations on the totality of war and thus of limiting the fear and arousing the hopes of mankind.

The hydrogen bomb was wrong morally. The radius of damage produced by a nuclear weapon scales as the cube root of the yield. At Hiroshima, buildings were obliterated within a one-mile radius of ground zero. A hydrogen bomb, with the yield of a thousand Little Boys, would produce similar devastation to a radius of ten miles. The only targets with a size comparable to such a damage radius are metropolitan areas. "By its very nature it cannot be confined to a military objective but becomes a weapon which in practical effect is almost one of genocide."

...It is clear that the use of such a weapon cannot be justified on any ethical ground which gives a human being a certain individuality and dignity even if he happens to be a resident of an enemy country.... Its use would put the United States in a bad moral position relative to the peoples of the world.
...The fact that no limits exist to the destructiveness of this weapon makes its very existence and the knowledge of its construction a danger to humanity as a whole. It is necessarily an evil thing considered in any light.
For these reasons we believe it important for the President of the United States to tell the American public, and the world, that we think it wrong on fundamental ethical principles to initiate a program of development or construction of weapons in this category.

On 31 January 1950, three months after the GAC report, an important meeting took place at the White House between President Harry Truman, Defense Secretary Louis Johnson, Secretary of State Dean Acheson, and Atomic Energy Commission Chairman David Lilienthal. They met to finalize the hydrogen bomb decision. Lilienthal began describing the reasons for not building the hydrogen bomb. Seven minutes into it, Truman cut him off: "Can the Russians do it?" When his visitors nodded yes, despite the GAC recommendation Truman said, "In that case, we have no choice. We'll go ahead." [Bird and Sherwin(2005)][428]
Even though Truman did not follow their advice, to this day, the GAC's arguments of October 1949 still deserve a hearing whenever new weapons

are proposed. It so happens that such a discussion has been going on in recent years regarding US Air Force proposals to station offensive weapons in low-Earth-orbit. Such a topic merits wider public discussion than it had so far received.

In 1950 Edward Teller, Stan Ulam, and John Wheeler, and many others (*not* including Robert Oppenheimer) set to work to deliver on the President's order. The breakthrough Teller-Ulam design that eventually worked was a staged "booster" device. A plutonium fission bomb was attached to one end of the fusion fuel. Stage one occurs when the fission bomb detonates. Its intense light flash sweeps through the fusion fuel ahead of the shock wave, raising the temperature to around ten million degrees. Within the high temperature and pressure of this intense light, and with the fusion fuel well tampered, stage two occurs when, for a millionth of a second, conditions mimic the core of a star, resulting in the fusion explosion.

The first hydrogen bomb, code-named Ivy Mike, used liquid hydrogen as the fusion fuel, requiring refrigeration equipment that made the bomb too big to carry. It was detonated on November 1, 1952, yielding 10.4 megatons, turning the Pacific island of Eugelab into a mile-wide crater. A deployable hydrogen bomb was on the drawing boards before the Mike shot, replacing liquid hydrogen with a lithium-deuterium paste. This design was the subject of the Castle Bravo test of March 1, 1954, on the Bikini Atoll. Its yield was expected to be four to eight megatons. The actual yield was 15 megatons. [Rhodes(2005)]

In his review of Teller's *Memoirs*, Professor Dyson reminds us that "Hydrogen bombs on both sides of the Cold War were essential to keeping it cold." He recalls having a beer one evening in the 1960s with a German infantry officer, a veteran of the Russian front during World War Two:

> *Then he pointed a finger at me and said, "If it were not for your damned hydrogen bombs, we would be back in Russia today." At that moment I was thinking, "Thank God for Edward Teller and his bombs."* [Dyson(2002a)]

McCarthyism

Eight months after Ivy Mike, on 12 August 1953 the Soviet Union successfully tested their first hydrogen bomb. In an environment of fear and suspicion many Americans—notably Senator Joseph McCarthy—began seeing Communists under every bed. For reading a Communist magazine, or finding common cause with the Communist Party in seeking better working conditions for California's migrant farm workers, or for having friends with Communist sympathies, you could be summoned to testify before the House Committee on Un-American Activities. Summoned witnesses had no good options.

1 May 2001
Dear Professor Dyson,
Once again as we near the semester's end, our Science, Technology, and Society class sends greetings to you and your family....
What decision by scientists has most affected the scientific community in a negative way?...

3 May 2001
Dear Dwight,
Thank you for the May Day message and thanks to the students for their list of questions....
It is hard to find examples of scientists doing things that affected the whole scientific community, either for good or for bad. The community is diverse, and divided up into a thousand little communities with different interests and different problems. The best example I can think of comes from the "McCarthy era" in the 1950s, when many scientists lost their jobs because they were accused of being Communists. The victims were questioned publicly by congressional committees in Washington, who demanded that they talk about (a) their own political activities, and (b) the activities of their friends. The victim then had a choice of two responses. Either (c) refuse to answer all questions by claiming the protection of the Fifth Amendment to the US Constitution, which says that nobody can be compelled to testify against himself, or (d) answer freely the questions about their own activities but refuse to answer questions about their friends. Among my own friends at that time, David Bohm chose (c), Wendell Furry and Chandler Davis chose (d). If you chose (c) you were legally protected. If you chose (d) you might go to jail. But the effects of people choosing (c) were disastrous for the scientific community. To plead the Fifth Amendment was generally understood to mean that you were guilty and had secrets to hide. This played into the hands of the politicians like Joe McCarthy who were scaring the public with scare-stories of Communist conspiracies. What happened to the individual victims? David Bohm came out of it badly. He was indicted for contempt of Congress, tried and found not guilty, but this did not do him any good. He lost his job at Princeton anyway, and

had to leave the USA to find a job in Brazil. Chandler Davis went to jail for a year and is now a distinguished professor in Toronto. Wendell Furry was never indicted and continued his life at Harvard without interruption. If everyone had chosen (d) and accepted the risk of going to jail, the damage to the country would have been much less.

Last year we had a similar witch-hunt with the accusations against Wen Ho Lee at Los Alamos. Wen Ho Lee went to jail for a year and the accusations that he was a spy collapsed. With luck, this witch-hunt may now be coming to an end. The courage and honorable behavior of Wen Ho Lee certainly helped to limit the damage.[95]

The reactions of some American politicians and Administration officials after the terrorist attacks of September 11, 2001 were reminiscent of McCarthyism. For expressing the opinion that the Iraq war was started on false pretenses, one could be labeled "unpatriotic." Administration reactions sanctioned the torture of prisoners, contradictory to American ideals and reminiscent of the tactics of the dictator whose brutality the invasion was supposed to end. [Mayer(2009)] Congress passed the Patriot Act which authorized warrantless searches contrary to the Bill of Rights.

12 November 2007
Dear Professor Dyson,
We hope that the 2007 Thanksgiving season finds you and all your family doing well....
What are your feelings about the Patriot Act? Do you believe it infringes on basic human rights? We ask this question in light of possible parallels with the McCarthy hysteria of the early 1950s.

23 November 2007
Dear Dwight,
...Yes, to me the Patriot Act is a big step backward. It is just as Benjamin Franklin said, people who give up a little freedom to obtain a little safety end up by losing both freedom and safety. Our present-day Patriot Act and our bad treatment of prisoners are even worse than the hysteria of the McCarthy era. McCarthy tried to put innocent people in jail, but he did not try to hold them in jail without trial, and he did not advocate us-

---

[95]Wen Ho Lee is a Taiwanese-American physicist who created computer simulations as part of the Stockpile Stewardship program. Lee was falsely accused of stealing US nuclear arsenal secrets on behalf of the People's Republic of China. Some time after Professor Dyson's May 2001 letter about him, Dr. Lee received $1.6 million from the federal government and five news organizations in a civil suit, and an apology from a federal judge.

ing torture to make them talk. I think this country is behaving much worse today than we were in the 1950s, and the rest of the world knows it. Our bad treatment of prisoners dismays our friends and encourages our enemies.

When circling the wagons, it's best to not shoot inward.

9 Arsenals of Folly

Correspondence on the Militarization of the Economy

> *"Even more significantly, NSC-68 began the historic uncoupling of the U.S. defense budget from fiscal policy."*–Richard Rhodes[96]

***

Investment Paid Off In Full

About the time Professor Dyson and his German officer friend were enjoying a beer together, I was a grade-schooler living in Salina, Kansas. In those days Salina was home to Schilling Air Force Base of the Strategic Air Command. Schilling kept a fleet of combat-ready bombers, plus a dozen Atlas missiles in hardened silos. My encounters with the Cold War at that time were typical of my generation living in the US Midwest. All across town we saw SAC parking decals on cars; we heard the roaring six-engine B-47s taking off for practice runs. The Cold War economy was worth a lot of jobs and contracts to the people of Salina. A 1957 public relations statement said that "Today Schilling Air Force Base represents 15 years of development and a tremendous financial investment. The total value of the base is more than $370,000,000. Almost $216,000,000 worth of jet bombers and four-engine tankers operate from its runways. It costs more than $35,000,000 per year and takes 6000 men to keep the two bomb wings operating and combat ready. If Schilling Air Force Base never again sends its planes to war, this investment will have paid off in full." [Waggoner and Carey(2015)][97]

The strategy of both sides during the Cold War was Mutual Assured Destruction, or MAD. If you nuke us, you get nuked back. Whatever the wisdom and follies of MAD as policy, the weapons systems backing it up were frightfully expensive.

The Cold War dominated international relations and industrialized economies for forty years. It was produced by post-WWII mistrust

---

[96][Rhodes(2007)][106]. Secretary of State Dean Acheson would later admit that the purpose of NSC-68, a 1950 national security report, was to "bludgeon the mass mind of 'top government...'"[103–104].

[97]This statement was issued when the airbase was renamed in honor of distinguished fighter pilot Col. David C. Schilling.

between the West and the Soviet bloc, accelerated from the US side by neo-conservatives who consistently over-estimated Soviet capabilities.[98] Pressure to over-estimate on the US side came from foreign policy zealots and from those in industry who had weapons systems contracts. [Rhodes(2007)][102–106] According to data from the Bulletin of Atomic Scientists, throughout the 1950s and '60s, the US was always ahead of the USSR in stockpiled nuclear weapons; for instance, in 1964 the US had 31,139 stockpiled weapons to 6,129 in the USSR. [Kristensen and Norris(2010)] Professor Dyson recalled his time with the Arms Control and Disarmament Agency in the 1960s, when he studied Soviet policies:

For example, in 1960 we enjoyed a superiority in offensive missiles while the Soviet Union concealed its weaknesses by maintaining a missile bluff. We then demolished the Soviet missile bluff as conspicuously as possible with public statements of the results of U-2 photography, and so forced the Soviet Union to replace its fictitious missile force by a real one. It would have been much wiser for us to have left the Soviet bluff intact. [Dyson(1979a)][137]

The USSR achieved parity with the USA in stockpiled nukes (about 25,000 each) around 1977 and surpassed the US until the collapse of the Soviet Union. The stockpiles of both sides drastically declined with the Strategic Arms Reduction Treaty (START) signed in 1991. As of 2015, the stockpiles had been reduced to about 7,500 nukes in Russia and 7,100 in the US. [Kristensen and Norris(2015)] During most this time, the number of strategic weapons *deployed* have been approximately equal.

During the Cold War years (ca. 1948–1991) programs to develop, stockpile, deploy, and guard nuclear weapons cost the USA an estimated $10 trillion, or 250 billion dollars per year. [Rhodes(2007)] Defense is expensive, and those who bear the responsibility for protecting the US population would be derelict in their duties if they did not err on the side of caution. In addition, the USA has treaty obligations with numerous countries around the globe. One could argue that if we do not maintain sufficient stockpiles of nuclear weapons, other nations that rely on us for their defense might be tempted to produce nuclear weapons themselves, accelerating proliferation.

---

[98]Threat exaggeration occurred on both sides. Nikita Khrushchev's comment on Churchill's "iron curtain" speech noted the role of US industry in Stalin's threat inflation: "Furthermore, the Cold War was sure to profit big American monopolistic capital.... It was largely because of Churchill's speech that Stalin exaggerated our enemies' strength and their intention to unleash war on us..." [Khrushchev and Talbott(1974)][355]

But wars and rumors of wars are also good for business. Technology gets pushed forward, but resources that could meet human needs are diverted. In October 1952, physicist Melba Phillips[99] warned about the unprecedented influence of military funding on science during and following World War Two:

The greatest humanitarian opportunity ever offered to science—namely, the technological development of vast backward areas of the earth—has become manifest and realizable in our epoch...[But this] has received only the most paltry governmental support and is largely ignored. What has displaced it? A vast program of military research, which transforms the humanitarian aim of science into its opposite. [Phillips(1952)]

On the evening of 17 January 1961, three days before the inauguration of John F. Kennedy, President Dwight Eisenhower delivered a televised farewell speech. He warned the American public against growing alliances between defense and industry. These remarks were especially credible being uttered by the President who had been Supreme Commander of the Allied Forces in the European theatre of World War Two, when US industrial might was essential to winning the war.

Until the latest of our world conflicts, the United States had no armaments industry. American makers of plowshares could... make swords as well. But now we can no longer risk emergency improvisation of national defense; we have been compelled to create a permanent armaments industry of vast proportions.... In the councils of government, we must guard against the acquisition of unwarranted influence, whether sought or unsought, by the military-industrial complex. The potential for the disastrous rise of misplaced power exists and will persist. [Eisenhower(1961)][100]

Eisenhower saw it coming. When a major defense contractor wins a large contract, say a new jet fighter whose development and manufacture will span several decades, the corporate executives engage in "district engineering." Subcontractors and factories and suppliers are dispersed to every State, making it almost impossible politically to cancel the program.

---

[99]Melba Phillips was Robert Oppenheimer's first woman graduate student. After her PhD, she and Oppenheimer discovered Oppenheimer–Phillips effect in nuclear physics. The month before her *Science* article was published, Phillips was called before the McCarran Committee, during its Second Session on Subversive Influence in the Educational Process. She pled the Fifth and was unemployable for four and a half years.

[100]An accessible source is http://www.youtube.com/watch?v=8y06NSBBRtY.

Has the US economy been unduly militarized? The following figures are sample line items from the 2014 fiscal year budget submitted to the United States Congress by President Obama. [Federal Budget(2014)] The left column shows the relative ranking of each department's funding; the middle column is the President's 2014 budget request in billions of dollars; the third column shows how many dollars the Department of Defense would have for every dollar budgeted to the department on that line. For example, the Department of Education had the fourth largest funding at 71.2 billion dollars, and for every dollar Education has in this budget, Defense has $7.40.

(1) Department of Defense	526.10	1.00
(2) Health & Human Services	80.10	6.57
(4) Department of Education	71.20	7.40
(7) Department of State	47.80	11.02
(10) Department of Energy	28.40	18.54
(13) NASA	17.10	29.75
(15) Environmental Protection Agency	8.20	64.22
(20) National Science Foundation	4.70	69.20

Dollars spent are not always an accurate measure of underlying values. Aircraft carriers are more expensive than office buildings with the same square footage, and the military has a huge payroll, so perhaps Defense needs $11.02 for every dollar budgeted for State. The generals and admirals cannot send people into lethal combat with inferior equipment. They cannot afford to be blind-sided by an adversary with better technology, and high tech is expensive. On the other hand, how many weapons systems are genuinely necessary, and how many are the result of wish lists or corporate pressure that sees Defense as a cash cow? It is difficult for an average citizen-taxpayer to say. But others closer to the facts have seen distortions in our national priorities. Richard Rhodes' history of the Cold War, *Arsenals of Folly*, recalls that "[Federal Reserve Chairman] Eccles argued as long ago as the 1960s that 'over-kill spending of the military' was 'responsible for our financial inability to adequately meet the problems of our cities and our rapidly expanding educational requirements.' " Rhodes continued,

...the superpower nuclear-arms race and the corresponding militarization of the American economy gave us ramshackle cities, broken bridges, failing schools, entrenched poverty, impeded life expectancy, and a menacing and secretive national-security state that held the entire human world hostage.... The politics of both sides were not moral because they put the human world at mortal risk, with no reasonable gain in security, for domestic advantage and the international play of power. [Rhodes(2007)][306–308]

One wonders what impact the $370,000,000 spent between 1946 and 1957 on creating Schilling Air Force Base would have had on the schools, medical care, and infrastructure of Salina.

In our first correspondence with him in April 1993, Professor Dyson was asked what piece of technology he would remove if he had the power. The existence of nuclear bombs determined his answer.

> *9 April 1993*
> *Dear Professor Neuenschwander,*
> *...What piece of technology would I remove if I had the power? My answer to this is nuclear fission technology, assuming that both the bombs and the power-stations would disappear together. Although I do not consider nuclear power-stations evil, it is clear that the benefits of nuclear power-stations are outweighed by the evil of nuclear bombs. There are other benefits of nuclear technology, such as the medical use of radio-isotopes for diagnosis and treatment of many diseases. But on balance, I would be happy to get rid of the power-stations and the medical uses of isotopes if we could get rid of the bombs too.*
> *...Yours ever,*
> *Freeman Dyson*

This response is all the more remarkable since it was written by the designer of the Triga reactor, the most commercially successful of nuclear reactors. In 1956, when the new lithium-deuteride hydrogen bombs were being tucked into the bomb bays of Strategic Air Command's long-range bombers and the Cold War was in full swing, in the midst of the MADness, ten people in San Diego found something uplifting to do with nuclear fission. Let us take a small digression.

Little Red Schoolhouse

In the summer of 1956, Freddy de Hoffman and General Dynamics Corporation organized a working group to develop commercial nuclear reactor designs. They set up shop in a rented little red schoolhouse. The small TRIGA reactor, its name an acronym for Training, Research and Isotopes–General Atomic, came from their summer work. Professor Dyson was part of the ten-member team, including Edward Teller, that designed and built it. Some seventy Trigas have been sold, licensed, and operate around the world for nuclear reactor education and isotope production.

The beauty of the Triga resides in its "inherent safety," in contrast to "engineered safety." Ordinary nuclear reactors will dangerously overheat if the control rods that absorb secondary neutrons are suddenly yanked out. A control system must be engineered to prevent a sudden withdrawal of the rods. In contrast, the Triga's metallurgy makes the reactor inoperable even if the rods are suddenly withdrawn. The Triga in inherently safe.

Professor Dyson remembers that "Working with Teller was as exciting as I had imagined it would be. Almost every day he came to the schoolhouse with some hare-brained new idea... I used his ideas as starting points for a more systematic analysis of the problem. His intuition and my mathematics fit together..." [Dyson(1979a)][98] But the environment has changed in the nuclear reactor industry. Today, he writes, "Nobody builds reactors for fun any more. The spirit of the little red schoolhouse is dead." [Dyson(1979a)]105] We are stuck with existing reactor designs. One can imagine what motoring would be like today if before 1905, the adventurers had been driven out of the nascent automobile industry, and replaced by rigid bureaucracies.

> *5 December 2001*
> *Dear Professor Dyson,*
> *I hope you and your family are looking forward to a wonderful time together over the holidays. The events of the past several months have caused us all to remember what is truly important....*
> *You say in chapter 9 that the spirit of the little red schoolhouse is dead. Do you believe that there are still little red schoolhouses? If there are not, that would paint a rather bleak picture of modern science.*

> *8 December 2001*
> *Dear Dwight,*
> *...Are there still little red school-houses? The answer is emphatically yes. When I wrote in the school-house chapter, "The spirit of the little red school-house is dead," I was referring explicitly to the nuclear power industry. The statement is true for the nuclear power industry, but it is certainly not true for modern science in general, or for modern industry in general. Side by side with the big projects and big companies, there are thousands of little projects and little companies where the spirit of the school-house is alive and well. For example, we have here*

in Princeton a delightful project run mostly by students, to look for optical flashes in the sky using a one-meter telescope on the Princeton campus. The idea is that alien societies in the sky might be signaling to us with laser pulses rather than with radio messages. The whole project costs only 28 thousand (not million) dollars, to refurbish the telescope and operate the system. We probably will not discover any alien civilizations, but there is a chance we may discover something almost as interesting and unexpected, since nobody has looked for nanosecond pulses in the sky before.[101]

8 December 2003
Dear Professor Dyson,
Thank you once again for your patient willingness to consider our questions....
If nuclear chain reactions had not been possible (e.g., had fission released no more than one neutron per nucleus), so that nuclear weapons and reactors were not possible, what do you envision Freddy de Hoffman (given the same resources) might have had you and the others doing in the "Little Red Schoolhouse" at that time in San Diego? In other words, in that setting, with that assembly of talent and resources, what other problem might have captured your imaginations at that time? What would such a group turn its attention to today?

9 December 2003
Dear Dwight and students,
Thank you for the new set of questions. I congratulate you on finding fresh questions which make me think before I can answer them. Also thank you for adding your names and majors to the message, so I know a little bit about who you are. I give you my answers quickly so you have them before the end of term.
This is a very interesting question that I never heard anybody ask before. If fission chain reactions had not been possible, the Manhattan Project would not have existed, and physicists would not have become the politically important elite that they were after World War Two. Physics would still have been exciting for scientists, but not for generals and politicians.
During WW2 there were serious programs to develop biological weapons in America, Britain and the Soviet Union. The Soviet Union used a tularemia weapon with some success in the battle of Stalingrad in 1942. The USA and Britain had stockpiles of anthrax bombs. My guess is that if nuclear weapons had not existed we would have had a Cold War arms race in the 1950s

---

[101][Schultz(1999)]

*based on biological weapons, and biologists would have replaced
physicists as the politically important scientists. Los Alamos
would have been a biological warfare lab, Freddy de Hoffman
would have been working at Los Alamos as a biologist, and General Atomic would have been a biotechnology company. (In real
life, Freddy did switch to biology and became director of the Salk
Institute in San Diego after he retired from General Atomic.)
So the little red schoolhouse would have been filled with biologists exploring the new world of biotechnology opened up by the
Watson-Crick discovery of the double helix structure of DNA in
1953. I would probably have been happy to switch to biology if
Freddy had invited me to work in the schoolhouse in 1956. We
would probably have spent the summer working on the genetic
code and the possible ways of sequencing DNA. We might have
invented ways of using DNA to diagnose genetic diseases and
synthesize new drugs. If we had been very clever we might have
invented the basic tricks of biotechnology which actually arrived
twenty years later, the polymerase chain reaction for multiplying
DNA and the gene-splicing technique for moving genes around
from one creature to another. The polymerase chain reaction is
to biology as the neutron chain reaction is to physics, similar
in basic concept and similar in power.*

*If we had a similar group in the little red schoolhouse today,
I imagine it would be looking into applications of nanotechnology, which is now the fashionable new technology as nuclear
technology was in 1956. Nanotechnology is the art of constructing structures and devices on an ultramicroscopic scale. One
idea I would like to work on would be to build a machine that
would attach itself to a molecule of DNA and read out the sequence as it walks along the molecule. If we could do that, we
might reduce the cost and increase the speed of sequencing by a
factor of a thousand. All kinds of medical applications of sequencing would then become affordable. Another application of
nanotechnology might be a molecular imaging device that would
wrap itself around an unknown molecule and read out an accurate picture of its shape. I leave it to your imaginations to think
of other inventions we might make and other ideas we might explore....*

*By the way, I recently received some E-mail from Gordon Per-
mann, a volunteer helper at the Barnard School in San Diego,
which was the original little red school-house. The school has
survived some good times and bad times. Permann says, "Over
the summer we rounded up thirty Navy volunteers who painted
and scrubbed the place back into some semblance of order, clear-
ing out twenty years of neglect." So the school is still functioning and hoping for better times to come. Permann has written*

*a history of the school since its beginning as a Navy school in
1943.*

Most Pressing Fear, Greatest Hope

Most of today's university students were born after the Soviet Union collapsed in December 1991. For them, the Soviet Union and the Confederacy are equally remote. They know that a war fought with nuclear bombs remains a physical possibility, but they have other things to think about. Perhaps the luxury of shifting such gloomy thoughts to the back of one's mind should be celebrated as a consequence of the Cold War's demise.

However, thousands of nuclear weapons and the platforms to deliver them still exist. Weapons, or technical specifications or parts for them, might be stolen or bought on the black market. Although Cold War leaders could be brutal and aggressive, most of them were not suicidal. The same assumption does not hold for today's terrorists. While one cannot live in state of perpetual worry, one should be aware. Professor Dyson's responses to our letters on the topic of nuclear weapons have been consistent across the years.

> *1 May 1998*
> *Dear Professor Dyson,*
> *...How would you respond to the following passage from John Steinbeck ("Grapes of Wrath")?– "Fear the time when the bombs stop falling while the bombers still live, for every bomb is proof that the spirit has not died."*

> *2 May 1998*
> *Dear Dwight and Class,*
> *...I like the Steinbeck quote. So far as the present situation is concerned, I take it to mean that we should get rid of nuclear weapons as quickly and completely as possible. So long as the bombs exist, there will be people with the power to use them, and with the spirit that is willing to use them in anger.*
> *Yours ever, Freeman*

> *13 April 2009*
> *Dear Professor Dyson,*
> *I bring you greetings from the Spring 2009 section of the Science, Technology, and Society class...*
> *...What should the generation now young be most concerned about?...*
> *On behalf of the students,*
> *Warm regards, DEN*

17 April 2009
Dear Dwight,
...The generation now young should have many different con-
cerns, depending on their individual circumstances and tastes.
One size does not fit all. One of the concerns that should re-
ceive much more attention is the abolition of nuclear weapons.
I think the time is ripe for the generation now young to take
this problem seriously and do something about it.
Yours ever, Freeman

29 April 2011
Dear Professor Dyson,
We trust that 2011 so far has been a splendid year for you and
your extended family....
What is your most pressing fear, and your greatest hope?
Thank you for all you have done for us, through your books,
articles, letters, and influence. Best wishes to you, to Imme,
your children, and your grandchildren.
STS class, Spring 2011

29 April 2011
Dear Dwight,
...Most pressing fear is still a war involving nuclear weapons.
Greatest hope is a public campaign to eliminate nuclear weapons
both unilaterally and multilaterally.
...Best wishes to you all, yours ever, Freeman Dyson.

In April 2010, a new START treaty was signed that would cut in half
the number of strategic nuclear missile launchers, and limit the number of
deployed strategic warheads held by the US and Russia to 1,550 each. In
December 2010, the US Senate voted to ratify the treaty. The 2010 START
treaty does not address the number of stockpiled nuclear weapons. The
United States presently has between five and ten thousand nuclear weapons
deployed and stockpiled. [Kristensen and Norris(2015)] These numbers are
down sharply from the more than ten thousand deployed and over twenty
thousand stockpiled by the USA alone at the height of the Cold War. But
given that only two nuclear bombs were needed to bring World War Two
to an abrupt end, one wonders why we still need fifteen hundred today.
At whom are we going to shoot them? The summer session of 2012 asked
Professor Dyson, "Why does the USA maintain a stockpile of something like
10,000 nuclear weapons? Wouldn't 100 or 10 hydrogen bombs be enough?"

17 July 2012
Dear Dwight,

I agree that a hundred nuclear weapons are more than we need for any reasonable purpose. I believe we would be better off with zero, even if our enemies have more. My friends are all worrying about nuclear weapons in North Korea or Iran, when they should be worrying about our own weapons. Our own weapons are more dangerous to us, being spread around the world in places where they might be captured or stolen. And the best way to get rid of the weapons is to do it unilaterally, as George Bush senior did in 1991, when he got rid of more than half our weapons. He got rid of all the weapons belonging to the army and the surface navy. Now we have only those belonging to the air force and the submarine navy. The military-industrial complex did not oppose Bush's decision. The soldiers and sailors in the army and surface navy were glad to be rid of the nukes, which got in the way when they had to fight real wars.

There are of course big vested interests which oppose getting rid of nukes; but the vested interests are mostly civilian rather than military. The politicians are generally worse than the soldiers. The soldiers know what war is like, and they know that nukes are not likely to be useful when they have to fight. The politicians mostly like nukes because nukes bring jobs to their districts. George Bush senior had the great advantage of being a right-wing Republican, so he was not afraid of the politicians. To conclude, I wish you all a great future, whether you are Democrats or Republicans. Although I would never vote Republican, I have to admit that Republicans are not all bad. George Bush senior twice showed great wisdom, once when he got rid of more than half of our nukes, and once when he avoided occupying Baghdad after defeating the Iraqi army.

Yours ever, Freeman Dyson

Recently as a class we wrote a letter to one of our US Senators regarding America's nuclear policies. We are grateful to live in a nation where we can freely tell our leaders what we think. One who does not exercise this right has no advantage over one who lacks it. Our letter asked the Senator, who served on the Armed Services Committee, why the US needs 1,500 deployed nuclear weapons. Wouldn't 100 or 10 be enough? Could we not unilaterally reduce our stockpile by, say, ten percent, then see what other nations do?[102] Before sending the letter to our Senator, we asked Professor Dyson to review a draft of it.

---

[102] As this goes to press, we have not heard back from the Senator. In fairness, he has responded to earlier letters. The one about nuclear stockpiles had some forty signatures.

22 April 2015
Dear Professor Dyson,
...Attached to this message is a long-overdue draft of a letter to
[our US] Senator... The class made some suggestions for the
letter (e.g., one student suggested "The USA considers itself to
be a leader, so reducing our nuclear arsenal unilaterally offers
an opportunity to show leadership")…. If you have a moment
to look it over and make suggestions, corrections, additions or
deletions, the class and I would be very grateful…. You have
much experience in conversations on these matters with power-
ful people who know more about them than the general public….

Professor Dyson suggested we delete one paragraph about hydrogen
bombs. He clarified our understanding of the types of nukes that have been
decommissioned in recent decades, and the composition of the present US
arsenal:

23 April 2015
Dear Dwight,
...The fact is that ten-megaton hydrogen bombs were taken out
of the stockpile a long time ago. One-megaton bombs were taken
out more recently. Today the biggest bombs in the stockpile are
less than half a megaton. The Air Force generals and Navy ad-
mirals understood a long time ago that small bombs are more
useful than big bombs, and so the bombs in the stockpile have
been getting smaller as time goes on. At the time of the big de-
bate about hydrogen bombs when Oppenheimer spoke, everyone
was thinking of the hydrogen bomb as a ten-megaton monster.
That is no longer true. I like to say, if you look at the stockpile
today, it is almost the same as it would have been if the hydro-
gen bomb had never been invented. In the end, the big debate
about the hydrogen bomb turned out to be unimportant. If we
had only fission, the bombs would look almost the same.
Of course, even if you do not have hydrogen bombs, half a mega-
ton kills a lot of people, and there are plenty of reasons why it
would be a good idea to get rid of it….
Yours ever, Freeman

Compared to a Castle Bravo-scale weapon (15 MT), 500 kilotons—half a
megaton—sounds small, but that's still 40 times the yield of Little Boy.
We have a long way to go. But such trends are encouraging. Somewhere,
the ghosts of the 1949 General Advisory Committee are saying, "We told
you so…."

In 1968, the US signed the nuclear Non-Proliferation Treaty (NPT). By its terms some 190 signatory nations without nuclear weapons pledged to not pursue them. In exchange, the five signatory countries already in possession of nuclear weapons—the USA, the Soviet Union (now Russia), Great Britain, France and China—agreed to share peaceful nuclear technologies with the non-nuclear weapon states, and eventually eliminate their own nuclear weapon stockpiles. In recent years, the US has sharply scolded NPT co-signers Iran and North Korea for pursuing the development of their own nuclear weapons.[103] The following letter to Professor Dyson came not from the class but from its professor:

> *17 October 2006*
> *Dear Professor Dyson,*
> *With the recent events in North Korea and Iran, I would like to continue raising the awareness of students to issues surrounding the international control of nuclear weapons.... You have been personally involved in nuclear weapons disarmament negotiations. I am therefore writing to inquire if you might have a statement you would like to pass along concerning the current situation regarding the North Korean nuclear test....*

> *17 October 2006*
> *Dear Dwight,...*
> *Your message arrives just as I am leaving for California, so I answer it briefly. Here is what I would say to the students.*
> *Don't believe the media hype about the North Korean bombs. Whether they have bombs or not is not important to the United States. Nuclear bombs are important to the North Koreans as a political status symbol. We only increase their value to the North Koreans by making such a fuss about them. The best thing for us to do is to ignore them. If in the future we want to get rid of North Korean bombs, it can only be done by international agreement, and then we must also be prepared to get rid of our own.*
> *Yours sincerely, Freeman*

Following the Ukrainian revolution of February 2014, tensions between Ukraine and Russia escalated into armed conflict. Separatists in Ukraine pushed for a part of that country to join Russia, and Russia appeared to encourage them. Since Professor Dyson was a veteran of the Arms Control and Disarmament Agency and knows a lot about Russian culture

---

[103]North Korea withdrew from the NPT in 2003, and Iran has been accused of violating the treaty.

and policies, we asked him about his views on the clash between Russia
and Ukraine.

> *24 April 2014*
> *Dear Professor Dyson,*
> *We hope the first half of your 91st year has been one of joy, time
> with family, many conversations with grandchildren, interesting
> work to do, and new adventures.*
> *Once again our STS class risks wearing out our welcome by
> sending you some questions. If you have a few moments to an-
> swer some of them, we would be grateful.*
> *What do you make of the way Russia is treating Ukraine? What
> would you like to see happen there? What should be the response
> of the US and NATO to this situation?*
> *With your experience at the Arms Control and Disarmament
> Agency and your work with the Jasons, along with your knowl-
> edge of Russian history, language, and culture, we thought you
> might have some needed perspectives on current events going on
> between Russia and Ukraine. On the one hand, many Ukrainian
> citizens speak Russian as their first language, and Russian cul-
> ture, so we have read, owes much to Kiev in addition to Moscow
> and St. Petersburg. If Ukraine or part of it genuinely wants to
> join Russia, there should be a way to facilitate that transition
> without violating Ukraine's constitution, international law, or
> human decency. On the other hand, we recall that Hitler an-
> nexed parts of Europe before WW II (ironically, shortly after
> Germany hosted the Olympics), saying to the world that Ger-
> many was merely protecting Germans. That did not turn out
> well. The motivation behind this question occurred after dis-
> cussing the history of atomic bombs and the Cold War. Since
> President Putin is a former KGB officer, perhaps he still views
> the world through Cold War spectacles. We read in class one
> of your letters where you said our goal should not be to destroy
> our enemies, but turn them into friends. We would like to be
> friends with Russians and with Ukrainians.*

> *28 April 2014*
> *Dear Dwight and Students,*
> *Thank you very much for your questions. These are good ques-
> tions and the discussions that came along with them are very
> helpful....*
> *What do I make of the way America is treating Ukraine?*
> *I know very little about Ukraine, but it seems extremely unwise
> for the USA to become involved in a power-struggle in a place
> where we have no power. There have been two occasions when
> countries in Europe divided peacefully into separate parts, Nor-*

*way and Sweden a hundred years ago, the Czech Republic and
Slovakia more recently. The best solution for Ukraine would
probably be a peaceful division into West and East. After that,
East Ukraine might or might not be swallowed by Putin. West
Ukraine might or might not join the European Union. The USA
has no reason to be involved in either decision. It is not useful
for us to tell Putin how to behave. We could give some help
and encouragement to West Ukraine, but not tell West Ukraine
how to behave. We should have learned from our experiences in
Vietnam and Afghanistan and Iraq that we have as little power
to control our friends as to control our enemies. I would like to
be friends with Russia, but it takes two to make friends.
Yours ever, Freeman*

Rods from God

In January 2001, a Congressional commission led by the newly nominated
Secretary of Defense Donald H. Rumsfeld recommended that the US military should "ensure that the president will have the option to deploy
weapons in space." The next year President George W. Bush withdrew
the US from the Antiballistic Missile Treaty that bans offensive weapons
platforms from being stationed in Earth orbit. The Air Force immediately began seeking presidential policies allowing them to deploy weapons
in space. Pete Teets, acting secretary of the Air Force, speaking at a
space warfare conference in 2004, was quoted in a *New York Times* article, [Weiner(2005)] as saying "We haven't reached the point of strafing and
bombing from space. Nonetheless, we are thinking about those possibilities." General Lance Lord, commander of the Air Force Space Command,
testified to Congress, "...we must establish and maintain space superiority.
Simply put, it's the American way of fighting." According to the *Times*
article, Air Force doctrine defines space superiority as "freedom to attack
as well as freedom from attack... Space superiority is not our birthright,
but it is our destiny. Space superiority is our day-to-day mission. Space
supremacy is our vision for the future."

The space weapons technologies envisioned include Global Strike, a military space plane loaded with guided weapons that could strike targets anywhere in the world within 45 minutes; Rods from God, flinging cylinders of
uranium, tungsten or titanium to strike targets on Earth's surface at 7,200
miles per hour (naval fleets would be especially vulnerable); lethal laser
beams bounced off of satellites or high-altitude blimps; and radio waves

whose power range could go "from a tap on the shoulder to toast." These are the dreams of Air Force generals.

It will all be dreadfully expensive, another Cold War budget. Not reassuringly, advanced weapons systems typically cost far more and deliver less than promised. Of course, by the nature of research, not every scheme works as envisioned. The 2005 *NY Times* article continued with the unsurprising news that "Senior military and space officials of the European Union, Canada, China and Russia have objected publicly to the notion of American space superiority." One nation stationing weapons in space would inevitably trigger another arms race.

Does the public, who has to pay for all this and will bear the consequences of the general's dreams, get to say anything about it? The *Times* article quotes a Captain Hardesty who, in an article published in the Naval War College Review, sensibly called for "a thorough military analysis" followed by a "larger public debate" of these plans. It is instructive to compare the history of the hydrogen bomb with the push for weapons in space. When President Truman decided the US would build the hydrogen bomb, the number of people who had anything to say about it was small, even though the number of people affected by the decision was large. [Bethe(1950)] Today there are a few books and articles about weapons in orbit, [Grossman(2011)], [Arbatov and Dvorkin(2011)], [Gillon(2003)], [Godwin(2003)], [Yong(2004)] and a recent *60 Minutes* broadcast of 27 April 2015 called "The Battle Above" about threats to US satellites.[104] A 2002 report by the Rand Corporation pessimistically observed:

Space weapons have been debated extensively twice in the modern history of space. At the beginning of the Cold War, the issue was the possibility of bombardment satellites carrying nuclear weapons. At the end of the Cold War, the issue was the possibility of space-based defenses against nuclear missiles. Aside from these debates, there has been little public discussion of the topic. Now, well past the Cold War, the topic of space weapons is surfacing again. Military vision documents give space weapons an air of inevitability. [Preston *et al.*(2002)Preston, Johnson, Edwards, Miller and Shipbaugh][1]

---

[104]The report described the Chinese shooting their own satellite in 2007, and told viewers the Chinese have fired other test shots, including one in 2013 that went 30,000 km (18,000 miles) high, almost to geosynchronous orbit where civilian and military satellites are situated for communications and GPS.

12 November 2007
Dear Professor Dyson,
We hope that the 2007 Thanksgiving season finds you and all
your family doing well... If we may, we would like to present
you with a few questions....
Can you see any possible reason for the USA to attempt to put
weapons in space?

Professor Dyson took a broader view than our class on what "weapons"
in space means.

23 November 2007
Dear Dwight,
Thank you ... for your letter of November 12 with questions
from your STS class...
I would say we already have huge numbers of weapons in space.
At the moment we have hundreds of military satellites in space,
giving our army and navy the ability to communicate and navi-
gate and aim missiles accurately. Without these satellites, none
of our army and navy units could function. Do these satellites
count as weapons? I don't see why not. The big problems will
come when our enemies begin shooting them down. It will be
much easier to shoot them down than to put them up. In the
long run I think we have only two options. Either negotiate
an international treaty allowing such weapons to everyone with
the right of free passage, or stop relying on them and gradually
withdraw them.

As if to make the point about the ease of shooting them down, on
January 11, 2007, the Chinese shot down one of their own satellites. Should
we respect a treaty that bans offensive weapons in low-Earth orbit? When
recalling the Test Ban Treaty of 1963, Professor Dyson raised a point of
principle, still relevant today:

A total test ban would at least stop our side from developing these weapons.
If it were known that we had stopped work on them and did not consider them
to be militarily important, the incentive for the other side to put serious effort
into developing them would be greatly reduced. On the other hand, the one way
to make certain that our adversaries would soon possess these weapons would
be for us to develop and deploy them ourselves. [Dyson(1979a)][128–130]

The generals carry a heavy responsibility. They must anticipate what
a potential adversary *might* do. But we would like to ask General Lord:

Why must we establish a destabilizing space *superiority*? What's wrong
with *parity*?

After our first "weapons in space" letter to Professor Dyson, a later
class wanted to visit the question again, this time defining more precisely
what we meant by "weapons" in space.

> *26 November 2014*
> *Dear Professor Dyson,*
> *On behalf of the Fall 2014 Science, Technology & Society class*
> *I bring you warm greetings.... The class enjoyed seeing your*
> *responses to the questions of their predecessors...*
> *In November 2007 our STS class asked you what you thought*
> *about the US stationing weapons in space. You pointed out that*
> *with communication and surveillance satellites in orbit for mil-*
> *itary applications we already have weapons in space. We would*
> *like to narrow the definition of weapons in space and ask the*
> *question again if you don't mind. Let us define weapons in*
> *space as systems envisioned by Air Force generals following the*
> *2001 Rumsfeld Commission recommendation...*

The next few paragraphs of the letter quoted passages from the *NY Times*
article described above, including the recommendation of the Rumsfeld
Commission and the blusterings of Air Force leaders. We also mentioned the
Chinese shooting down one of their satellites. Putting these developments
together with Professor Dyson's chapter "The Ethics of Defense" brought
us to our question:

> *...We do not see how such policies can be consistent with "The*
> *Ethics of Defense." If we place in orbit the kinds of weapons*
> *that General Lord wants, we think that will guarantee other na-*
> *tions following suit. Then we will be back into another multi-*
> *trillion-dollar arms race similar to what we saw during the Cold*
> *War. What are your thoughts on this issue? To ask the ques-*
> *tion another way, what would you say to General Lord and his*
> *like-minded colleagues?*

> *3 December 2014*
> *Dear Dwight and students,*
> *I am back from our five-day trip to celebrate with daughter Mia*
> *and her family in Maine. The high point [was] a performance*
> *of "A Christmas Carol" in a local theater with twelve-year-old*
> *grandson Aidan on stage....*
> *Here are answers to your questions.... As usual, the questions*
> *are more interesting than the answers. The most important part*
> *of your education is to work out your own answers.*

I had not heard the remarks that you quote from General Lord. They are an extreme expression of the Air Force mentality that goes back almost a hundred years, to the slogan "Victory through Air Power" that drove the air forces (then divided between Army and Navy) in World War II. The idea is that we can win wars and enforce our political objectives by maintaining air superiority and killing our enemies from the sky. The idea is wrong and dangerous, now more than ever. It is unpractical because weapons in space are highly vulnerable and highly visible. Any attempt to achieve air superiority over China would be successfully resisted. The result would be retreat and withdrawal if we were lucky, a major war if we were unlucky.
To answer your question, the policies advocated by General Lord are totally inconsistent with "The Ethics of Defense." If I had the opportunity to talk to him, I would tell him that he is wrong militarily, wrong politically, and wrong morally. Wrong militarily because his policies give our enemies easy targets to shoot at. Wrong politically because bombing attacks and drone killings strengthen our enemies and weaken our influence. Wrong morally because his policies blur the distinction between war and peace, keeping the world in a permanent state of tension and unrest. Thank you once more for a good set of questions....
Happy Christmas to you and the class! Yours ever, Freeman.

If defense is more ethical than offense, why then, asks Professor Dyson, "have our scientific strategists become so fanatically devoted to the doctrine of the supremacy of the offensive?" He answers, "Nobody would describe an antiballistic missile system with the phrase that Robert Oppenheimer used to describe the hydrogen bomb. Defense is not technically sweet." [Dyson(1979a)][144] Rods from God is technically sweet.

7 December 1999
Dear Professor Dyson,
On behalf of the Fall 99 "Science, Technology, and Society" class, we wish you and your family a joyous and meaningful Christmas Season. We hope you will all have a wonderful time together, including ample time to spend with your beautiful grandchildren.
One student asked, "I don't want to sound like the crazy general in 'Dr. Strangelove,' but is there a possibility of having an affordable Strategic Defense Initiative? Was SDI consistent in spirit to the stand you make in 'The Ethics of Defense?'"

8 December 1999
Dear Dwight,
The questions from your students go immediately to the top of the pile of unanswered letters. The others can wait for a few days longer. Please give the students my greetings and thanks. Here are some off-the-cuff answers.
Yes, I agree there is a possibility of an affordable missile defense, and this is consistent with the defensive strategy that I was advocating in the book. But this only makes sense, politically and morally, if it is combined with drastic reductions in offensive forces. To build a missile defense now, when we have no intention of reducing offensive forces seriously, would be wrong from every point of view. It would be seen by the Russians as threatening, it would do nothing to counter the real danger of terrorist bombs arriving by boat or by airplane, and it would be a great waste of money. I would say, lets get rid of at least ninety percent of our offensive missiles first, and then missile defense might be part of a genuine shift to a defensive strategy.

Since 1992, the United States has shown some unilateral restraint through a self-imposed moratorium on nuclear weapons testing. That year President George H. W. Bush gave his approval of US participation in the Comprehensive Nuclear Test Ban Treaty that prohibits all nuclear explosions for any purpose. The treaty was approved by the United Nations and opened for signatures in 1996. The United States has signed but not ratified the treaty.

Jason

Professor Dyson has worked for the Arms Control and Disarmament Agency, has testified before Congress, and for fifty years has been a member of the Jasons, a group of civilian technical experts who advise the government with studies commissioned by a federal agency or branch of the military. The Department of Defense is a frequent Jason client.

4 June 2001
Dear Professor Dyson,
... Has your career ever been in conflict with your convictions?

6 June 2001
My career never came in conflict with my convictions, because
my career has always been concerned with abstruse mathemati-
cal science... The most questionable of my extra-curricular ac-
tivities is to be a member of Jason, a group of scientists who give
technical advice to the government in general and the Defense
Department in particular.... I think I do more good than harm
by working for Jason, but I have to weigh my actions carefully...
The most difficult time to be a member of Jason was during the
Vietnam war. Many people... felt it was wrong to have anything
to do with the people who were running the war. Several Jason
members resigned as an act of protest against the war. I did not
resign, because I thought it was more important to... give the
soldiers some contact with the world outside the Pentagon....

During the self-imposed US moratorium on testing nuclear weapons, the
US relies on the Stockpile Stewardship program, virtual testing by com-
puter simulations. We wondered if Professor Dyson had a role in Stockpile
Stewardship.

26 November 2014
Dear Professor Dyson,
...What was your role (perhaps as a member of Jason?) in con-
vincing President George H.W. Bush to stop nuclear weapons
testing, which then led to the present policy of Stockpile Stew-
ardship?

3 December 2014
Dear Dwight and students,
...I do not claim to have had any influence on the decision to
stop testing. So far as I remember, the decision was taken by
President Bush and three other people, the directors of the three
weapons laboratories, Los Alamos, Livermore and Sandia. The
three directors had to promise to Bush that they could continue
to provide reliable weapons without testing. Like other bureau-
crats, the directors were mainly concerned with maintaining the
budgets for their organizations. So they took this opportunity to
do a deal with Bush. They agreed to promise to provide reliable
weapons, and they demanded that Bush promise to provide re-
liable funding. To provide reliable funding for the weapons labs
after they stopped testing, Bush agreed to establish the Stock-
pile Stewardship program. In my opinion, Stockpile Steward-
ship is not really a program. It is a political device to make sure
that the weapons laboratories get a generous and reliable level of
funding. It is not needed for technical reasons. The bombs are

reliable and durable enough without any stewardship. Stockpile
Stewardship is needed for political reasons, to make sure that
the lab directors do not demand a resumption of testing. How-
ever, Stockpile Stewardship was officially approved by Jason,
and many of my friends sincerely believe that it is essential to
our security. It was probably worth paying that price to get the
testing stopped....
Thank you once more for a good set of questions....
Happy Christmas to you and the class! Yours ever, Freeman.

Three years after the preemptive strike by the United States against
Iraq, the Fall 2006 class had two back-to-back questions for Professor Dyson
because he is a member of Jason. The first asked about an incident during
the Vietnam War that he describes in *Disturbing the Universe*:

In 1966, at another such meeting, official Z said, "I think it might be a good
idea to throw in a nuke now and then, just to keep the other side guessing." ...
After the meeting ended, I checked with three other civilian scientists who were
present, to make sure that Z had really said what I heard him say. They were
all as shocked as I. [Dyson(1979a)][149]

With Defense Department approval, four Jasons carried out a study
on the probable consequences of using a nuke in Vietnam. "Our analysis
demonstrated that even from the narrowest military point of view, disre-
garding all political and ethical considerations, the use of nuclear weapons
would be a disastrous mistake." Although we do not know if the Jason
report was read by the Johnson Administration, we do know that nuclear
weapons were never used in Vietnam, even when President Johnson escalated the war in 1966–1968. Forty years after the Vietnam War escalation,
the Iraq conflict was escalated and, as in Vietnam, was not going well for
the American forces. We tied the two escalations together in a pair of
questions for Professor Dyson:

4 December 2006
Dear Professor Dyson,
We hope that you and your extended family are doing well this
fall. May the holiday season be a time when you will be able to
hold many grandchildren....
In the May/June 2003 issue of the "Bulletin of the Atomic Sci-
entists," we found an article by Peter Hayes and Nina Tan-
nenwald called "Nixing nukes in Vietnam."[Vol. 9, issue 3]
The article recalls a scene that we read about in "Disturbing

the Universe," where some Pentagon official remarked that "It might be a good idea to toss in a nuke now and then, just to keep the other side guessing." The BAS article describes how four members of Jasons: you, Robert Gomer, Courtenay Wright, and Steven Weinberg, were so appalled by the remark that you decided the best way to counter it would be to conduct a serious study of the effects of "tossing in a nuke." Here are our questions:

1. Given the present Administration's demonstrated willingness to use preemptive strikes against other states, as a co-author of the 1966 Jason study mentioned above what advice would you give the Administration—and we citizens—in today's global political environment?

2. What topics should be top priorities for a Jason study at present?

9 December 2006
Dear Dwight and students,
I just came back from a tour of family in various places, our minister daughter Mia in Maine, our son George in Bellingham and our step-daughter Katarina in Vancouver, with their various offspring. A great trip. Came back yesterday to find your message, luckily just in time for the Monday deadline [the last day of class]. Here are answers to the questions.

1. I find it encouraging that even an administration as immoral and incompetent as our present one has not been talking about "tossing in a nuke" as Maxwell Taylor did in 1967. Even Mr. Bush now understands that tossing in a nuke would not help to solve his problems in Iraq or in Iran or in North Korea. The advice I would give to the administration today is: talk to your enemies. There is one person still around today who knows how to run Iraq, namely Saddam Hussein. Take him out of jail and make use of him, as we did with the Japanese emperor in 1945. Give him the respect that is due to him as a head of state, and let him try to hold the country together. If he fails, if Iraq falls apart into three countries, with the Shia and the Kurds seceding, that is his problem and not ours.

2. Topics for Jason studies always depend on having a sponsor who pays for the study and wants to listen to our advice. If nobody in the government will pay for it, then nobody will listen to it. A Jason study of military strategy in Iraq would not be useful. Even though that is the most important subject, we do not have the credentials to give advice about it. The main topics for our up-coming Winter Study in January are the RRW (Reliable Replacement Warhead), and the protection of buildings against cars and trucks loaded with explosives. These are both

*technical problems for which we have the credentials to be taken
seriously. As you can imagine, the Oklahoma bombing provides
a lot of the data for the building study. The problem is to make
a building safe without making it look and feel like a prison.
The RRW is partly a technical problem and partly political. The
technical problem is to rebuild our nuclear weapons with control
systems built into the structure so that it is physically impossible for anyone who steals a weapon to explode it. If this were
done to the weapons in the stockpiles here and in Russia, it
would make the world a bit safer. It would mean that nuclear
terrorists would have to build their own weapons. The political
problem with the RRW is that it looks as if we are developing
new nuclear weapons, and so gives an excuse for other countries to develop new weapons too. On the whole I am against
the RRW for political reasons, but still it makes technical sense
and I agreed to work on it. The good thing about Jason is that
we are each free to choose which problems to work on.*

As we know, Sadaam Hussein was not taken out of jail and treated with
respect as a head of state. Instead, he was put on trial and, on 30 December
2006, was ignominiously hanged.

Role Reversal

A member of the Fall 2003 class proposed a splendid idea for turning our
question-and-answer practice around.

*25 November 2003
Dear Professor Dyson,
In the STS class today we were discussing some candidate ques-
tions the class might like to ask you. Before converging on the
final few, one student (a very insightful young lady named Zina
Z.) said, "I wonder if there's a question that Professor Dyson
would like to ask <u>us</u>." I thought I would pass that along to you.
May you have a joyous Thanksgiving.
Warm regards,
Dwight*

*26 November 2003
Dear Dwight,
Happy Thanksgiving to you and the class! I look forward to
seeing your questions next week. My wife and I are going up
to Maine to celebrate with Mia and her family (now one more
grandson since you saw them).
Since I have no time for a careful response to Zina Z., I ask*

the class to consider a political rather than a scientific question. How would you react if an army of young Arabs with lethal weapons and knowing nothing of your language and culture were occupying your country and dominating your lives? This question is outside the agenda of your course, but it is an important question and I would like you to think about it.

 Thank you, Zina, for inviting me to ask it.
Yours sincerely, Freeman Dyson.

Anything Professor Dyson chooses to ask us goes to the top of our agenda. His question and our response to it took place on consecutive class meetings (recall that we meet one evening each week).

2 December 2003
Dear Professor Dyson,
Our STS class meets on Tuesdays, so I brought your question to our collective attention yesterday. The question was: "How would you react if an army of young Arabs with lethal weapons and knowing nothing of your language and culture were occupying your country and dominating your lives?"
Answering this keen question was a struggle for us as a class (about 40 students). After presenting the question, I gave the class about five minutes for discussions between neighbors. This was followed by opening the floor to the entire class. Here are the responses, as defined by comments we collected on the blackboard, and in the approximate order in which these points were volunteered from the floor:
* "I wouldn't like it." (the first, immediate reaction, from several people)
* "If the tables are turned, they must be turned in every aspect—if they were liberating us from a dictator I would feel different than if they invaded to take away our freedoms."
* "But even if I lived under a brutal dictator, these guys are still taking over my home. Who are they, to take over my home?"
* "I would resent them telling me how to live-in going after me they're going after the wrong person; I am not the dictator."
* "Out of fear, I would hide in the basement."
* "Try non-violent resistance... Be like Gandhi. More terrorism is not the answer."
* "If they are overthrowing our government, we would not accept that."
* "It depends on their reasons for coming in—WHY they fight."
* "I would be scared—as are the Iraqis."
* "We assume that everyone thinks like us, we de-construct the Iraqis as not really human beings."

* *"We are used to being free. Losing our freedom would create a different sense of loss than if we were being liberated."*

As the class ended I invited the students to write further comments... and leave them on my desk.... Here are some of the non-redundant ones:

* *"Seeing how our country was so united and were very much a 'brotherhood' after 9/11/01, I would like to think that if a group of people came into our country to overthrow our government, that we would all unite and take up arms to protect the freedom we are so blessed to have. There is no way that I could hide out in a basement if people were threatening my country, my friends, my family, and my freedom. This freedom is worth dying for and I would, should it come to that. Nathan C."*

* *"If the tables were turned (in every respect) and we were living under a government that needed liberation, I would be glad.... If there were just some Arabs coming into our country to change the way we live, just because, then I would fight for my family.... Leslie C."*

* *"Some people would say that the situation here is not identical to the situation in Iraq before the invasion and to adequately turn the tables, they must be similar at every point. I would like to point out that what WE define as a dictator may not be considered as a dictator to THEM and THEY may define our President and/or form of government as a dictator or dictatorship while we envision ourselves as free. If 'young Arabs with lethal weapons' were occupying the US and 'dominating' our lives we would see it as an invading force coming to conquer us. Many of the Iraqis feel just that way. Becky S."*

Your question for us generated about 30 minutes of very interesting discussion. I saw a lot of introspective expressions. Many of the students had apparently not imagined before a role reversal between themselves and the Iraqis....

Thank you Professor Dyson for your willingness to engage our class in these discussions. Its a privilege and we appreciate it. Warm regards, Dwight

A week later the students sent Professor Dyson a postscript:

8 December 2003
Dear Professor Dyson,
We were also wondering how you would react "if an army of young Arabs with lethal weapons and knowing nothing of our language and culture were occupying our country and dominating our lives."

We wish a happy Christmas to you and your family. We also wish you a happy 80th Birthday, which we understand occurs this month. Our class is planning something for you to help celebrate that event.

...We thank you for sharing your life with us through "Disturbing the Universe," your other speeches and writings, and your correspondence.

The STS Class, Fall Semester 2003

9 December 2003

Dear Dwight and students,

...Thank you for giving me a chance to answer this question. Thank you also for your answers which Dwight sent to me a few days ago. Your answers were thoughtful and reasonable. As many of you said, we cannot give a definite answer to the question until we know more about the circumstances. Here is my answer for what it is worth.

I assume that there would be two kinds of opposition to the invaders, as there was in occupied countries in Europe during World War Two. There would be young people fighting with guns, and the mass of the population resisting passively with silent non-cooperation. I am too old to be a fighter myself. I would help the fighters as much as I could, and otherwise I would be a passive resister. I would do as much as possible to make the invaders miserable, so that the invaders' government would find it difficult to replace them when they went home.

Happy Christmas and New Year to all of you!

Yours ever, Freeman Dyson.

The Mailman is More Important

8 December 2003

Dear Professor Dyson,

Thank you once again for your patient willingness to consider our questions....

You have worked inside the government as well as outside, such as serving on the ACDA and testifying before Congress. What changes over the years have you seen from the inside, in how the government presents itself to the public?

9 December 2003

Dear Dwight and students,

Thank you for the new set of questions.... I give you my answers quickly so you have them before the end of term.

I have been working for government as an advisor for almost fifty years, and the main thing that strikes me is how little things have changed over that long time. The politicians at the top announce big changes, but the people who do the daily work in the government departments follow the routines and change as little as possible. On the whole I think this is good. Most of the things the government does are providing services to the public, and reliability is more important than being up-to-date with the latest technology. A good example of this is the monitoring of the environment by NOAA and various other agencies. Important things to measure when you are studying climate are the sea-surface temperature and salinity of the oceans. You measure sea-surface temperature and salinity by collecting water in a bucket as your ship passes by. It is important never to change the size and shape of the bucket, so that the measurements made this year can be reliably compared with the measurements made ten years ago or fifty years ago. If you change from a metal to a plastic bucket, the measurements will be affected and the comparison is no longer reliable. There is a noticeable difference between the present Bush administration and earlier administrations. The politicians at the top of this administration have less respect for technical competence than any other administration I have known. They seem to take advice only from their cronies and not from outside experts who know a lot more. In spite of the high level of incompetence and ignorance at the top, the government still functions quite well. Underneath the top political level, technical competence is still respected. Needless to say, when I am working for the government, I only talk with people below the top level.

You ask how the government presents itself to the public. I am not sure what this means. It might mean George Bush making speeches on television. Or it might mean the mailman delivering the mail every day, in spite of snowstorms and blizzards. In my opinion, the mailman is more important. And he has not changed much over the years.

My father-in-law worked for the US Postal Service for thirty years. He had the kind of job that the rest of us overlook and take for granted. It was usually a dull, routine job, but such jobs are essential to keeping the country running. Let's hear it for the people who quietly make the world work:

Raise your glass to the hard working people
Let's drink to the uncounted heads

> *Let's think of the wavering millions*
> *Who need leaders but get gamblers instead.*[105]

The history of nations, it could be said, is the study of gamblers and folly. One day during the Potsdam conference, President Truman was driven through Berlin on a tour of the ruined capital of Germany. He wrote in his diary:

Then we went on to Berlin and saw absolute ruin. Hitler's folly....
I hope for some sort of peace–but I fear that machines are ahead of morals by some centuries.... [Rhodes(1986)][683]

---

[105] "Salt of the Earth" by Mick Jagger and Keith Richards (*Beggar's Banquet* album, Decca, 1968), also performed by Joan Baez (*Blessed Are...*, Vanguard, 1971) and Judy Collins (*Judith*, Elektra Records, 1975).

10 To Touch the Face of the Stars

Letters on Our Place in the Universe

> *Ah, not to be cut off,*
> *not through the slightest partition*
> *shut out from the law of the stars...*
> –Ranier Maria Rilke[106]

***

The Sky People

You and other tribal members are sitting around the fire in a Cheyenne encampment two hundred years ago. Supper is long over, most of the camp is asleep, sentries are at their posts and the horses are tethered for the night. As the campfire dies down to glowing coals, eyes turn upward to the Milky Way. After a long silence, a grandfather retells the ancient story, how the Milky Way is the light from campfires that mark the pathways of souls that went before. As Grandfather speaks, the listeners meditate on life and death, earth and sky. [Littmann and Planetarium(1976)]

When planets and stars came to be understood as physical places, human beings could imagine going to them. It would not be so straightforward a task as told in the Algonquin or Chippewa tales, where a spunky maiden or lad shoots arrows into the sky to make a ladder, then climbs it to encounter the Sky People and have adventures. [Mayo(1987)] Professor Dyson is a sky person of another kind. His passion for the colonization of space motivates many an STS discussion.

Long before *Sputnik*, the public's imagination was already primed for visions of space travel to other worlds. The nineteenth century saw great popularity of tales such as *From the Earth to the Moon* (1865) by Jules Verne, where a capsule called *Columbiad*, bearing three crew members, launches to the moon by being fired from a cannon. For adventures in space exploration, the twentieth century began with the necessary conditions of imagination and anticipation. Only 104 years elapsed between Verne's ficititious *Columbiad* and Apollo 11's real *Columbia*.

Sometimes I almost feel sorry for my STS students who have no personal memory of mankind's first ventures into space. It was an exciting time to be

---

[106][Rilke(2015)]

alive. However, these things even out: In their time they will see adventures in space that I will not see. We are all becoming sky people.

Looming in the background of these developments were the new hydrogen bombs. A rocket capable of placing a satellite into orbit could deliver a nuclear weapon anywhere on the globe much faster than a bomber. In the 1950s, a Cold War missile race was on. It quickly morphed into a Space Race.

Sputnik and Explorer

During the International Geophysical Year, which ran from July 1957 through December 1958, the US and Soviet governments intended to place satellites in orbit. The Soviet Union did it first on 4 October 1957 with the 184-lb *Sputnik I*. The iconic beep-beep-beep emitted by the shiny sphere trailing its four antennae became an indelible memory to everyone aware of it at the time. The US had to answer, and do it fast. Modifying existing hardware, the Army Ballistic Missile Agency, together with the Jet Propulsion Laboratory, assembled in 84 days the *Explorer 1* satellite and Redstone launch vehicle. It was successfully launched into orbit on January 31, 1958. To launch this satellite weighing 31 pounds required a rocket weighing 32 tons.

In the Cold War environment, these events set off alarm bells in the US government, industry, and education. On 2 September 1958, the National Defense Education Act was signed into law, emphasizing mathematics and science education. In February 1958, the Advanced Research Projects Agency (ARPA) was formed in the Pentagon to coordinate US civilian and military efforts in making sure that US military technology would be the most advanced. In the summer of 1958, ARPA initiated the program to develop the Saturn family of rockets, which culminated with the mighty Saturn V, the largest of Werner von Braun's designs. The Saturn V first stage carried five engines, consumed 15 tons of fuel per second and produced 7.5 million lb of thrust.

Project Orion

Nuclear fission releases, atom for atom, about twenty million times more energy than chemical reactions. When NASA was formed in 1958, a small private group was pursuing an exotic proposal regarding nuclear propulsion.

This was Project Orion, organized privately by Ted Taylor. He had come "directly from Los Alamos, where he had been the pioneer of a new art form, the design of small efficient bombs that could be squeezed into tight places... Could these elegant little bombs be used to drive an elegant little spaceship around the solar system? [Dyson(1979a)][96, 109] Project Orion offered an attractive competitor to von Braun's thirsty rockets.

An example of a bomb that could be squeezed into tight places was the M-388 tactical nuclear weapon, with a yield of 10–20 tons of TNT, about one-thousandth of Little Boy. It was fired from a tripod-mounted recoilless rifle, the "Davy Crockett." In the hands of the Orion designers a small nuke like the M-388 could be used for a peaceful and inspiring purpose. Professor Dyson was invited to participate. He took a leave of absence from the Institute for Advanced Study and joined Orion full-time for a year.

Inspiration for Project Orion came from noticing components that survived the Trinity test at close range, such as Jumbo[107] and the rebar sticking up out of what was left of the vaporized tower's concrete foundation. [Dyson(2002b)] Professor Dyson recalls,

We worked together for a year, from summer 1958 to fall 1959, as full of enthusiasm as the VfR pioneers in their great year from 1931 to 1932. We, too, were working in a hurry...We knew that the government must soon decide whether to put its main effort into chemical or into nuclear propulsion... [Dyson(1979a)][112]

Unfortunately for the Orion team's dream of swooping around Saturn by 1970 in a nuclear-bomb-powered craft, Project Orion did not work out. The design became increasingly complicated; with later Air Force sponsorship, the project became more bureaucratic and the Air Force lost interest when they could see no military application; time was of the essence and von Braun's chemical rockets were already available. The coffin nail in the project was the radioactive wake that every Orion launch would leave behind it. The Test Ban Treaty of 1963 meant that a full-scale Orion prototype with nuclear bombs could not be tested. The Orion drawings were

---

[107] Jumbo was the 214-ton steel tank intended to house the plutonium bomb during the test, so the plutonium could be salvaged if the bomb fizzled. When Jumbo became superfluous, it was used to test the effects of the bomb. Suspended from a steel tower 800 feet from the bomb's tower, the blast swept Jumbo's tower away but Jumbo dropped to the ground essentially intact.

mothballed in the archives. But it was a great adventure and the Orion experience remains one of Professor Dyson's fondest memories.

Space and Imagination

While Project Orion was underway, NASA began deploying satellites with von Braun's chemical rockets and preparing for flights with astronauts. NASA's first meteorological satellite *Trios 1*, lifted off its launch pad on 1 April 1960, and the *Echo 1* communication satellite followed on August 12. As a second-grader playing outside in the evenings I began watching for satellites...

.... a bright gleaming "star" moves fast from horizon to horizon. In response to my shouts of "Come look, a satellite!" everyone rushes out of the house to gaze at this wonder. We realize that, in the long history of the world, no one has ever seen this before. We are grateful to be present as witnesses.... To this day, every time I see a satellite sweeping across the sky I re-live the wonder...[108]

Through the 1960s, NASA had a focused mission. The Mercury, Gemini and Apollo programs forged ahead,[109] reaching a sublime moment in December 1968...

...Christmas holiday, 1968, Apollo 8 carries the first astronauts to ever leave low-Earth orbit, outbound to the Moon. Every few hours we receive a live television broadcast from Apollo 8. The astronauts Frank Bormann, James Lovell, and William Anders aim their camera back at Earth. Each time our planet looks smaller than it did in the preceding broadcast. On Christmas Eve the astronauts hold what may be the most unusual press conference of all time. As they orbit the Moon seventy miles above its cratered surface, they read aloud verses 1-10 from the first chapter of the *Book of Genesis*, in the Elizabethan

---

[108]Some of these passages were adapted from the author's "NASA after the Shuttle: Begin in a Museum," *Radiations*, Fall 2011, 14–25, 29. This article was originally adapted from STS presentations.

[109]The tragic capsule fire of 27 January 1967, with the loss of Gus Grissom, Ed White and Roger Chaffee, set the program back 20 months. Grissom had written, "We are in a risky business, and we hope if anything happens to us it will not delay the program." The rockets may have come from Defense, but for Grissom, White, Chaffee and their colleagues, it was a poet's war of adventure.

English of the King James Version... Into that moment are compressed untold generations of humanity's yearning for adventure and meaning...

...The following summer, on 16 June 1969, the climax of the decade begins with the launch of Apollo 11. Three days later, as Michael Collins orbits the moon in the command module *Columbia*, Neil Armstrong and Buzz Aldrin fly the *Eagle* lunar lander to the Moon's surface. "Tranquility Base here, the *Eagle* has landed...."

It took over twenty billion 1960s dollars spread over that decade, and a third of a million people to manage the Mercury, Gemini, and Apollo programs. Eight years had elapsed since President Kennedy declared the lunar landing a goal of the US space program. But the human accomplishments in space during those years will be remembered long after their costs and Cold War motivations have been forgotten.

Twenty-four Apollo astronauts orbited the Moon, and twelve walked there. So far they are the only humans to see with their own eyes the Moon up close and Earth from afar. After the highs of Apollo 8 and 11, in a culture of perpetual entertainment, it was disappointing but not surprising to see how quickly so many people lost interest. Another trip to the Moon?–we've seen that already.... Apollos 18, 19, and 20 were cancelled.

The Apollo ships were superbly successful in taking men for short trips to the moon, and they looked beautiful on television, but as soon as mankind became tired of this particular spectacle, the Apollo ships became as obselete as the V-2. There was nothing else they could do. [Dyson(1979a)][110]

Before space travel can become routine, it must become cheap. Small groups of private adventurers have re-taken the initiative, resurrecting the spirit of *Orion*, as we saw in the impressive flights of *SpaceShipOne*. In the long view, a diversity of approaches will be good for space exploration. This was the message of Professor Dyson's chapter "Pilgrims, Saints, and Spacemen." *SpaceShipOne* now occupies its rightful place, near Apollo 11's *Columbia*, in the Milestones of Flight Gallery of the National Air and Space Museum.

> *17 July 2012*
> *Dear Professor Dyson,*
> *...Are projects such as SpaceShipOne what you had in mind as alternatives to NASA when you wrote "Pilgrims, Saints, and*

Spacemen"? What would you recommend for NASA's priorities now that the Shuttles have been retired?

17 July 2012
Dear Dwight,
...I am delighted that private companies are moving faster into the space business. The Falcon rocket is a big success.[110] But this is very far from the sort of independent ventures that I was writing about in "Pilgrims, Saints, and Spacemen." The companies that are active in space today are still heavily dependent on the government. Without government funding they would not survive. For truly independent ventures to be possible, space operations must become enormously cheaper. I believe this will happen, but it will take a long time. Perhaps a hundred years from now.
Meanwhile there are plenty of good things for NASA to do. NASA is already doing a splendid job with unmanned missions exploring the universe, and these will continue. The recent Kepler mission is a huge success, discovering hundreds of planetary systems orbiting around other stars. The big problem for NASA is to find something exciting to do with manned missions. Manned missions are not needed for science. To have a meaningful program of manned missions, we have to think in centuries rather than in decades. Kennedy started NASA in the wrong direction when he set the aim of the Apollo program, as putting a man on the Moon and bringing him back in ten years. As a result, the program was not sustainable and turned out to be a dead end. Kennedy should have said, we start with a modest and sustainable program that will bring people to live permanently on the Moon and planets in a hundred years. If he had said that, we would already be half-way there.

Although the Mercury, Gemini, and Apollo missions were more about quick results and less about long-term vision, by successfully making it to the Moon, that decade showed that human travel to other worlds would be a matter of time. But imagination must come first. Imagination lived the brains of Jules Verne, Orion designers, NASA and *SpaceShipOne* engineers. The space program was about more than Neil Armstrong stepping onto the Moon. It was also about a second-grader searching the night sky with wonder, and joyously shouting "Come look!"

---

[110]The Falcon Project, started by Daniel Jubb in the UK, builds rocket motors, and, as an aside, is part of the Bloodhound Project to break the land speed record by aiming for Mach 1.4. Falcon has received UK and US military support for a hypersonic plane along the lines of Global Strike.

Points Beyond

In his 1863 biography of English poet and artist William Blake, Alexander Gilchrist wrote that Blake did not write and paint for the many, but rather "for children and angels, himself a 'divine child,' whose playthings were sun, moon, and stars, the heavens and the earth." [Gilchrist(1998)] Like William Blake, the sun, moon and stars are playthings of Professor Dyson. Unlike William Blake, Professor Dyson approaches the heavenly bodies with physics and biology compressed into mathematics. Freeman Dyson is passionate about the prospects of humanity expanding into space. In *Infinite in All Directions* he quotes a few lines of Blake's poem of expansion, "America, a Prophecy":

> *On my American plains I feel the struggling afflictions*
> *Endured by roots that writhe their arms into the nether deep.*
> *I see a Serpent in Canada who courts me to his love,*
> *In Mexico an Eagle, and a lion in Peru;*
> *I see a Whale in the South Sea, drinking my soul away.*

Professor Dyson's prose following Blake's poem says "The destiny which I am preaching is not the expansion of a single nation or of a single species, but the spreading out of life in all its multifarious forms from its confinement on the surface of our small planet to the freedom of a boundless universe.... Perhaps we shall have to wait another two hundred years before we can translate the vision of William Blake into a wider cosmography: [Dyson(1988)][133–134]

> *I see a Serpent on Iapetus who courts me to his love;*
> *On Ganymede an Eagle, and a Lion on Miranda;*
> *I see a Whale in the Oort Cloud, drinking my soul away.*

When he envisions humanity expanding its frontiers into space, Professor Dyson is talking on timescales of centuries to many mellinnia. In our first correspondence with him in the spring of 1993, he responded to a question on the prospects for humans migrating to other habitats in space:

> *9 April 1993*
> *Dear Professor Neuenschwander,*
> *...When and how will people be living in space? This is discussed*
> *at length in the Tokyo talk.*[111] *The answer depends on what*

---

[111] "The Seven Ages of Man," lecture to the NTT DATA New Paradigm Session, 21 August 1992, Tokyo. The speech by Jacques in William Shakespeare's *As You Like It*— "All the world's a stage...", Professor Dyson uses as a metaphor for various timescales in human existence, and what can be accomplished by our species in them.

time-scale you are thinking about. If you are thinking about ten or a hundred years, then space-settlements will be unimportant if they exist at all. If you are thinking about a thousand years, then space-settlements will probably be all over the solar system. If you are thinking about ten thousand years on longer, then life will be fully adapted to space and will be spreading over the universe. This is my guess. Of course I may be totally wrong. The purpose of speculating about the future is not to make predictions but to suggest possibilities and broaden our horizons.

The tone of a long look to the distant future may be contrasted against a vivid moment from the past. *Disturbing the Universe* records a merry scene when Freeman and other young visiting scholars at the Institute for Advanced Study were smitten with spring fever: "A battered old Dodge convertible with the roof open...careening at breakneck speed down through the institute woods to the river...." [Dyson(1979a)][75] In a letter of 6 December 2005 to Professor Dyson we referred to this passage and asked "What is your fondest memory of the immaturies that are the privilege of youth?"

6 December 2005
Dear Dwight,
Thanks to you and the students for another thought-provoking lot of questions. 2005 has indeed been a good year for us and our tribe of fourteen grandchildren. We have much to be thankful for....
It is impossible to say which is the fondest among many memories of immaturity. Perhaps the fondest of all is night-climbing over the ancient buildings of my high-school in England, when war-time blackout was complete and the only light was moonlight. I used to go climbing the crumbling stone towers of our buildings with my friend Peter[112] in the early hours after midnight. We did not bother with such frills as helmets or climbing ropes. It was wartime and we took crazy risks, hanging onto medieval stone saints over a hundred-foot drop. Peter was killed two years later as a parachutist in the battle of Arnhem. I must be one of the few surviving people who remember him.
...Thanks again for your interest and your good wishes. Happy Christmas and New Year to all of you. Yours ever, Freeman.

---

[112]Young Freeman's climbing companion was Peter Sankey, who after Winchester became an engineering student before being taken by the war. [Schweber(1994)][486]

Winchester College, where Freeman Dyson went to school, was founded in 1382 by William of Wykeham, a contemporary of Geoffrey Chaucer. Today Wykeham's buildings still stand. Today we still read Chaucer.

I cannot remember how my obsession with the future began. I believe it may have had its roots in my upbringing among the medieval buildings of Winchester... I did not want to go back six hundred years into that dull old world... I would much rather go six hundred years forward. So while they talked learnedly of Chaucer and William of Wykeham, I dreamed of spaceships and alien civilizations. Six hundred years, for anybody who grew up in Winchester, is not a long time. [Dyson(1979a)][191–192]

Professor Dyson is interested in exploring developments that may be *possible*, when limited only by the laws of nature. He is not interested in making predictions. "In the long run, qualitative changes always outweigh quantitative ones.... I am interested in the long run, the remote future, where quantitative predictions are meaningless." [Dyson(1979a)][190–192]

> *29 April 2011*
> *Dear Professor Dyson,...*
> *You wrote that, in the long term, qualitative decisions are more important than quantitative ones. What are some of the important qualitative decisions being made today?*

Professor Dyson's humanist side, his caring about what happens to other people in the here and now, was clear:

> *29 April 2011*
> *Dear Dwight,...*
> *I suppose the most important qualitative decision being made today is whether equality of opportunity applies to communities or to individuals. In the USA recent legal decisions have outlawed affirmative action programs giving preferential treatment to communities. The result is increased inequality at all levels of society. I consider this an unmitigated evil....*

While we cannot make accurate quantitative predictions of the long-term future, we can try to understand the conditions that have made life possible on this planet. Borrowing a page from Robert Pirsig's *Zen and the Art of Motorcycle Maintenance*, we look at astronomical habitat from two perspectives, the Classic and the Romantic modes of understanding. We will begin with the Classic mode, looking beneath the surface at the nuts and bolts of how the system works. Then we will move into the Romantic mode, with awareness of and appreciation for our experiences that are made possible by our astronomical habitat.

Astronomical Habitat: Classical Mode[113]

> *"In 1956, at the age of three, I was walking home with my father, physicist Freeman Dyson, from his office at the Institute for Advanced Study, when I found a broken fan belt lying in the road. I asked my father what it was. 'It's a piece of the sun,' he said."* –George Dyson[114]

The conditions necessary for life as we know it to exist include real estate, energy, time, stability, and the right chemistry.

Life requires a real estate on which to make its home. For now and the foreseeable future this means living on a planet (or a planet's moon) orbiting a star.[115] In life, as in business, it's all about location, which for life means the availability of liquid water. Too close to the star, and every drop of water boils away; too far, and every drop freezes solid. The range of distances from it where liquid water can be found is a star's "life zone."

Stars and their planets form together in the gravitational contraction of a nebula—a giant cloud of mostly hydrogen and helium. The star's core lights up when the temperature reaches about 15 million degrees Celsius and ignites hydrogen fusion. The collapsing cloud's rotation flattens it into a disc, and planets, moons, and comets coalesce from the disc material.

The Earth is about 93 million miles from the Sun. Traveling at 186,000 miles per second, light makes the trip from Sun to Earth in eight minutes. At the speed of a commercial airliner (600 mph) traversing the Sun-to-Earth distance would take 17 years; Sun-to-Jupiter, 45 light-minutes apart, would take 89 years. The Sun's closest neighboring star, Alpha Centauri, is about four light-years away. At airliner speed it would take 4.6 million years to get there! To visualize these distances, rescale the Sun to a grapefruit sitting in Washington DC. The entire solar system fits within two blocks of the

---

[113]See any introductory astronomy text for further discussion of the points described in this section.

[114][Dyson(2012)][xiii]

[115]Making a home on asteroids or comets might eventually come to pass; we have already landed probes on both.

Washington Mall.[116] Alpha Centauri is another grapefruit in San Francisco. Our spiral Milky Way galaxy, with a hundred billion stars, is about 100,000 light-years in diameter. Our solar system resides about 30,000 light-years from the galactic center. If you can find a dark night sky, follow the broad sweep of the Milky Way over your head. You are gazing into one of the galaxy's great spiral arms. Our Sun is one of the stars in that arm.

The light we receive from the Sun is a by-product of hydrogen fusing to helium in the solar core. The luminosity, or energy cranked out per second by the Sun, is about 4×10^{26} watts. Thanks to $E = mc^2$, that figure means the sun consumes itself, turning its mass into light, at the rate of about four million tons per second. The Earth intercepts a tiny fraction of the Sun's outpouring of light energy. Plants use sunlight energy to drive photosynthesis, where carbon dioxide from the air, along with water and nutrients from the soil, are assembled into carbohydrates. When we eat the plants, our metabolism disassembles the carbohydrates to yield carbon dioxide and water and release energy. We and the plants need each other.

The timescales for life to evolve from the primordial slime to multi-cellular species requires hundreds of millions of years. For life to have a fighting chance, the host star must shine that long with stability. A star is a contest between nuclear fusion at its core trying to blow the star apart, and gravity trying to crush it. For a star to endure, those effects must balance one another throughout the star's lifetime.

Since it carries a finite amount of fuel, asking how long a star will last is like asking how far you can drive your car on one tank of fuel. The answer depends on the size of the fuel tank and the consumption rate. The fuel capacity of a star is proportional to its mass m, and its fuel consumption rate goes as the mass to the 3.5 power. Therefore the lifetime of a star is proportional to $m/m^{3.5} = m^{-2.5}$. The more massive a star, the shorter its lifetime. A red dwarf star has a tiny "fuel tank," but sips fuel like a mo-ped scooter. A blue supergiant carries an enormous supply of fuel, but wantonly burns through it like a Saturn V stage 1 booster. From the Sun's mass and luminosity and the fraction of its interior hot enough to sustain fusion, we estimate the Sun's lifetime will be about 10 billion years. A star with half the Sun's mass will shine for 50 billion years; a star with ten times the mass of our Sun will last only 20 million years. Geology tells us the

---

[116] A scale model at the Smithsonian Institution in Washington, D.C., places the Sun at the east end of the National Air and Space Museum on Constitution Avenue; Uranus sits at the west end of Air and Space, and Pluto sits near the entrance of the original Smithsonian "castle" in the next block.

Earth is four to five billion years old. Since the planets formed along with the Sun, the Sun is about halfway through its lifetime.

Let us put the Sun's ten-billion-year lifetime into visualizable terms. Imagine hiking from New York City to Los Angeles, a distance of about 3,000 miles. Let this distance represent the 10-billion-year lifetime of the Sun. If you take a 3-ft stride, then one step corresponds to about 2,000 years. On that hike we are presently somewhere in Oklahoma. Standing in my classroom in Oklahoma, facing southwest toward Los Angeles, my location represents the present time in solar system history. If I take one step backwards, it's 2000 years ago, the time of Jesus. Two steps back puts me at 4,000 years ago, the time of Eleventh Dynasty pharaohs in Egypt. Three, four, and five steps back leaves me still in the classroom, representing 10,000 years ago when agriculture was invented. The dinosaurs were wiped out 65 million years ago, about 18 miles back. Photosynthesis started about 600 miles ago, a hundred miles east of St. Louis. Most STS students are in their early twenties. They have lived so far about one percent of one step, one-third of an inch.

Compared to a frog or a flower, stars are relatively simple—think of the complexity in a frog's respiratory system, nervous system, digestive system, its ability to see and vocalize, secrete hormones, make decisions, move about, make little frogs. While a star shines, the inward pressure from gravity and the outward pressure from nuclear reactions balance out. Compared to the busy doings of a frog, the ongoing stellar contest between gravity and nuclear reactions is relatively simple. That is why we know a lot about stars.

> *12 November 2007*
> *Dear Professor Dyson,*
> *We hope that the 2007 Thanksgiving season finds you and all your family doing well....*
> *Our professor observed that a frog is many orders of magnitude more complex than a star. Do you agree?*

> *23 November 2007*
> *Dear STS class,*
> *...There are many kinds of stars, some of them much more complicated than others, but all of them less complicated than frogs. The star we know best is our sun, which has many complicated details such as sunspots and flares and prominences which we do not know how to model. But it is still much simpler than a frog....*
> *Please say thank you to the students for signing your letter.*

That gives me a glimpse of who they are. I find it interesting
that seven of them are theology majors and seven are science
majors, with the big majority doing more practical things.
Since Thanksgiving is over, I wish you all Happy Christmas.
Yours ever, Freeman Dyson

When the fusion of hydrogen to helium at the core nears completion, this reaction shuts down. Relentless gravity becomes dominant and squeezes further on the core, raising its pressure and temperature. When the core temperature reaches around 100 million degrees, helium starts fusing to carbon.

Before the core reaches 100 million degrees, the layers around the core hit 15 million degrees, igniting a shell of hydrogen fusion, swelling the star into a "red giant." When this happens to our Sun, it will engulf the inner planets, including the Earth. As the helium gets depleted and the core becomes mostly carbon, helium fusion shuts down and gravity again squeezes tighter on the core. Our Sun has insufficient mass for the core temperature to reach the 600 million degrees required to fuse carbon to nitrogen and oxygen and silicon. Our Sun will therefore end its days of nuclear fusion with a carbon core at a hundred million degrees. It will settle down as a "white dwarf" star, a compact object about the size of the Earth, and very slowly cool down.

To carry life for a long time, a planet must orbit its star with stability, avoiding calamities such as collisions with other planets, falling into the star or being flung out of the solar system. Most of the major collisions between planets happened early in the history of planet-building; today we live with the survivors. Stars in the galaxy's spiral arms are far enough apart that collisions between them statistically happen only about once every hundred thousand solar lifetimes.[117] However, comets and asteroids still cruise around the Sun; every streaking meteorite continues the planet-building process. Most of the meteors that hit the earth are small, but occasionally a piece of wandering debris can pack enough punch to be catastrophic.[118]

Life as we know it requires the right chemistry, including carbon for protein, calcium for bone, phosphorus for DNA, iron for hemoglobin, oxygen

---

[117]The stars would not have to literally crash together to produce disaster; they would only need to draw close enough that each one's gravity disrupts the orbits of the other one's planets.
[118]The best explanation that fits the data for the event that wiped out the dinosaurs about 65 million years ago is a collision between a six-mile-diameter asteroid and Earth. Imagine Pikes Peak crashing into the earth at, say, 60,000 mph.

for water. These were already loaded into the nebula from which the Sun and its planets formed. Chemistry comes from ancient nuclear physics.

Let us go back to the stellar death scenario. If the star is massive enough to create the necessary core temperatures (600 million degrees and higher), carbon fuses to silicon, neon, magnesium, and so on. If the original star began with a mass at least eight times that of the Sun, successive episodes of fusion continue until the core material fuses to iron, the most stable of all nuclear species. Stars that have fused their core material to iron have reached the end of fusion possibilities—out of fuel, the core collapses one last time. The infalling outer layers rebound off the iron core, exploding the star.[119] In the violence of the nuclear collisions within the explosion, fusion overshoots past iron to make heavier elements such as gold and uranium.

The debris ejected by the explosion moves outward at a significant fraction of the speed of light, laden with the elements fused in the exploding star. In the jargon of astronomers, elements beyond hydrogen and helium are "metals." When neighboring nebulae contract, the new stars and planets inherit metals from previous generations of stars that exploded. The metallicity of our solar system is about 2%. The calcium in our bones and the iron in our blood are remnants of stars that lived and died before our solar system formed. Made of stardust, we are sky people.

Here Today, Gone Tomorrow

> "The sun is the same in a relative way but you're older
> Shorter of breath and one day closer to death..."
> – "Time" by Pink Floyd[120]

The Sun will eventually swell up and engulf the Earth about five billion years from now. Is this depressing? Yes and no. Yes, because everything attached to this planet is doomed. No, for two reasons.

First, the Sun's remaining lifetime is so long compared to human institutions that for all practical purposes the Sun may as well last forever. On the timescale of human civilizations mountains seem permanent. But on a timescale of one billion years—one-fifth the Sun's remaining lifetime—the Rocky Mountains are as ephemeral as clouds. Do we realistically envision our cultures and monuments outlasting the Rockies? By the time the Sun

---

[119]This is a Type II supernova. Neutrino pressure also helps explode the star. Other types of supernovae, e.g., Type 1a, occur when a white dwarf star accretes matter off a nearby normal star, until the accreted matter explodes.

[120] "Time" by Pink Floyd, from *The Dark Side of the Moon* (Capitol Records, 1973).

is ready to swell into a red giant, will our descendants and institutions and artifacts still be here, or will they have long since washed to the sea or migrated to younger star systems?

Second, and more important, life is worth living for what it *is*, regardless of *how long* it lasts. The beauty of a sunset is not lessened because it is fleeting; the joy of a small child climbing into your lap is no less even though children grow up fast. It is *because* the sunset and a child's dimpled face are so ephemeral that we cherish our moments with them.

In December 1999, Professor Dyson wrote in reply to one of our questions, "The worst thing I can imagine would be if the doctors find a cure for death." The full reply and the question to which he was responding will be told in their place. But the sentence as it stands suggests that death is not the worst fate that can happen to us. Lack of meaning is worse. Life's meaning is not a treasure sitting out there waiting to be discovered. Rather, Life puts the question *to us* and watches to see how we respond.[121] Life is measured not by its length, but by its depth.

In his 1986 speech to the Conference of Catholic Bishops, Professor Dyson added a stunning insight to the perpetual questions on the meaning of life. It came in the form of a hypothesis:

> **The hypothesis is that the universe is constructed according to a principle of maximum diversity.... It says that the laws of nature and the initial conditions are such as to make the universe as interesting as possible.** [Dyson(1988)][298]

This changes the interpretation of bottomless questions such as why life includes struggles and disasters. We are perpetually on the knife-edge between great tragedy and great adventure. There are no tornadoes on the Moon, but neither are there springtime mornings. Thoreau wisely observed that the only way to avoid danger is to avoid life itself: "The amount of it is, if a man is alive, there is always *danger* that he might die." [Thoreau(1960)][105–106]

---

[121]Viktor Frankl beautifully discusses this point of view in *Man's Search for Meaning*, [Frankl(1963)].

Astronomical Habitat: Romantic mode

The STS professor says that although he spent over an hour presenting the Classical mode for understanding astronomical habitat, the Romantic mode will take five minutes. The Romantic mode is no less important than the Classical mode. The Classical mode takes longer because it requires ideas to be expressed through words, data, and logical reasoning. Billions of years of astronomical, geological, and biological processes have brought us here. But they recede from consciousness when we ride our first bicycle, experience that first kiss, or cradle an infant in our arms. The Romantic mode needs no words.

The classroom lights go down. Music begins with an elegant simple cello solo that savors every measure. "Drifting," by Enya, a soulful instrumental, reaches deep. On the screen, photographs are choreographed to the music. Wife, children, scenery. Mountains, waterfalls... Acadia beach in Maine; Mt. Manganui in New Zealand, Havasaupi Falls in the Grand Canyon; Lake Superior stretching clear and blue below the Upper Peninsula's Sugarloaf Mountain... The music builds without hurry... Haast Pass and Mt. Cook in the New Zealand Alps; the Grand Canyon from the south rim; golden aspens shimmering on Colorado's Independence Pass... In the penultimate photo, a two-month-old grandchild, held in arms, looks into his grandpa's eyes. The cello glides gently into the last measure, and we behold Earth from Apollo 8, cruising above the Moon. Chimes pronounce the benediction, then... peaceful silence.

Within the lingering silence, while gazing at the blue Earth from above the mountains of the Moon, the scene changes to a barred spiral galaxy, with a quote from the Psalms: "What is man, that Thou art mindful of him?"[122] What is mankind indeed, who lives so brief a time on this small rocky planet orbiting a modest star—but contemplates the entire universe!

The image on the screen changes again, showing the *Voyager 1* photo of the Earth seen from four billion miles away. That blue dot contains all our history, civilizations, arts, sciences, religions, quarrels, tragedies, joys and aspirations. We are small, but our imaginations are not small. This is the backdrop against which our exploration of the universe begins. The story of humanity has just begun.

The image on the screen changes again. A Hubble Deep Field photograph shows the first-generation galaxies. They formed when the universe was young, a billion years after the big bang. Their light arrives here

---

[122]Psalms 8:4a

twelve billion years later. Alongside the Deep Field photo appears lyrics from "Dante's Prayer" by Loreena McKennitt, the song that was playing when the students assembled this evening for class:[123]

> *Though we share this humble path alone*
> *How fragile is the heart*
> *Oh give these clay feet wings to fly*
> *To touch the face of the stars...*

Despite tragedies and broken dreams, despite our lack of social justice, it is still a beautiful world. Do we respect and appreciate what we have? The Earth does not need us. Nature can take us out any time she wants. Like so many others, I have had my house swept off its foundation by a tornado. But as Luther Standing Bear (1878–1934) wisely observed, it is pointless to rage at the storms. [Standing Bear(1933)] They are part of life. They are experiences to grow on. We should be grateful, even amid the storms. The out-of-equilibrium thermodynamics that makes tornadoes possible also makes life possible. [Grinspoon(2009)] "The laws of nature and the initial conditions are such as to make the universe as interesting as possible."

A few years ago, while on a motorcycle trip from Phoenix, Arizona to Oklahoma City, at dusk I came upon the Very Large Array.[124] The VLA consists of two dozen radio telescopes arranged in a giant Y on the high San Augustin plain, ringed by mountains, fifty miles west of Socorro, New Mexico. Each telescope carries a parabolic dish sixty feet in diameter. All the telescopes work together as one, receiving faint signals from galaxies across the universe. At that hour the visitor's center was closed. For all practical purposes I had the plateau all to myself. I turned off the highway and headed up the service road. At the intersection of the service road and the railroad tracks on which the telescopes are moved about, a nearby telescope was bolted to its concrete pier. I stopped, got off the bike, and stood there for a long time in the profound silence. It was an indelible moment of being truly *alive*. In the deep blue evening over the wide silence, the scattered clouds were tipped with rose by the sun's fading rays. In front of me waited the machine that was carrying me smoothly across deserts and mountains, while behind it another machine was busily receiving faint signals sent forth from some distant galaxy a hundred million years ago. Thoreau's words echoed in my mind, "Why should I feel alone? Is not our

---

[123]"Dante's Prayer" by Loreena McKennitt, from *The Book of Secrets* (1997), Warner Bros. Records.
[124]The VLA is formally named after Karl G. Jansky, a pioneer of radio astronomy.

Fig. 10.1 *"I was not a spectator of the universe, but a participant in it."* (author photo)

planet in the Milky Way?" [Thoreau(1960)][92] I was not looking *at* the universe; I was *in* the universe, not as a spectator, but as a participant.

> ...*Cast your eyes on the ocean*
> *Cast your soul to the sea*
> *When the dark night seems endless*
> *Please remember me*
> *Please remember me...*[125]

Ultimately we do not own anything. We merely borrow it from our grand-children.

---

[125]More lyrics from "Dante's Prayer" by Loreena McKennitt.

11 Silence

On Seeking Serenity and Peace of Mind

> *"Vladimir Kosma Zworykin was a pioneer of television who would live to regret that his invention's capacity for the transmission of intelligence had become a channel for so much noise."*[126]

***

As part of his work on Project Orion, Professor Dyson visited an Atomic Energy Commission nuclear weapons test site in Nevada.

Only once in my life have I experienced absolute silence. That was at Jackass Flat under the midday sun.... It is a soul-shattering silence. You hold your breath and hear absolutely nothing.... You are alone with God in that silence. There in the white flat silence I began for the first time to feel a slight sense of shame for what we were proposing to do. Did we really intend to invade this silence with our trucks and bulldozers, and after a few years leave it a radioactive junkyard? The first shadow of doubt about the rightness of Orion came into my mind with that silence. [Dyson(1979a)][128]

Jillian B. wrote about this passage, "I identify with Dyson when he stands in a silent salt flat and begins to shift his priorities. He is a human first and a scientist second. This is something I respect him for."

Professor Dyson's experience at Jackass Flat offers an excellent opening to another poignant class discussion. How many of you, I ask the students, have ever experienced a moment of absolute silence? After a brief pause, out of forty students one or two hands go up, then a few more. We hear of hiking experiences in the Rocky Mountains, starlight on an Oklahoma farm, exploring a limestone cave in Missouri, or sitting alone on a Costa Rican cloud forest trail. Follow-up questions are raised: Why is silence so difficult to find in modern society? When we do find a moment of silence, why are we so quick to drown it out?

In 1916, amid the thundering cannons of World War I, Edgar Lee Masters paid homage to silence: [Masters(1916)]

---

[126][Dyson(2012)][64]

I have known the silence of the stars and of the sea,
And the silence of the city when it pauses,
And the silence of a man and a maid,
And the silence for which music alone finds the word,
And the silence of the woods before the winds of spring begin,
And the silence of the sick
When their eyes roam about the room.
And I ask: For the depths
Of what use is language?...

Professor Dyson and I have this common: We have experienced the absolute silence of the Great Basin desert. Through photographs and artifacts and stories I try to bring that setting into the classroom as best as I can. During my graduate school days I spent three consecutive summers in the deserts of western Utah and eastern Nevada, not far from Jackass Flat. After being immersed in such silence, you are a different person. My friend Doug and I explored the Great Basin with a 1964 Volkswagen bus loaded with camping gear, geologist's field equipment, water jugs, gas cans, tools, spare parts, and a battered copy of J. R. R. Tolkien's *The Lord of the Rings*. During these trips we tied our wristwatches onto the VW's wiring under the dashboard, out of sight. Even before smart phones, we made it a point to be deliberately disconnected. Out there, we experienced the "white flat silence" that Professor Dyson describes. We had the planet to ourselves.

Doug and his twin brother Dudley have been brothers to me since we met at age thirteen.[127] During those summers Doug needed an assistant for his geology field work, and I immediately volunteered. His dissertation project included mapping the ancient continental shelf that forms part of the Great Basin. We did a "section" by measuring the strata, taking photographs and notes, and collecting samples for Doug's lab work back at his university. Between sections we explored abandoned mines, hiked canyons and climbed 13,000 foot peaks.

Our favorite deserted mining town was Frisco, Utah. An historical marker on the state highway describes the millions of dollars' worth of gold that was extracted here between 1885 and 1910. In the Frisco cemetery the words on several grave markers were still legible. Most of them were memorials to young mothers and children, showing the real cost of digging all that gold:

---

[127]Dudley, a biochemist, joined us for a few days on one of our expeditions.

Fig. 11.1 *Evening as Sevier Lake salt flat, Utah. Notch Peak stands in the background.* (Doug Strickland photo)

Rachel
Age 10
Darling We Miss Thee
1908

In Utah's House Range, dominated by Notch Peak, we did sections at Swasey Peak and Week's Canyon. In the House Range and, to the south, in the aptly named Confusion Range, our companions were rattlesnakes and wild horses. We measured sections in Nevada among the abandoned mines at Steptoe and beneath eagles riding updrafts at Patterson Pass. The best part of being in the field, sixty miles from the next drivable car, is the awesome silence. When you stop and listen you hear absolutely nothing beyond your own thoughts. The silence of deserts and salt flats, mountains and sky, soaks into your soul. If you appreciate this place for what it is, you are rewarded. In that silence, with the right attitudes, the spirits of the Shoshone and Paiute draw up softly beside you...

When...the memory of my tribe shall have become a myth among the white man, these shores will swarm with the invisible dead of my tribe, and when your children's children think themselves alone in the field...they will not be alone. [McLuhan(1971)][30]

In this vast silence comes a deep, nourishing peace. Silence in our modern society grows increasingly difficult to find. Although I cannot go to Swasey Peak or the Sevier salt flat right now, it's good to know they exist. I go there mentally every day. When no wild quiet places are left, when everything has been "developed," something irreplaceable will be lost. The tragedy is, most people will not realize they have lost it.

When you experience profound silence, you can listen to your own thoughts. When we do find a rare moment of silence in modern life, so often we quickly drown it out by pulling out the smart phone, plugging in the earphones or switching on TV blather. Maybe we are afraid to be alone with our own thoughts. Maybe we are afraid we will have no thoughts. Maybe we fear that something greater than ourselves will make its presence known to us...

We love quiet, we suffer the mouse to play; when the woods are rustled by the wind, we fear not. [McLuhan(1971)][5]

At night we made a rice and veggie stew over the campfire. To make coffee we dumped the grounds straight into an iron pot, set it on the fire and brought the water to a rolling boil. Lift the pot off the fire, the grounds settle to the bottom, leaving the coffee rich and strong. The night desert air became chilly, so we put on army field jackets and enjoyed our campfire coffee over the shimmering glow of red-hot coals. From our campfire we looked up to the campfires marking the pathways of departed souls...the Milky Way. We were not looking *at* the universe, we were *in* the universe. Alone in the silence we were not lonely; we were connected to all things and could hear God thinking.

Dark skies are getting harder to find nowadays too. It's sad how the light trespass of a single mercury vapor lamp wipes out your view of the entire universe. The tragedy is, most people never look up. They do not know what they're not seeing. There are places for noise and artificial light, but it's not *every* place.

On a talus slope we split fragments of black shale with rock hammers. We sometimes found the fossilized body of a trilobite, extinct arthropods that prowled the ocean shallows from Early Cambrian through Permian times. The connection between the moment of this fellow's burial in the soft offshore mud 500 million years ago, and the moment when I split the shale to bring him once again into the sunlight, telescopes time itself. One acquires a sense of time that frenetic city dwellers cannot fathom. Every

day we looked at timescales for which a million years is but an instant.
The last words of Crowfoot (1821–1890) of the Blackfeet nation asked the
ultimate question:

What is life? It is the flash of a firefly in the night. It is the breath of a
buffalo in the winter time. It is the little shadow which runs across the grass
and loses itself in the Sunset. [McLuhan(1971)][12]

On the east side of Nevada's Snake Range we explored abandoned mines
and their rusting machinery, including two marooned World War Two vintage halftracks and a 1948 Chrysler that somehow ended up here. We
wanted to take them home, these interesting machines with a story. Whoever brought them here used them to scratch around on the land, and then
just walked away, disrespecting both the landscape and the machines. It reminds one of the sad words of a Wintu woman who spoke of the destruction
of her homeland where mining had torn the earth during the California gold
rush: "How can the spirit of the earth like the White man? Everywhere
the White man has touched the earth it is sore." [McLuhan(1971)][15] One
wonders what the land and the trees have to say. We do not listen to them,
or to the vanished peoples who were here first, whose value system differed
from ours. They had much to teach us. But we wanted their land, not their
philosophy. One wonders who was the most civilized.

A few days later we headed back to the other world of campuses and
clocks, to resume the kind of education certified by diplomas. But I would
not trade those three summers for three decades in *anyone's* cubicle. In the
desert, amid stars and the silence, we lived a priceless education of another
kind.[128]

Rediscovering Silence

The topic of "Silence" keeps recurring in student letters even weeks after
we have moved on to other subjects. Evidently our meditations on silence
strike a chord in the student's lives.

This week [our professor] talked about the summers he spent
in Utah and Nevada...Dyson, like [our professor], experienced

---

[128]This section adapted from "Rattlesnake University" by the author [Neuenschwan-
der(2003)]; the article itself was adapted from presentations in STS class as described
herein.

silence in Nevada... Feeling like we are in the universe and
looking at the beauty of the skies makes us question our
world with its busyness, tight schedules, and
overstimulation... It is tragic that we can't see the stars
because of our billboards, lights, and cars. In a way, this
makes us lose sight of who we are and distracts us from the
big picture... --Drew V.

26 November 2014
Dear Professor Dyson,
*...Your description of "absolute silence" at Jackass Flat,
Nevada, offers an opening for discussing questions about silence
(both audio and visual), such as: Why is silence so difficult to
find in our society; When we do find it, why are we so quick
to drown it out; Why do we not push back hard against the in-
your-face noise to which we are continually bombarded; Why is
our eagerness to embrace the latest technology not accompanied
by reflection over what it displaces...? and so on. Professor
Dyson, where do you go, and how often do you go there, to be
alone with your own thoughts, to find a moment of silence?*

3 December 2014
Dear Dwight and students,
*...I am lucky to have an office at the Institute for Advanced
Study where I work. Although I am retired, they let me keep the
office as long as I can make use of it. I usually keep the door
open so that the young Institute members are not afraid to walk
in. But whenever I need to have silence, I can shut the door. I
usually shut the door only when a visitor is with me and wants
to talk privately. But I can also shut it when I am alone. I
remember long ago reading the book, "A Room of One's Own,"
by Virginia Woolf. That book was written a hundred years ago
when families were bigger and fewer people had rooms of their
own. It encouraged a whole generation of women to claim the
right to silence. I am lucky to have silence available whenever
I want it. I do not need it to be as quiet as Jackass Flat.
I find it horrible to be at a party with loud music, often so loud
that it is impossible to have a serious conversation. The habit of
playing loud music at parties is doing permanent damage to the
hearing of young people. It is also depriving them of the opportunity to have serious conversations. Since I always like to look
on the bright side of things, I rejoice to see that the railroad on
the regular route through New Jersey has "Quiet Cars," where
passengers may not use cell-phones or carry on conversations.*

These cars are not totally silent, but they allow passengers to read or work in peace. They are a good step in the right direction....
Thank you once more for a good set of questions...
Happy Christmas to you and the class! Yours ever, Freeman.

I have a confession. I do not know how to live life to the fullest. I do not know how to be spontaneous. And I don't know how to enjoy silence anymore.... We're bombarded by so many things, whether it be busy tasks, media, or other people. I confess that I have fallen into the rhythm of living in noise. And honestly, I am quite annoyed with it. I don't have time to think and reflect on things that are important in life.... I also feel as though American society has become very task-oriented and because of our busy schedules we have become eager to just check things off our lists and move on to the next task. What about enjoying life?... Do I want to be responsible? Yes. But I also want to LIVE. I want to value two new concepts. Concepts that one would think to be old, but to me are brand new -- Silence and Adventure. I know that I need them both. --Jennie L.

Sherry Turkle, a researcher from MIT who studies the social and psychological effects of technology, documents the growing frustration with a world where anyone can yank your chain at any moment:

We insist that our world is increasingly complex, yet we have created a communications culture that has decreased the time available for us to sit and think uninterrupted. As we communicate in ways that ask for almost instantaneous responses, we don't allow sufficient space to consider complicated problems... [Turkle(2012)][166]

The Internet is a phenomenonal source of information, but with all its popups, scrolling pictures, sidebars and hyperlinks it is also an instrument of distraction that encourages superficial skimming at the expense of deep reading and reflective thinking. "The Internet...wasn't built by educators to optimize learning," writes Nicholas Carr. "It presents information not in a carefully balanced way but as a concentration-fragmenting mismash. The Net is, by design, an interruption system, a machine geared for dividing attention." [Carr(2011)][131]

In contrast, when Doug and I camped in deserts and mountains of Utah and Nevada, cut off from the rest of the world, we had time to look. We had time to listen. We had time to think. Thoreau felt this too, at Walden: "I have, as it were, my own sun and moon and stars, and a little world all to myself... I never found the companion that was so companionable as solitude." [Thoreau(1960)][90,94] The Internet offers a flood of noisy information; Grandfather Dyson offers quiet, deliberative wisdom...

> ...And there is the silence of age,
> Too full of wisdom for the tongue to utter it
> In words intelligible to those who have not lived
> The great range of life....

22 April, 2015
Dear Professor Dyson,
On behalf of the Spring 2015 STS class, I bring you greetings, with good wishes to you and all your family. Please give my regards to Imme as well....
...If you could "get away from it all" anywhere in the world, where would you go and what would you do? We know that you and Imme enjoy traveling, and have been to practically every country on the planet, including exotic places such as the Galápagos Islands. This question is similar to a recent one we asked you about where you go to find a moment of silence. But the difference between the two questions, I think, is asking what kinds of environments on this planet would most resonate with who you are deep down (we know you would also like to go to Saturn and would not mind visiting an asteroid).
Thank you Professor Dyson for your consideration of our questions. Do not feel obliged to answer all of them. We do not want to take your time for granted.
Warm regards, on behalf of the students, Dwight

1 May 2015
Dear Dwight,
...I cannot give a useful answer to this question because I would hate to "get away from it all." I need friends and I need family and I need the community in which I lived for sixty years. Humans are social animals, and most of us like to be constantly interacting with friends and family and community. I enjoy visiting exotic places like the Galápagos, but even there it is not the solitude that I enjoy. I enjoyed the Galápagos because I lost my suitcase and some young girls on the boat lent me their colorful

*blouses, so my wife and I joined the group of young people and
became friends right away. Losing the suitcase turned out to
be lucky. We even found it again when we flew back to Quito.
I can only answer the question by saying, I would love to get
away from it all for five minutes, but not longer.*

*By the way, I just published a new book with the title "Dreams
of Earth and Sky," a collection of book reviews published by the
New York Review of Books. Yesterday the local book-store in
Princeton had an evening session, half an hour of me reading
aloud from the book, then half an hour of question and answer
discussion, and finally a book-signing with me signing books for
people who bought them. I was amazed to see how many books
we sold. A big crowd came and they were all my friends. That
is why I like to stay here and not to get away from it all.*

*With all my good wishes and thanks to all of you, yours ever,
Freeman Dyson.*

Whatever the external circumstances, the most important silence is inner peace of mind.

Long before we sold our souls to smart phones and diluted our minds with multitasking, long before our days began with commuter traffic and road rage, long before television screens stood over the lobbies of every bank and post office and airport gate, long before we replaced the real world with the small screen—the desert and mountains stood in silence, millennium after millennium. As William Shakespeare observed, mankind appears, makes noise for a season, and exits. In the long run the silence remains...

Fig. 11.2   *An anonyomous grave in the cemetary at Dalamar, Nevada.* (author photo)

...And there is the silence of the dead.
If we who are in life cannot speak
Of profound experiences,
Why do you marvel that the dead
Do not tell you of death?
Their silence shall be interpreted
As we approach them.

***

This chapter dedicated to the memory of Douglas K. Strickland
June 28, 1952 – May 4, 2011

"We should come home from afar,
from adventures, and perils, and discoveries every day,
with new experience and character."
–Henry David Thoreau

12 The Chainsaw and the White Oak

Letters about the Environment

"How can you expect the birds to sing when their groves are cut down?...Instead of calling on some scholar, I paid many a visit to particular trees." –Henry David Thoreau[129]

***

As the students enter the classroom this evening, they hear the music of a Costa Rican band called Editus. Their distinctive musical style features crisp violin, guitar, and percussion artistry; birds and children's laughter may occasionally be heard in the background. From our Latin American neighbors, with their brightly-painted houses, joyous music, easy laughter and propensity to dance, we North Americans have much to learn about the pure enjoyment of life. *Pura vida* (pure life) is the motto of Costa Rica. Our university has a field station in that country's Talamanca Mountains. A few STS students have been there. The others have something left to live for. Professor Dyson's influence has reached here too.

Our Costa Rica field station offers a gorgeous setting for discussing our relationship with the environment. We frame the discussion with four questions: (1) What does "environmental sustainability" mean? (2) How well do we practice it? The third and fourth questions are motivated by a rich passage from *Disturbing the Universe*: "Sanity is, in its essence, nothing more than the ability to live in harmony with nature's laws," [Dyson(1979a)][237] By this standard, we raise questions (3) and (4): Are we living in harmony with nature's laws? If not, does it follow that our society is insane?

In this chapter, "The Greening of the Galaxy," Professor Dyson distinguishes two types of technology, "gray" and "green:"

In everything we undertake, either on earth or in the sky, we have a choice of two styles, which I call the gray and the green... Factories are gray, gardens are green. Physics is gray, biology is green. Plutonium is gray, horse manure is green. Bureaucracy is gray, pioneer communities are green. Self-reproducing machines are gray, trees and children are green. Human technology is gray, God's technology is green. [Dyson(1979a)][227]

---

[129][Thoreau(1960)][132, 138]

Professor Dyson's first letter to us included his response to a question that requested elaboration on the meaning of gray and green technologies:

> *9 April 1993*
> *Dear Professor Neuenschwander and STS class,*
> *...What is the meaning of grey and green? The distinction here is not between god-made and man-made. Both grey and green may be god-made or man-made. The distinction is between dead and living materials. Grey is made of metal and glass and steam and electricity. Green is made of leaves and roots and cells and enzymes and genes and bugs and brains. Up to now, grey technology has mostly been done by engineers, green technology by farmers. In the future the roles of engineers and farmers will become blurred.*

After Ted Taylor had done all he could to prevent nuclear terrorism, he designed "solar ponds," large ponds surrounded by dikes and covered with transparent plastic air mattresses. In summer, the mattresses prevent evaporation while allow sunlight to heat the water, trapping heat for indoor heating the following winter. In winter, the water in other ponds can be allowed to freeze and the ice covered with the plastic mattresses to save it for home cooling the next summer. Thinking of the latter application, the term "ice pond" was used in our first letter to Professor Dyson. In *Disturbing the Universe* he describes Taylor's proposal to build enough ponds to provide heating and cooling for the apartments that house families of visiting scholars at the Institute for Advanced Study. We asked what became of the proposal. Professor Dyson's response went beyond answering the immediate question. He included a story and broke the situation down into parts with a well-organized list:

> *9 April 1993*
> *Dear Professor Neuenschwander and STS class,*
> *...What happened to the ice-ponds? The scheme to use ice-ponds here in Princeton never materialized. The problem with ice-ponds is that they need a lot of attention. They have not yet been packaged so that you can install them and then forget about them. They are being used only by people who enjoy tinkering and taking care of them. I have visited the Kutter Cheese Factory in New York State, which uses ice-ponds successfully and saves a lot of money which would otherwise be spent on electricity for refrigeration. Three facts make this project successful.*
> *(a) Mr. Kutter loves his ice-ponds and does not grudge the time he spends messing around with them.*
> *(b) The cheese factory has a predictable demand for refrigera-*

tion all the year round.
(c) The factory is out in the woods and does not need to look
elegant. None of these three facts would be true for an aver-
age home-owner or for our Institute housing project. Until the
ice-ponds can be packaged so as to be neat-looking and easy to
maintain, it will not be sold and used by home-owners on a large
scale.

If all the technical and aesthetic problems of Taylor's ponds could be solved, and if all communities on Earth decided to rely on them, Professor Dyson calculated they would cover about one percent of Earth's surface. [Dyson(1979a)][229] He pointed out a precedent for public works on such a scale: about one percent of the United States has been paved to serve the automobile.

Meeting our needs for energy, living space, nutrition, recreation and tranquility promises to be an ever-growing challenge. In front of the class the image on the screen announces tonight's topic of discussion: "Environmental Sustainability" and lists the four questions mentioned above. As with other topics, we split this one into components of appreciation and awareness.

To illustrate the appreciation sector we embark on a photographic tour of some glorious places in Costa Rica. For half a dozen years, environmental biologist and *mi amigo* Professor Leo Finkenbinder and I team-taught a course there that we called "The Astronomical Basis of Life on Earth."[130] A ten-day trip to Costa Rica over spring break provided the field study component of the course, with our base of operations at our university's field station high in the cloud forest of the Talamanca Mountains, nine degrees north of the equator.

You don't have to go to Costa Rica to think about environmental sustainability. You can go outside right where you are. But when we visit a foreign land we often see there with clarity what we take for granted at home. William Blake's poem "Auguries of Innocence" (1803) begins with a celebration of seeing beneath the surface:

> *To see the world in a grain of sand*
> *Heaven in a wildflower*
> *Hold Eternity in the palm of your hand*
> *And Infinity in an hour...*

---

[130]Portions of this astro-habitat course spilled over into the STS course, showing up here in Ch. 10.

In Costa Rica, every surface is *alive*. The diversity among the birds and flowers hits you with in-your-face intensity.

The story that follows should be told by Leo and by a Costa Rican farmer named Efrain Chacón, because it is *their* story to tell. Before Leo retired, he routinely visited our class to share it with us. [Finkenbinder and Neuenschwander(2001)] Now I have to sub for him.

The story began about 1950 when Efrain Chacón, a dairy farmer who had lost his farm due to an extended El Niño drought, learned that he was eligible for land in a Costa Rican homestead act. His homestead was in the San Gerado de Dota valley of the Talamanca Mountains, which was then still a wild undeveloped place. The Talamancas are the newest range in Central America. Their rise completed the land bridge between North and South America some three million years ago. The forest that Efrain moved into is part of one of the largest contiguous oak forests in the Western Hemisphere.

Efrain entered the valley in 1952. He hiked alongside the Rio Savegre carrying his axe, watched by the Brockett deer, yellow flycatchers, and Resplendent Quetzals (*Pharomachrus mocinno*). This was a new beginning. He and his wife Caridad, with their infant son Marino, lived the first few weeks in a cave by the Rio Savegre while Efrain built a snug house. Then with his axe he began felling the ninety-feet-tall oak trees and burning off the understory to clear the steep mountainsides for pastures.

Efrain was hard-working and innovative. His fine cheeses sold well at shops on the Pan-Am Highway. Over the years he built a herd of prize-winning Holstein cattle. Over sixty trophies his cattle won at international shows are proudly displayed in his living room.

With the clear cold Rio Savegre running through his canyon farm Efrain saw another business opportunity. After consulting with fish and game authorities, he built spawning ponds for rainbow trout, *cabinas* for fishermen, a small restaurant run by Caridad, and placed a notice in a San José sports shop. Trout fishermen came. Seeing another opportunity, because apples were imported from the States, by the time they landed on San José grocery shelves their fresh juicy crispness was lost. Efrain and his sons found in Israel the Ana apple tree that grows well on the Talamanca mountainsides which lack seasonal variations. They converted some pastures into orchards. The family thrived with the business triad of the dairy supplemented by trout fishing and orchards.

In the early 1980s, through a mutual acquaintance Leo went to Costa Rica and met the Chacóns. Leo and his wife Zana and the entire Chacón family hit it off at once. Leo began bringing students to conduct research in the Chacón's cloud forest. The biologists tell me that, when hiking a hundred yards through this forest, you pass by more species than exist on the entire North American continent! Over time, Leo and Zana became like members of the Chacón family. I saw this with my own eyes on my first visit. The moment Leo stepped out of his Trooper a crowd of boisterous Chacón grandchildren came rushing from all directions and swarmed around him with gleeful shouts of "Leo! Leo!"

In 1982 Leo and some students were visiting the Chacón's farm to carry out a field study. On their last night in the valley, as they were having dinner in Caridad's restaurant, in came Marino with survey drawings. He proudly unrolled them on the floor to show them to his friends from Oklahoma. At that time the Chacóns had almost eighty acres of mountain pastures. Marino excitedly explained to the biologists how he and Efrain were going to triple the size of the pastures. Telling about it later, Leo said that at the time "Our hearts were crushed, to think of that magnificent forest destroyed for pasturage." But they said nothing.

The next day during the flight back to the States, Leo and his students discussed what, if anything, could be done. They had no right to tell the Chacón family what to do. But the university students had become good friends with members of the family, and during their farewells in San Gerado de Dota, they promised to keep in touch. On the airplane that day the university students resolved that, in their letters to the Chacón family members, they would always express what that spectacular cloud forest meant to them.

A year later as Leo returned to his office from microbiology class his telephone was ringing. It was Marino, who said "Leo, we have decided to sell all the cattle and not cut any more trees. Can you come down?" When Leo got there, the family put a cup of Costa Rica Terrazu coffee in his hand and debriefed him on what had happened.

One evening after a long day of chopping oak trees with their axes, before hiking down the steep mountainside to home and supper, Efrain and Marino sat down on the ground to rest. They leaned their backs against the next tree they intended to chop down, a ninety-foot-tall white oak. As dusk drew on, they noticed lights coming on in the houses of various family members—Efrain's family had grown to eleven children and many grandchildren by this time. Efrain and Marino could clearly see each house. Suddenly a realization hit them. They could see each house because no trees stood in the way. Efrain began reminiscing about coming to this forest, seeing the quetzals and the tiny Brockett deer,[131] the moss-covered trees, the wildflowers. Efrain loved this forest. He wanted his grandchildren to see it *the way he saw it originally*. But here he was, chopping and burning his way up the mountain. He and Marino began talking about those letters from the Oklahoma students that showed what other people saw in this forest. Efrain and Marino began asking themselves if chopping down the rest of it was necessary. They realized that if they returned to this spot the next morning and chopped down this white oak, they would go on chopping and burning up this slope and down the other side. Normally they left their axes at the work site so they would not have to lug them back up the next morning. That evening they carried their axes home.

The next day, instead of chopping down that white oak, they called a family meeting. They discussed the forest, and each person shared what it meant to them. They discussed the letters from their student friends in Oklahoma. Then they turned to the hard business decision of whether they should continue with their plans to cut down more forest, or consider other options. At that moment they had eighty acres in pastures. They looked at what extending the pastures would gain. Crucially, they also looked at what those extended pastures would displace. The orchards and trout fishing businesses were doing well. The family had options.

The Chacós decided, and made a plan. They would cut no more trees, sell all the cattle, convert existing pastures into orchards, and tear down the cow barns. Since the barn sites were already leveled, more tourist *cabinas* would replace the barns. The restaurant would be upgraded and expanded. This was a big gamble with the extended family's livelihood. The dairy had been the backbone of their income. Having done their research and made their plan, Marino telephoned Leo.

When I first visited the Chacón operation, all the cattle were gone, neat cabins replaced the barns, and eighty acres of pastures had become eighty acres of orchards. Other than two narrow hiking trails, the rest of the forest was intact. At that time, our university had recently negotiated with the Chacóns a renewable long-term lease of a site next to Rio Savegre that the Chacóns had previously cleared and leveled when they were planning to build a large milking barn. The milking barn was never built, but thanks to the support of our alumni, built on that site instead was a two-story laboratory, classroom, dormitory and small natural history museum under one roof, the Quetzal Education and Research Center (QERC), known to

---

[131]Brockett deer are 18 inches tall at the shoulder, fully grown.

Fig. 12.1 *Left to right: Efrain Chacón, granddaughter Matilda, and Marino. To Efrain's right stands the white oak tree that figures prominently in the family's decision to save their forest.* (photo courtesy of Marco Saborio and Leo Finkenbinder)

locals as the "flower of the forest." As part of the lease agreement, four hundred acres of the Chacón's tropical cloud forest are accessible for field studies. Students from our university and others come here to conduct research.[132]

On the hiking trails one can spend the day surrounded by tall oak trees covered with moss and epiphytes, watching the small frisky bright yellow flycatchers. We witness almost every day the lovely sinusoidal flight of a Resplendent Quetzal. The Brockett deer are making a comeback. William Blake would be glad:

> The wild deer, running here and there
> Keeps the human soul from care...

The course that Leo and I team-taught, "The Astronomical Basis of Life on Earth," was designed to enlarge to astrophysical scales our interpreta-

---

[132]At the time of this writing the lease was recently extended for another twenty-five years, and the QERC field station was named in honor of Leo and Zana Finkenbinder.

Fig. 12.2   *A Resplendent Quetzal at the QERC.* (photo courtesy of Marco Saborio)

tion of the word "habitat." What astronomical conditions are necessary for life to exist on a planet? Stellar evolution provides energy, elements, and timescale for biological evolution, a relationship colorfully displayed here with immediate clarity.[133] For example, when studying the nuclear reactions that power the Sun, we hike into the cloud forest and discuss under the trees the proton-proton cycle of hydrogen fusion at the Sun's core. Then Prof. Leo takes his turn. Standing in the forest with the sunlight filtering through the leaves, he points out various light-gathering mechanisms among the plants all around us, such as the spiral gingers (family *Zingiberaceae*) whose leaves are arranged on the stem like a spiral staircase so the leaves above do not cast shadows on their fellows below.

At least once per visit to the QERC, we leave each student alone on the trail, from thirty minutes to two hours. They are to sit there with only their field notebook and pencil, their senses, the forest silence and their

---

[133]In astronomy, "stellar evolution" means the progression of single star through the stages of its life cycle. In biology, "evolution" means natural selection over many generations.

thoughts. Here, instead of calling on a scholar we pay a visit to the trees. Swasey Peak in Utah and the QERC in the montane cloud forest show something that we all need: time to be alone with our own thoughts—not to *do* anything, but to *be*. How do we integrate this need for quiet reflection into our economy?

Our studies also take us farther afield to sites across Costa Rica. When discussing tides we stand up to our necks in one on the Pacific beach at Manuel Antonio National Park. The physics professor uses two coconuts to illustrate the Earth and Moon, while the real Moon stands watch over our heads. When discussing the role of volcanoes in planet-building, we stand a respectful distance from the active Arenal Volcano. We smell the hydrogen sulfide and watch as boulders the size of houses (glowing red at night), flung out of the crater, bounce noisily down the mountain's pyroclastic cone. We stand among the craters, some thirty feet in diameter, at the site of the former villages of Tabacon, Pueblo Nuevo, and San Luis. During Arenal's large 1968 eruption, 87 people perished here, most of them in Tabacon. They did not respond quickly enough to evacuation warnings. Nature can be dangerous as well as beautiful. She must be treated with respect.

Environment and Economy

How did their business gamble work out for the Chacóns? Several times I have stood outside their restaurant as big tour buses pull up in front of the cabin registration office. Stepping off the buses are serious birdwatchers, identifiable by expensive cameras with colossal telephoto lenses. This is one of the few places in Central America where one can still see in the wild the rare, engendered, glorious Resplendent Quetzal.[134] Efrain's neighbors have taken notice. Their cattle are disappearing too, their barns giving way to *cabinas*. Over ten thousand ecotourists visit the Rio Savegre valley every year.

Considering the alternative, everybody wins. The forest ecosystem remains essentially intact, the quetzals and other species have sanctuary in their natural habitat, and the birdwatchers fulfill a dream. Efrain's family and his neighbors are prospering. Because the trees still stand, the mists still form every day to water the cloud forest, and megatons of sediment are not sliding off these mountains and moving downstream every year. The

---

[134] Another is Monteverde to the north.

July 2005 establishment of the nearby Los Quetzales National Park helps protect the entire Savegre watershed.[135]

Efrain says "I thank God every day that I did not have a chainsaw when I came to this valley. This forest is still here because I had an axe." He expresses through personal experience a general truth articulated many years ago by pioneering ecologist Eugene P. Odum who wrote, "Man's power to change and control seems to be increasing faster than man's realization and understanding of the results of the profound changes of which he is now capable." [Odum(1959)][26] A chainsaw works so fast that we do not always pause to think through the consequences of what we do with it. Most technologies are invented to speed things up. Problems arise when technology advances faster than the speed of reflective thought.

Efrain owns a chainsaw today. When a tree falls from natural causes and blocks the trail, Efrain cuts a gap in the fallen log so the hiking birdwatchers will not detour around it and damage the adjacent forest floor. A chainsaw is not intrinsically evil. What matters are the principles and values that reside within the mind to which it is connected.

Costa Rica has made exemplary success in retarding deforestation, but deforestation there has not stopped. In southwest Costa Rica, the landscape flattens out as we catch a whiff of Pacific Ocean breeze and pass through plantations of teak and mahogany, palm oil and bananas. These vast acreages of trees in neat rows are crops, not ecosystems. My biologist colleagues call them "green deserts." The biological diversity and symbiotic relationships that make ecosystems are gone. As we drive by the corporate-owned banana towns with their dusty soccer fields surrounded by identical brightly-painted houses, we learn that the huge blue plastic bags used to trap gases in the growing banana bunches end up, by the millions, in the ocean where leatherback sea turtles choke to death on them when they mistake the bags for their meal of jellyfish. Whenever I pass through the fruit section of an Oklahoma grocery, I ponder the hidden costs behind those rows of bananas aligned so smartly in the display.

---

[135]The Chacón experience has been the subject of conference presentations; e.g., L.F. "The White Oak Model: Sustainability in a Cloud Forest" at various meetings of the Oklahoma Academy of Sciences; L.F., invited paper in "The Global Dilemma" session, conference on "An Aging Population, an Aging Planet, and a Sustainable Future: Thinking Globally, Acting Locally," University of North Texas, Feb. 1995; L.F. and D.N. "Astronomical Ecosystems" (Denver, CO, May 2004) and "To See Cosmology in a Quetzal" (Albuquerque, NM, June 2002), meetings of the American Astronomical Society.

At the inland Costa Rican town of Los Chiles, three kilometers from the border with Nicaragua, we climb aboard narrow boats and cruise the Rio Frio Wildlife Refuge. This serpentine haven, the river plus a few hundred yards on either side amid agriculture beyond, offers a lively ribbon of sanctuary. We watch a caiman stalking a grebe, an ahinga drying his wings after fishing, a small "Jesus Christ lizard" run with slapping webbed feet across the top of the water as howler monkeys swing in the branches overhead. Although the country has numerous national parks and wildlife refuges, due to habitat fragmentation around them, enclaves of wildlife become trapped and isolated. Environmental scientists have found it necessary to introduce the new sub-discipline of "island ecology."

Another excursion takes us to Manuel Antonio National Park, which sits on the Pacific coast adjacent to the town of Quepos. From our hotel deck we hear buses in the town below, but our view of the Pacific Ocean is unobstructed. An ordinance prohibits the construction of buildings higher than the tree-tops, an instructive counterpoint to the high-rise hotels of Honolulu. Although it's a small town compared to Honolulu, Quepos has morning and evening rush hours. In the mornings a nation of squirrel monkeys (*Saimiri oerstedii*, the "organ grinder monkeys") migrate down the mountain and pass chattering through the town enroute to their foraging sites near the beach. In the evening they move back up the mountain to their nesting sites, sweeping again through Quepos. You are standing in an open-air restaurant late in the afternoon. The squirrel monkeys pass through on their homeward commute, jumping chair-to-chair and onto lamp-posts. Some of the jumpers are mothers with babies hanging tightly onto their backs.

When tourism became the dominant industry here after World War II, the car traffic produced carnage in squirrel monkey nation. The people of Quepos strung ropes high across the roads, the monkeys use them as bridges, and the number of squirrel monkeys run over by cars has dropped to approximately zero. The people of Quepos care about the wildlife, and are proactive in keeping their town hospitable not only to tourists, but also to monkeys, birds, sloths, coati ("like a raccoon with an attitude"–Leo) and other species who were here first. As the Chacóns discovered in San Gerado de Dota, intact wildlife habitat is good for the wildlife *and* the economy. Tourists come here because they want to see nature as close to its original state as possible. They crave reality, not a staged Disneyfied world of robotic animals.

Costa Rica has a viable network of national parks because this small nation can afford them. When the Spanish came to this part of Central America, despite the name they gave it they found no gold and moved on. Costa Rica thereby avoided much of the tragedy of Latin America, where in country after country a few dozen families own practically all the sources of wealth. For decades, Costa Rica has enjoyed a stable democracy and a large middle class.[136] Among Latin American nations it has favorable rates of life expectancy, living standards and literacy. [World Bank Statistics(2015)] Other than a national guard, Costa Rica does not have a standing army.[137] A 1962 treaty exists between the USA and Costa Rica for "providing defense articles and services to Costa Rica for the purpose of contributing to its internal security." [Treaties Between the US and Costa Rica(1962)] This has freed resources for education and health care, contributing to Costa Rica's stability and internal security and posing no threat to its neighbors.[138]

As the Chacóns and the residents of Quepos have shown, strategies for keeping the environment approximately intact must make scientific *and* economic *and* cultural sense if they are to work. If the world's environmental sustainability problems are going to be solved, young people around the world who are passionate about solving them need to find each other. Such a network "forms another kind of ecosystem, a habitat for the growth of ideas and awareness of stewardship." [Finkenbinder and Neuenschwander(2001)]

The astrohabitat course that Leo and I taught in Costa Rica is merely one of several directed study opportunities that the QERC field station offers students from our university and others. But the expenses of traveling to Costa Rica can prevent qualified students from going there. In 2000, Professor and Imme Dyson learned of our Costa Rica field station and its mission. They endowed a scholarship fund to help defray travel expenses for students who wish to study and conduct research at the QERC. The Dyson Travel Scholarship has enabled several dozen students to go there and become part of the solution to environmental and sociological challenges.

---

[136]Other democracies could learn a thing or two from the Costa Ricans. National election day is an official holiday, so everyone goes to the polls. Voting is a family excursion. Even the children vote—their votes do not count officially, but the children's vote is reported and the practice encourages attitudes of responsibility and habits of participation.

[137]When a platoon of pelicans flying in V-formation patrols the coast, the locals point and say "the Costa Rican air force."

[138]US military spending that stands behind treaties such as the one with Costa Rica, and produces results visible in the well-being of the populace, makes sense.

For Professor Dyson's generosity and the support of his family we are deeply grateful.

> *21 February 2001*
> *Dear Professor Dyson,*
> *Just a quick note to let you know what's happening with the Dyson QERC Scholarship. We had five highly qualified candidates apply this first time... By university policy the interest earnings of the fund will not be available until the elapse of one year, but we are going to go ahead and kick in some departmental budget to get the program off the ground this spring without touching the Fund itself this round. That way we can hit the ground running. You gave us the kick to get this part going.*
> *The QERC lab/classroom/dormitory building is essentially finished. There's a VIP room in it with a reservation already on hold for you and Imme!*
> *Thank you again for your interest in what we're doing here and in Costa Rica. I'll also send you information about what the students will be doing in Costa Rica this spring and summer.*
> *George's boats are pretty amazing. It's nice to now have a picture of the six-seat boat that you mention in "Back to Earth."... Beautiful craftsmanship.... Lots of similarities in attitudes and caring, in crafting quantum field theory and baidarkas.*
> *Warm regards, Dwight*
>
> *1 May 2001*
> *Dear Professor Dyson,*
> *Once again as we near the semester's end, our Science, Technology, and Society class sends greetings to you and your family. We also have some questions...*
> *Before going to the questions, I want to thank you again for your support of our work in Costa Rica. Your generosity helped three students visit our Quetzal Education Research Center in the Costa Rican high-altitude cloud forest. In addition, [they] visited the Arenal Volcano area and the Pacific coast at Manuel Antonio National Park. I have some mementos of the trip to send you and they will follow shortly.*
>
> *10 June 2001*
> *Dear Dwight,*
> *... I also have a cheerful postcard from [university development VP] Michael Crabtree in Costa Rica reporting the official opening of QERC. Please give him my thanks and congratulations. I guess the public-relations people hadn't noticed that you were already teaching there in March. Anyhow, I am happy that*

the project now has official status and formal blessing from the Costa Rica government.

20 November 2001
Dear Professor Dyson,
I am mailing to you this evening two boxes laden with treasures for you.... There are two sweatshirts and two t-shirts from the Quetzal Education Research Center in Costa Rica....

More recent projects conducted by students who have gone to the QERC on a Dyson scholarship include[139] a 2011 study by Macey Lawson to assess pollination in fruit production in the upper Rio Savegre valley. That same year Matthew Wilkowske monitored the microclimate of the Talamanca range. In collaboration with the University of Oklahoma and *Parque Nacional Los Quetzales* the microclimate data will be used to shape local conservation policy and monitor climate change.

In 2013, Becca Cossel studied the effects on mammal wildlife of varying the flash level of infrared trail cameras. This project, in collaboration with Point Loma Nazarene University, was part of the first systematic study of large mammals in the Rio Savegre watershed, a buffer zone for the mammal wildlife populations in the contiguous forest that extends to Panama.

Also in 2013 Dan Wilkin carried out a predation risk assessment for the colorful male lizard *Sceloporus malachiticus*. In 2015, Natalie Lemay studied the spatial ecology of that same species, while Chase Yager followed ground-dwelling arthropod communities in the primary and secondary forests.

While at the QERC, the students become part of the local community. When they return home, we have reason to think their vision of global community has been enhanced.

Sustainability—Or Not

In the 1980s, the United Nations commissioned a study of global environmental sustainability. A former Prime Minister of Norway, Madame Gro Harlem Brundtland, was named chairperson. The Brundtland Commission defined environmental sustainability in terms of a principle: "Meeting the needs of the present without compromising the ability of future generations to meet their own needs." [Brundtland *et al.*(1987)] The definition implies

[139]See "Research" and "Study Abroad" at the QERC website, http://qerc.org.

that if you must have a mahogany door, that's fine—provided you are not depriving future generations of mahogany. In other words, Thou shalt not steal from thy grandchildren.

Our industrialized society's insatiable appetite for petroleum offers an obvious example of unsustainable behavior. Globally about eighty million barrels are consumed every day. The global rate of deforestation displays another unsustainable behavior. According to a recent United Nations report, [UN FAO(2015)] the global deforestation rate during 2000-2010 was about 13 million hectares (32 milllion acres) per year, one acre per second. The timber going down today includes primary forest that was heretofore unmolested by human activity.

Of course, some trees are replanted, as in Oregon with its vast stands of corporate-owned pine and Douglas fir. Such forests serve an important purpose—most of us live in wood-framed dwellings. But like the Central American plantations that raise bananas, palm oil, mahogany and teak, these stands of timber are green deserts—they are crops, not ecosystems. Left alone, it would take five hundred years to restore the ecosystem—assuming the seed bank survives. [Finkenbinder and Neuenschwander(2001)]

In the long view, the lack of environmentally sustainable economies leads to social problems whose costs are vast but not as quantifiable as the number of board feet in an acre of timber. Costa Rica faces on its northern border an immigration crisis similar to the one faced by the USA on its southern border. When we turn the corner in Los Chiles to meet the boats for the Rio Frio float trip, we pass an immigration office. Every time we drove by, a long line of Nicaraguans were waiting in line for documents. Nicaragua and Haiti must import rice because they cannot feed their own populations. There are political and economic reasons for such endemic distress—histories of exploitation and interference by colonial powers, and after independence a tragic parade of corrupt dictators and civil wars. Environmental contributions to abject poverty can be seen in the destruction of forests. When flying out of San José in the daytime, you can tell when the aircraft passes from Costa Rican to Nicaraguan airspace—the landscape below goes from green to brown. After being deforested the coastal plain soil becomes hard-baked lateralite and mountain watersheds become mudslides.

On our way to Los Chiles, we drive across the northern Costa Rica plains. The locals call it "McDonaldland." Starting around 1960, in response to the explosive growth of the fast food hamburger market in North

America, much Central American low-elevation forest was bulldozed. The oak and teak and mahogany trees were piled up and burned to make pastures for cattle. The hamburgers were proudly advertised as "American-raised beef." The ads neglected to mention that it was Brahma cattle from Central America, not Herefords from Texas, where much of the beef was raised.

In "Auguries of Innocence" William Blake laments such losses:

> *...A robin redbreast in a cage*
> *Puts all heaven in a rage...*
> *A dog starved at his master's gate*
> *Predicts the ruin of the state.*
> *A horse misused upon the road*
> *Calls to heaven for human blood...*
> *A skylark wounded in the wing,*
> *A cherubim doth cease to sing...*

While planning this chapter, I hesitated to mention the town of Quepos by name. No small group of tourists who practice appreciation and awareness will trash the place; but *en masse* the sheer numbers of them will. For now Quepos coexists harmoniously with the monkeys and the sloths. But I am worried. The last time I was in Quepos I saw billboards promoting new gated communities marketed to Americans looking for retirement paradise. Back in the States I have seen cable TV commercials promoting retirement communities in Costa Rica. I do not begrudge anyone who seeks a pleasant retirement in Costa Rica. If I could afford it I might be tempted to be one of them myself. But a flood of North Americans bringing money and a taste for the conveniences they left behind will transform a unique place like Quepos into just another Aspen or Jackson Hole. Does the First Commandment apply to the God of Convenience?

For a landscape, could being seen as a paradise be the kiss of death?[140] One feels the urgency of Thoreau, who wrote "I was in haste to buy it [the Hollowell farm], before the proprietor finished getting out some rocks, cutting down the hollow apple trees,...or, in short, had made any more of his improvements." [Thoreau(1960)][57]

Professor and Imme Dyson appreciate unspoiled places. The January 2009 Dyson Family Chronicle described their visit in 2008 to the Galápagos

---

[140]I often play in class "The Last Resort" by the Eagles (Asylum, 1977). The last lines go "They called it paradise / I don't know why / Call someplace paradise / Kiss it goodbye..."

Islands, to celebrate their golden wedding anniversary (where they made friends because of a lost suitcase). "In May, the islands were green and food was abundant for birds and reptiles after some heavy rains...." The Chronicle described how 97% of the Galápagos is national park, and the remaining 3% was occupied before the park was established in 1959. The number of settlers remained small for forty years, but now that this remaining 3% has been opened for development, people are "pouring into" it in large numbers. "It is the settlers and not the tourists who threaten to disturb the natural ecology of the islands."

On the various islands Imme and Freeman walked among albatrosses, boobies, penguins and scarlet-breasted firgate birds...

...Enough variety to keep us happy for seven days of walking.
The most dramatic event happened when we were cruising on the boat one evening. An Orca whale was swimming close alongside the boat, immediately underneath us while we stood at the edge of the deck. Suddenly a big sea-turtle appeared in front of the whale and the whale bit it in half. The sea turned red, and in a few seconds about fifty frigate birds appeared out of nowhere, circling over the bloody patch and dipping into it for scraps. Nature is beautiful but she is also cruel.

The following April we sent a note of thanks to Professor Dyson for the Chronicle. His response showed the Dyson clan to be looking ahead to their next adventure:

> *17 April 2009*
> *Dear Dwight,*
> *Thanks to you and the students for your friendly response to my little newsletter. The next newsletter will be full of another adventure, a family reunion at the Russian space-launch center in Baikonur, Kazakhstan. My wife and I came back from this trip three weeks ago and are still absorbing the impact of it. The Russian space culture is radically different from ours. For us space-travel is an adventure. For them it is a vocation....*

In the fall of 2008, Esther Dyson trained as a back-up cosmonaut for the Soyouz TMA-14 mission to the International Space Station. The scheduled cosmonaut retained his seat, but the Dysons met in Kazakhstan anyway to watch the launch—its not every family that has a cosmonaut daughter!

Esther's cosmonaut training points in the direction of Professor Dyson's thoughts. The gray technologies of the Soyuz vehicle and International

Space Station are stepping stones to humanity colonizing other regions of the solar system—and beyond. "The Greening of the Galaxy" envisions how biological diversity can be adapted, through accelerated evolution by conscious selection, to other environments beyond Earth. Instead of having to always take metal pods to Mars and seal themselves inside it, perhaps human colonists will eventually use green technology to genetically engineer their eyes and lungs to walk bare-faced on the Martian surface.

Harmony and Sanity

"If we are not crazy, and we will assume we are not, why is it that humanity seems determined to spiral ever faster towards self-destruction?" –Richard Leakey and Roger Lewin[141]

In "The Greening of the Galaxy" Professor Dyson writes that as humanity expands to other systems across the galaxy, insane behaviors will be weeded out, for "Sanity is, in its essence, nothing more than the ability to live in harmony with nature's laws." Linking sanity to living in harmony with nature's laws offers an irresistible opportunity to provoke thought.

In our fast-paced, consumptive, image-conscious lifestyle that sees mankind's purpose to be the aquisition of more stuff, one can present the case that our society fails to live in harmony with nature's laws. If that is so, then perhaps by Professor Dyson's definition our society is insane. Let the prosecutor make the case for insanity. The defense will raise objections.

Although everyone knows our economy depends on non-renewable fossil fuels, attempts to introduce sustainable alternatives bring out fervent opposition. For example, in the rural communities that lie within a day's drive of Oklahoma City, energy companies are building "wind farms," vast arrays of windmills that turn electric generators. Although the giant spinning blades kill hundreds of thousands of bats and birds every year[142] this is an otherwise clean energy source that will last as long as the winds blow. But few want to see these giant propellers looming over their back fence, and the soothing proposals of the companies that build them are met by howls of opposition.

The frustration of the protestors goes beyond the prospect of these giant whirlybirds changing the landscape while sending power to distant Florida. The real frustration is that the shots seem to be called by strangers from

---

[141][Leakey and Lewin(1978)][10]

[142]In a 13-to-15 mph wind, the tips of the turbine blades move over 120 mph, and top 180 mph in strong winds. The largest turbine blades sweep out an area of about an acre.

afar who come with money to buy influence and steer events the way they want them to go—and there is little that ordinary people, to whom this place is home, can do about it. I empathize with the opposition's distress about the disappearance of original landscapes. Photographer David Plowden summarized it well in his 2007 interview when discussing fifty years of photographs collected into his book, *Vanishing Point*: "No one a hundred years from now will recognize the America that I show in my photographs." [Gordon and Plowden(2007)], [Plowden(2007)] These events remind me of a similar phenomenon that I witnessed when living in Phoenix during the construction of a nearby nuclear power plant. Protests were a frequent occurrence. The protestors were motivated by authentic concern for the environment. But the defense could jump in to ask the protestors, in Phoenix and in Oklahoma, "While your concerns deserve a hearing, how many electrical appliances are you willing to do without? You can't have it both ways."

> *1 May 1998*
> *Dear Professor Dyson,*
> *...After fossil fuels are depleted, will nuclear energy be our primary energy source? Thank you once again for touching our lives....*

> *2 May 1998*
> *Dear Dwight and Class,*
> *...I see no reason to rule out nuclear energy as a major source of power after the oil is gone. But is likely that solar energy will be the primary source, because it is more abundant and distributed more evenly over the earth. Solar energy has many advantages in flexibility and adaptability to local conditions. At the moment solar energy is more expensive than nuclear energy, but in the long run solar energy will probably be cheaper. And solar energy is most abundant in the tropics where most of the people live.*
> *...Please give my greetings to the students and tell them I feel honored that they read my stuff. Yours ever, Freeman*

Wind energy is indirect solar energy. But non-nuclear alternatives to fossil fuel are so far a small factor in the total energy picture. Meanwhile, demand for energy continues to grow. Perhaps we are content to let future generations fend for themselves, as we bequeath to them a ride on a path that seems headed towards a collision with reality. Could this be the onset of insanity?

The prosecution rests and we bring the case before Professor Dyson. The class of the spring 2014 semester suggested to him that perhaps our society is insane. In our question, we explained our reasoning.

> *24 April 2014*
> *Dear Professor Dyson,*
> *I hope the first half of your 91st year has been one of joy, time with family, many conversations with grandchildren, interesting work to do, and new adventures.*
> *Once again our STS class risks wearing out our welcome by sending you some questions. If you have a few moments to answer some of them, we would be grateful....*
> *...What social reforms will be necessary if nuclear energy turns out to be our only long-term energy source that can provide the quantity of energy needed to maintain national and global economies?*
> *In class we discussed environmental sustainability issues. For example, at present rates of consumption the USA goes through 8 billion barrels of oil (the reserve thought to be under the Arctic National Wildlife Refuge) about every 400 days. Clearly our dependence on fossil fuel is not sustainable. The business-driven response has been to look for more fossil fuel, at least for the time being.... Meanwhile, wind power is very controversial in this part of the country, as windmills seem to be popping up everywhere, resulting in citizens committees, town meetings, and passionate letters to the editors of newspapers. Everyone wants cheap electricity, but no one wants a windmill or a nuclear reactor in their back yard. Curtailing our consumption of electricity, or pricing it to reflect its true costs (including, for example, light pollution) does not seem to be in the cards anytime soon. Everyone wants cheap power but no one wants the costs to the landscape that go with it. In the long view we can't have it both ways. These discussions occurred under the motif of one of your lines from the chapter "The Greening of the Galaxy:" sanity, in its essence, is living in harmony with nature's laws. By that definition, our society is insane.*

To our surprise, Professor Dyson strongly disagreed with us. His reply showed that the definition of insanity can be approached from a larger perspective. Significantly, he puts people first.

> *28 April 2014*
> *Dear Dwight and Students,*
> *Thank you very much for your questions. These are good questions and the discussions that came along with them are very helpful. You have already gone deeply into each of them. I*

*will disagree with some of your opinions, but I do not expect to
change your minds....*

*...What social reforms will be necessary to provide us with a per-
manent and ample supply of energy?ˉ Here I disagree strongly
with your discussion of the energy problem. I disagree particularly with your last sentence, where you say our society is
insane. On the contrary, I think we are handling the energy
problem much better than we are handling other problems such
as poverty and inequality and gun-violence and education and
public health. The obsession with energy is distracting attention
from these more serious problems.*

*As I see it, nuclear energy is unimportant, a minor player in the
energy game, not as good as its advocates claim, not as bad as
its enemies claim. There are two major players, fossil fuels and
solar energy. Fossil fuels are ample for at least the next hundred
years and are allowing China and India to become rich. Solar
energy is enormously abundant and will give us a permanent
supply of energy as soon as we develop the technology to use it
cheaply. I would be surprised if it takes as long as a hundred
years to make solar energy cheap and available to everyone.*

*So my answer to your question is, no social reforms are needed
to deal wisely with energy. Social reforms are needed to deal
with the more serious problems, especially with inequality. Political actions to make fossil fuels more expensive make inequality worse.*

Yours ever, Freeman

Professor Dyson's definition of insanity in "The Greening of the Galaxy"
has proved more provocative than we originally imagined it would be. In
his writings and interviews he frames such issues in terms of a disagreement about values, represented by two groups he calls "naturalists" and
"humanists." In his book *The Scientist as Rebel*, when discussing humanity's relationship with nature Professor Dyson describes what he means by
naturalists and humanists:

*Naturalists believe that nature knows best. For them the highest value is to
respect the natural order of things. Any gross human disruption of the natural
environment is evil. Excessive burning of fossil fuels is evil. Changing nature's
desert, either the Sahara desert or the ocean desert, into a managed ecosystem
where giraffes or tuna fish may flourish, is likewise evil. Nature knows best,
and anything we do to improve upon Nature will only bring trouble.*

*The humanist ethic begins with the belief that humans are an essential part
of nature. Through human minds the biosphere has acquired the capacity to*

steer its own evolution, and now we are in charge. Humans have the right and the duty to reconstruct nature so that humans and the biosphere can both survive and prosper. For humanists, the highest value is the harmonious coexistence between humans and nature. The greatest evils are poverty, underdevelopment, unemployment, disease, and hunger, all the conditions that deprive people of opportunities and limit their freedoms. The human ethic accepts an increase of carbon dioxide in the atmosphere as a small price to pay if worldwide development can alleviate the miseries of the poorer half of humanity. The humanist ethic accepts the responsibility to guide the evolution of the planet. [Dyson(2006)][65]

This partitioning of attitudes into "naturalist" and "humanist" has been helpful to the students and to me personally. It helps us articulate the poles of conflict that make life interesting and bewildering. All my life I have tried to reconcile my naturalist and humanist sides. I love to ride motorcycles on back roads, but regret the intrusion of those roads into the habitat of the wild creatures who were there first. I love working on antique cars, but lament the environmental damage done by the sheer number of cars that are driven daily. Perhaps the dilemma can be resolved with a fulcrum word, harmony.

Perhaps humanists and naturalists can find common ground in the maxim "the highest value is the harmonious coexistence between humans and nature." Two-lane roads winding through forests are harmonious; wide swaths of interstate highways that cut down hills to fill scenic valleys are not. Raising buffalo on prairie grassland is harmonious; destroying forests for pasturage in steep mountain canyons is not. Using a car for weekend outings is harmonious; two hundred million cars each carrying one person on a thirty mile daily commute is not. Stringing ropes across tropical highways for monkey bridges is harmonious; bulldozing their habitat for gated communities marketed to rich invaders is not. Reducing one's electricity consumption is harmonious; having a television set in every room of the house while protesting the construction of wind-powered generators or nuclear power plants is not. Cafés and coffee shops and stores in repurposed old buildings are harmonious; a hundred and sixty thousand cookie-cutter franchise outlets strategically located to intercept you at every major intersection is not.

At the outset of the STS course we observed that human beings are part of nature, not detached from it. Humanity being part of nature originally meant to us that we are subject to nature's realities. If we poison ourselves with pollutants or overwhelm the planet's carrying capacity, nature will not suspend its laws to get us off the hook. But as Professor Dyson has emphasized, being part of nature also means we can reconstruct the world, with consequences for lives and species and times beyond our own. Whether we choose to be naturalists or humanists or something in between, the challenge is to proceed harmoniously, so that "humans and the biosphere can both survive and prosper."

The Chacón family's experience illustrates that harmony can be found if we are willing to imagine other ways of doing things, showing respect for lives besides our own. The beauty of the Chacón's model of environmental sustainability can be seen in how they manage to keep most of the original cloud forest ecosystem intact while making a comfortable income from it for their families. At least in the valley of San Gerado de Dota, they have managed to be naturalists and humanists at the same time.

Long-term vision must harmoniously meet the human needs of today. If my family is hungry, I will go hunting and wood-gathering, regardless of the legal status or environmental importance of the forest and its wildlife. To set aside vast tracts of land for national parks and wildlife refuges means society can afford to let them be. Fossil fuels will make China and India rich over the few decades while the level of carbon dioxide and sulfur and soot in the atmosphere will continue to rise. But if after those decades their populations are well-to-do (and if any forests are left), they may have the disposable incomes and the vision to create more systems of parks and preserves than they would if subsistence farming remains the norm. Our grandchildren shall see.

Professor Dyson's emphasis on the problems of poverty and injustice being more important than energy supplies leads to another thought about the past connecting to the future. Problems with energy began with the Industrial Revolution. Problems with poverty and social injustice are far older. The energy problem, though large, is small compared to the problems of poverty and injustice.

The STS class following the one that sent our "insanity letter" wanted to raise the question again, and thus broadened it.

> *6 November 2014*
> *Dear Professor Dyson,*
> *...The STS class last April asked you what social reforms will be necessary if nuclear energy turns out to be our only long-term energy resource that can meet the needs of national and global economies. That question grew out of our discussions of*

environmental sustainability, including our dependence on non-renewable fossil fuels. Since our economies are dependent on a resource that will no longer be available within another human lifetime or two, we wondered last April if such dependence qualifies as "insanity," given the definition of insanity that you offered in "The Greening of the Galaxy:" "Sanity is, in its essence, nothing more than the ability to live in harmony with nature's laws."

*Your reply was very instructive because you put people first....
You went on to describe how fossil fuels are enabling China and India to become rich, and in the meantime we should develop solar energy so that when fossil fuels are depleted we will have sustainable, adequate energy for all. You said "Political actions to make fossil fuels more expensive make inequality worse." Point well taken.*

We appreciate that you put people first. We understand too that preserving the environment means that today's immediate needs must already be met, so that we can afford to set some parts of nature aside. Henry David Thoreau expressed it well when he wrote in Walden, "A man is rich in proportion to the number of things which he can afford to leave alone."[143] Thus the problems of poverty and environment form a strongly coupled system.

At last we come to this question from the Fall 2014 class: We would like to enlarge the scope of last spring's question about environment and insanity. We see ongoing destruction of forests, continuing pollution, over-fishing in the oceans, loss of wildlife habitat and biological diversity, and so on. At what point will our consumptive, short-sighted lifestyle tip over into insanity as you have defined it?

3 December 2014
Dear Dwight and students,
...I answer this question the same way as I answered your question in April. I think you are wrong in seeing our life-style as only destructive and short-sighted. In the real world, we are doing a lot of destruction and a lot of preservation. The media give us a false impression by giving us only the bad news and not the good news. One of the advantages of being ninety years old is that I can see the good news more clearly.

I happen to live in New Jersey, a state that is heavily populated and heavily industrialized. It is proud to give itself the name, "The Garden State." Fifty years ago, visitors to New Jersey considered the name to be a joke. On the main highway driving

---

[143][Thoreau(1960)][56]

South from New York, there is an enormous oil refinery. Fifty years ago, the whole region near the refinery stank of sulfurous fumes. Visitors had to shut their car windows and drive through as fast as possible. Now the refinery is still there but the stink is gone. The Garden State is no longer a joke. The state has learned how to clean up a bad mess. All that it takes is time and money and political will.

The forests in New Jersey are also growing. A hundred years ago, the natural forests had been destroyed, mostly to grow hay for the horses in nineteenth-century cities. Now the hayfields are mostly growing back to forests, and the animals and birds that live in forests are returning. In the last ten years, a substantial population of bears has returned to the state. At the same time, a substantial population of humans has returned to small-scale farming as a hobby. Friends of ours near to Princeton are raising cows on grass, producing meat that tastes better than meat from animals raised on feed-lots in Iowa. Other friends are campaigning to preserve wetlands and bird sanctuaries. I do not see any signs of our population tipping over into insanity.

Of course, rich people do better than poor people in caring for the environment. That is why the worst destruction of nature is happening in the poorest countries. The poor people are not insane. They only lack the time and money that are needed to save forests and fish.

Thank you once more for a good set of questions....

Happy Christmas to you and the class! Yours ever, Freeman.

This question about whether our society is insane has been very stimulating to classroom discussion. We also see, again, the importance of consulting with the tribe's elders, for walking with Grandfather.

One might argue that our society *would* be insane if we never changed course, cutting and slashing with no regard to consequences. But while some sectors of society seem to do that, other sectors push back. For every Monsanto and Wal-Mart there is also a Greenpeace and a Sierra Club (although they do not all have comparable finances). American society, in particular, seems to operate in the Pearl Harbor mode of response: Despite warnings, little is done until the crisis strikes, but when it strikes we respond with everything we have. While not a reassuring strategy, in the past it has been effective. We can only hope that our grandchildren, and their grandchildren, will be able to enjoy starry skies and pristine landscapes that we have been privileged to experience. As Professor Dyson observed, our sense of brotherhood with all mankind is an anchor "essential to our sanity." [Dyson(1979a)][169]

> It is right it should be so;
> Man was made for joy and woe;
> And when this we rightly know,
> Thro' the world we safely go.
> –William Blake

Fig. 12.3   *Collage that was Sierra P.'s "STS Museum" project.*   (photo courtesy of Sierra P.)

13 "Why Should I Care?"

Discussions about Values and Ethics

"It occurred to me that there is no manual that deals with the real business of motorcycle maintenance, the most important aspect of all. Caring about what you are doing..."
–Robert Pirsig[144]

***

One evening about eight years ago as we were wrapping up a class discussion on unsustainable practices, a young lady raised her hand and said, "I get it, but I also need to play devil's advocate. An oil spill on caribou habitat in Alaska does not affect my everyday routines, so why should I care?" That was a fair question. It was raised about one minute before class was to dismiss. We could not do it justice in the little time remaining that evening, so I suggested that we all think about it and discuss it as our first topic at our next meeting. The next class meeting saw a lively discussion. Hands popped up and together we converged on three broad reasons why we should care. Similar reasons have been articulated by other classes since then. They may be grouped under the broad headings of (1) Survival, (2) Quality of Life, and (3) Ethics.

Survival

A pragmatic reason why we should care is the self-serving one of survival: the Earth does not need us, but we need the Earth. If for whatever reason the Earth's lithosphere were to become too poisoned for our survival, this planet would continue spinning on its axis while orbiting the sun. After a few million years, life would re-organize into some new form. For a few billion more years, the Earth and life will go on with or without us. If we want to be part of life's story for a long time, we had better treat this oasis with respect.

Quality of Life

The quality of life reason emerged in response to the question, "In what kind of world do we want to live?" What does "quality of life" mean, and

---
[144][Pirsig(1999)][34–36]

how should it guide our actions? Here we are not talking about medical care or transportation or communication. Nobody wants to go back to surgery as practiced in Civil War field hospitals, and other than historical re-enactment enthusiasts, nobody wants to creak across the Great Plains in a covered wagon. Here we are asking about the long-term consequences for ourselves, and for our descendants, that come from our short-term lifestyle choices. A *Newsweek* essay, "Once Unique, Soon a Place Like Any Other" illustrates the concern. Essayist Abe Whaley lamented

> It's heartbreaking to watch the Appalachia I love disappear under endless condos and cabins.... It seems that no ridge is too steep, no mountaintop too high, no creek too pristine to bulldoze and build on... Its not the single-family homes that are so irritating... What bothers me is the way developers feel the need to put a subdivision on the most beautiful piece of mountain farmland they can find.... It is obvious that nothing is sacred....[145]

You see it everywhere—another stand of woods bulldozed, another meadow paved over, another orchard leveled, another historic farmhouse with two dozen century-old oak trees cleared away to make room for...what?—another big-box store with a parking lot vast enough to land an airplane? How many more of those do we *need*? Of course, they are not built because they are needed. They are built because they generate income for somebody. Along the way they provide jobs. But the trees we used to climb when we were kids, the stream where we built miniature dams out of rocks, the open spaces where we used to play impromptu soccer games are gone—which means our grandchildren cannot do these things—and replaced with a line item on some distant corporate spreadsheet.

On the other hand, the ubiquitous big-box and dollar stores make accessible to struggling families some basic household decency. They continue a trend that began in the Industrial Revolution where, amid its cruelties and gritty ugliness, thousands of families were lifted out of impoverished rural cottages surrounded by seas of manure and mud, as Jacob Bronowski reminds us:

> It is comic to think that cotton underwear and soap could work a transformation in the lives of the poor. Yet these simple things—coal in an iron range, glass in the windows, a choice of food—were a wonderful rise in the standard of life and health. [Bronowski(1973)][279]

---

[145] Abe Whaley, "Once Unique, Soon a Place Like Any Other," *Newsweek*, Nov. 14, 2005, p. 13.

From a business point of view the developers know what they are doing: Build and they will come—especially if it's ten minutes closer. "Build it and they will come" succeeds because there are more of them to come this year than there were last year. Population growth drives oil consumption and greenhouse emissions and urban sprawl and the loss of wildlife habitat. Twenty-five years from now my grandchildren will be looking for places to live.

The world population stands at about 7.4 billion at this writing, and is projected to exceed nine billion by mid-century. [Geohive.com(2015)] Although the global population continues to increase, the over-all rate of growth has slowed.[146] However, the population grows the fastest in societies that can least afford it. [Geohive.com(2015)][147]

Insect on the Leaf

Anyone completing a university education should be acquainted with the basic arithmetic of exponential growth. When a population's growth rate is proportional to the population, then the time for the population to double is determined. A growth rate of 2% per year implies a doubling time of 35 years; at 7% per year the doubling time is 10 years. Generally, if the growth rate is n percent per year, then the doubling time is $70/n$ years.[148] So long as the growth rate stays constant, so does the doubling time. If at time zero the population equals 1 unit, then the population after one doubling time is 2 units; 4 units at two doubling times, then 8, 16, 32, 64, 128, 256 units, and so on with the elapse of each successive doubling time.

Let us put exponential growth in a finite environment into a visualizable context.[149] Imagine a one-celled microorganism that multiplies by dividing. Suppose this species of creature undergoes a cell division every minute. Thus the doubling time is one minute. Let us put one of these little guys

---

[146]In 2015 the global growth rate is 1.132%, giving a doubling time of about 61.2 years. To go from 4 billion to 5 billion took 13 years (1974–1987), 5 to 6 billion 12 years (1987–1999); 6 to 7 billion back to 13 years (1999–2012). The projections say the population will go from 9 to 10 billion in the 22 years from 2040 to 2062.

[147]For example, the number of births per woman in 2015 stands at 1.48 in Italy and 1.66 in China; 6.86 in Mali and 7.58 in Niger.

[148]More accurately, the doubling time is $69.3/n$, because the natural logarithm of 2 is about 0.693. This is also the mathematics of a fission chain reaction, although the doubling time for the human population measured in years instead of microseconds.

[149]I am indebted to the late Professor Albert Bartlett of the University of Colorado who popularized this illustration.

inside a bottle at 11:00 a.m., and adjust the size of the bottle so it will be filled one hour later, at 12:00 noon. When is the bottle half full?

Most students, unconsciously assuming linear growth, guess the bottle will be half full at 11:30. But a doubling time of one minute means the bottle will be half full at 11:59. It will be a quarter full at 11:58, and one-eighth full at 1:57. It takes fifty-seven minutes to go from a single individual to the bottle being one-eighth full, and only three minutes to fill the remaining seven-eighths of the bottle!

Suppose that in the society of these little creatures, their version of Greenpeace sounds the alarm at 11:57. The business communities and political leaders shout them down, saying "What are you worried about?– we have been here for fifty-seven lifetimes and still have seven-eighths of our world open for development!"

If this society is to survive until 12:01, they will need to find a second bottle. To make it to 12:02, they will need two more bottles, then four more to get through the next minute, and so on. In the absence of an unlimited supply of bottles, this cannot continue. Likewise, the problem of overpopulation on Earth will not be solved by colonizing Mars. If we do not control our population deliberately, Nature will, and her methods will not be pretty. Before we reach that day, do we really want to live in a world saturated with people? What will "quality of life" mean then?

But the answer to overpopulation is *not* genocide or infanticide. As we speak of an overcrowded Earth, let us not forget What—or Who— the increase is. Every single life is precious; everyone has an equal right to be here. The values at stake were beautifully articulated by Charles Dickens in *A Christmas Carol*, first published in 1843. The story begins with Ebenezer Scrooge hard at work in his office on Christmas Eve. He is visited by two gentlemen. "Scrooge or Marley?" they ask, referring to their list. Scrooge identifies himself, saying that his partner, Jacob Marley, passed away seven years ago, this very night. No doubt, says one of the gentleman, his liberality is well represented in his surviving partner. "At the ominous word 'liberality,' Scrooge frowned, and shook his head..."

"At this festive time of year, Mr. Scrooge," said the gentleman,...
"it is more than usually desirable that we should make some slight provision for the poor and destitute, who suffer greatly at the present time. Many thousands are in want of common necessaries; hundreds of thousands are in want of common comforts, sir."
"Are there no prisons?" asked Scrooge.
"Plenty of prisons," said the gentleman...

> "And the Union workhouses?" demanded Scrooge. "Are they still in operation?"
> "They are. Still," returned the gentleman, "I wish I could say they were not.... What shall I put you down for?"
> "Nothing!" Scrooge replied.
> "You wish to be anonymous?"
> "I wish to be left alone," said Scrooge. "...I help support the establishments I have mentioned: they cost enough, and those who are badly off must go there."
> "Many can't go there; and many would rather die."
> "If they would rather die," said Scrooge, "they had better do it, and decrease the surplus population...."

That night Marley's Ghost visits Scrooge. The Ghost informs Scrooge that he will be visited by three Spirits. By showing Scrooge his former self and long-forgotten youthful hopes, the first Spirit starts a small tentative thawing of Scrooge's icy heart. The second Spirit takes Scrooge unseen to the hardscrabble home of his clerk, Bob Cratchit. Bob comes cheerfully through the door carrying on his shoulder one of his little children: "Alas for Tiny Tim, for he bore a little crutch, and had his limbs supported by an iron frame!" After keenly watching the family enjoy Christmas together, Scrooge asks the Spirit if Tiny Tim will live. The Spirit says that if these shadows remain unaltered by the future "No other of my race will find him here; the child will die." "Oh no, kind Spirit!" exclaimed Scrooge. "Say he will be spared." The Spirit retorted, "If he be like to die, he had better do it, and decrease the surplus population."

"Scrooge hung his head to hear his own words quoted by the Spirit, and was overcome with penitence and grief." The Spirit lets Scrooge have it:

> "Man," said the Ghost, "if man you be at heart, not adamant, forbear that wicked cant until you have discovered What the surplus is, and Where it is... Oh God! to hear the Insect on the leaf pronouncing on the too much life among his hungry brothers in the dust!"

In the Christmas season of 1999 the students asked Professor Dyson about population.

> 7 December 1999
> Dear Professor Dyson,
> On behalf of the Fall '99 Science, Technology, and Society class, we wish you and your family a joyous and meaningful Christmas Season. We hope you will all have a wonderful time together, including ample time to spend with your beautiful grandchildren.

As is our custom (one we hope has not grown burdensome to you), the students have proposed a few questions.... If you can find some time to answer one or two of them, we would be obliged....
1. Do you think the world will naturally take care of overpopulation through plagues and starvation? Medicine continues to prolong life—what do you think the expected life span for humans will be by the year 2050?
2. Why would cloning be considered when were already worried about over-population? What are the long-term implications of cloning for the diversity of humans?

8 December 1999
Dear Dwight,
The questions from your students go immediately to the top of the pile of unanswered letters. The others can wait for a few days longer. Please give the students my greetings and thanks. Here are some off-the-cuff answers....
1. I was delighted to read recently that the average number of children in Mexican families dropped from 7 to 2.5 in the last thirty years. In Italy, the birthrate is so low that the Italians are saying, in a hundred years there will be nobody here but Albanians. Somehow the women of the world are getting the message, you don't have to have a lot of babies. This is the cure for overpopulation, not plagues and starvation.
Medicine increases the average life-span but does not do much to increase the upper limit. Sophocles wrote his last play at the age of ninety. Ninety remains the upper limit for practical purposes. I hope this remains true. The worst thing I can imagine would be if the doctors find a cure for death. On Sunday, we went with our grandsons to sing carols to the patients in the local nursing home, most of them ninety-year-olds stuck there until they die. They loved the boys and the carols, but it is a sad and depressing place. Living longer than ninety is not much fun.
2. Cloning of humans is not a big deal. It may be a preferred option for a small fraction of parents who are unable to get babies by other methods, but it will not change the total population significantly.
The serious problems raised by genetic engineering do not come from cloning but from the genetic manipulation of human embryos. Many parents, not only those who have fertility problems, may want to give their babies a better chance in life by putting in a few extra good genes or taking out a few bad ones, as soon as the technology is available. This could be a severe problem, especially if the good genes are only available to rich

parents. The children of the rich could quickly become a hereditary caste. I recommend the book, "Remaking Eden" by Lee Silver, who discusses the possibilities and the dangers realistically. As Lee Silver remarks, fertility clinics are a huge and profitable branch of medicine all over the world, and the technology is driven forward and paid for by the parents, not by the governments.

When he wrote this letter Professor Dyson was within a week of celebrating his 76th birthday. As I write this, he is approaching his 92nd birthday and is still going strong. He sometimes says he is too old for this or that, but to this day he keeps popping up all over the world, from New Jersey to California, Singapore and Japan to England, still traveling and speaking and writing. The STS students and I wish him well every moment of his life. While we hope we will be doing as well should we live so long, we also hope that, like him, in the evening of our lives we will be able look back with satisfaction to a life well lived, and look ahead with a cheerful spirit of gratitude. His legacy will extend well beyond his mathematics, his physics, and his writings. He is blessed with a loving family. He has friends around the world, including the appreciation and good wishes of some three thousand students who attended a small college in Oklahoma.

I had the pleasure of teasing a nephew and his wife who recently had their fifth child, and said to them "It's projected that the world population will reach nine billion by mid-century. But it's not all up to you." While few should follow their example, everyone would prefer to live in a society where parents have the *freedom* to raise large families. The crucial statistic is the average number of children per family. My nephew's children and the Dyson grandchildren and my grandchildren are growing up in a society where the average number of births per woman is 1.97. [Geohive.com(2015)] Whatever the size of the family, *every* child is a precious gift.

Ethics

"When you come, we die." –Chiparopai (Yuma)[150]

Ethics forms our third reason for why we should care. We frame this reason as another set of questions: When we hold title to a piece of land, do we also own the lives of the creatures already living there? Why do we think we have the right to take the lives of other creatures who value their own

---

[150][McLuhan(1971)][113]

lives? Since we are the ones wielding the chainsaws, what are our ethical responsibilities towards the other lives with whom we share this planet?

One of the saddest examples of sudden and fatal habitat loss that I ever witnessed with my own eyes occurred during my time as an undergraduate student in southern Colorado. The campus sits about two miles east of Interstate 25. In my student days, a two-lane highway carrying traffic east and west connected I-25 to our campus. North of the two-lane highway, between the campus and the Interstate, lived a large population of prairie dogs, or gophers. I often ate lunch in my car, parked at the edge of the parking lot, so I could watch their antics as they popped in and out of their holes and chattered to one another. They were alert, social and active. When you stepped in their direction they dove into their burrows. As far as I could tell, gophers value their lives.

One day the giant earth-moving scrapers came to prairie dog town. Between my arrival at school that morning and my departure that evening the topography was reshaped for a new housing development. The scrapers were that day engaged in unwitting genocide, skimming several inches of topsoil and animal parts into their huge trailers with each pass. That evening the highway connecting our campus to I-25 was heavily covered with the flattened bloody corpses of countless prairie dogs who escaped the scrapers only to be run over by commuter automobiles. I wonder if the university students and faculty, or the nice people living in the lovely homes that now sit west of campus, ever give a passing thought to the costs, besides the economic ones, of those splendid homes and our fine campus.

One of my nephews worked for a housing developer in Colorado Springs. One day I asked him, "When your company buys a piece of untouched land on which to build houses, before sending in the bulldozers do the managers meet around a conference table to discuss the wildlife that was there first?" His answer was as revealing as it was direct: "No. That subject never comes up." This side of the business is not mentioned in the glossy brochures (TAKE ONE) prominently displayed in the smartly staged model homes of Deer Springs.

Most house builders are genuine craftsmen who care deeply about their work. In my student days I worked for some of them. They have an essential role in a society that does not live in tipis. The rest of us want what they have to offer. Like being part of a traffic jam I can shake my fist at the problem, but am part of it. Do we have awareness enough to muster even a little post-mortem regret?

Different Meanings of "Civilization"

The abandoned shot-up 1954 Cadillac in Delamar, Nevada, that was shown early in the semester was not merely a victim of bullets. Before the bullets flew it was already a victim of lack of respect. I suggest that the *attitude* towards the victim that exists in the heart and mind of one who can shoot up a car is not much different from the *attitude* of Nazi officers that shot their victims in Polish forests and the Russian steppe. [Shrier(1961)][953] Of course, the two shootings are not on the same moral plane. Shooting a machine is not murder. But I am suggesting that the *attitudes* of both shooters towards their victims were similar. Before the rifle could be raised and the trigger pulled, both shooters had to convince themselves that their victims were expendable objects. Such attitudes easily transfer to other species, to the ecosystem, to other cultures and peoples.

For example, throughout the nineteenth century US federal policy was to force Native Americans off their ancestral lands and onto reservations. The Indian Removal Act of 1830 during Andrew Jackson's administration forcibly removed the Cherokee, Chickasaw, Choctaw, Muscogee and Seminole peoples to Oklahoma Territory, the Trail of Tears (1831–1838). [Jahoda(1975)][151] The policy of ethnic cleansing tuned to the Great Plains tribes after the Civil War. One tactic was to starve the tribes by exterminating the buffalo. General Philip Sheridan summarized postwar federal policy and his own opinion by saying "Let them kill, skin, and sell until the buffalo is exterminated, as it is the only way to bring lasting peace and allow civilization to advance." [Brown(1971)][265] General Sheridan's concept of civilization stands in stark contrast to that of Luther Standing Bear, a Lakota we met earlier, who lived in both cultures:

The man who sat on the ground in his tipi meditating on life and its meaning, accepting the kinship of all creatures and acknowledging unity with the universe of things was infusing into his being the true essence of civilization. And when native man left off this form of development, his humanization was retarded in growth. [Standing Bear(1933)][250]

---

[151]The Potawatomi refer to their forced removal in 1838 from northern Indiana to Kansas as the "Trail of Death." See "The 1867 Potawatomi Treaty: Encroachment in Potawatomi Land and the Move to Indian Territory" by Kelli Mosteller, *HowNiKan* (newspaper of the Potawatomi nation), March 2015, p. 1.

In front of the classroom, images from the organized bison slaughters of the 1880s give way to contemporary parallels: A scene from the documentary *The Cove* that filmed with hidden cameras the annual dolphin slaughter at Taiji, Japan; [Freeman(2012)] whales thrashing in bloody water beneath an industrial whaling ship....

Abe Whaley lamented that there is nothing sacred. Everything is for sale. "Talk of Heaven! ye disgrace earth!" wrote Thoreau. [Thoreau(1960)][138] An economy of respect would be sustainable if it were founded on an ethic of reverence for *all* lives.

Reverence for Life

By the time he was into his twenties, Albert Schweitzer (1865–1965) had studied theology, earned a PhD in philosophy and an international reputation as a Bach concert organist. As a youth he promised himself that he would pursue his music and philosophy careers until he was thirty. Then he would retool to become a medical missionary and spend the rest of his life in service to others. When he turned 30 he went to medical school. Upon completing his medical degree, in 1913 he was sent to Lembarené, in French Equatorial Africa (now Gabon). There Schweitzer founded a hospital and spent the next five decades, the rest of his life. Today the Albert Schweitzer Hospital still stands as one of the premier medical institutions on the African continent.

Schweitzer's writings on philosophical subjects did not stop when he went to Lembarné. He could no more live without philosophy than Frank Thompson could live without poetry or Freeman Dyson could live without mathematics. After a day in the clinic, in surgery and visiting surrounding villages, Schweitzer wrote books by lamplight.

One of his major literary goals was to write a philosophy of civilization. Long before he left for Africa, Schweitzer sensed that Western civilization was living on its inheritance without being worthy of it; that "progress" was not guaranteed to be always upward and irreversible. The outbreak of World War One made it clear to him that "civilization" had to mean more than technological accomplishment. He struggled to articulate a principle that would serve as a universal foundation for ethics across all cultures.

One day in 1915 while concentrating on his problem during a steamboat journey up the Ogowe River, he was gazing at the life all around him—birds, monkeys, hippos. Suddenly his prepared mind saw a profound connection: "I am a life which wills to live in the midst of life which wills to live." All life struggles to survive, and sentient creatures give every indication of valuing their lives. Schweitzer developed this observation into a philosophy of ethics known as "reverence for life." [Schweitzer and Campion(1949)][156–157] Ethical philosophies have long recognized that human beings should treat one another decently because we share a common humanity. John Donne eloquently summarized this awareness in *Meditations XVII* (1624):

No man is an island, entire of itself; every man is a piece of the continent, a part of the main. If a clod be washed away by the sea, Europe is the less... Any man's death diminishes me, because I am involved in mankind, and therefore never send to know for whom the bells tolls; it tolls for thee.

Schweitzer offers a sweeping generalization: We are connected to *all* life:

A man is ethical only when life, as such, is sacred to him, that of plants and animals as that of his fellow men, and when he devotes himself helpfully to all life that is in need of help.... The ethic of the relation of man to man is not something apart by itself: it is only a particular relation which results from a universal one. [Schweitzer and Campion(1949)][158–159]

Albert Schweitzer never taught that nothing should ever be killed. Some creatures we raise for food. Some are predators, others are prey. Because death is part of life, what strategy should guide one who wishes to live in accordance with the principle of reverence for all life? Schweitzer's distinction was the "pressure of necessity:"

The farmer who has mown down a thousand flowers in his meadow to feed his cows, must be careful on his way home not to strike off in thoughtless pastime the head of a single flower by the roadside, for he thereby commits a wrong against life without being under the pressure of necessity. [Meyer and Bergel(2002)][143]

This prompted Jordan S. to write,

```
Last week in STS we talked about reverence for life.  I
must admit that this hit me quite hard...  The line about
having reverence for life means that we don't carelessly
destroy even the head of a wild flower as we walk along has a
```

special meaning for me.... I have a part time job as a
grounds keeper, so I work with plants every day, and thinking
about this reverence for life, even for plant life, has given
me a new perspective on my work. I used to think that what I
did was just a menial job for low pay, but I now like to
think of myself as a steward, someone who promotes life.

Joseph Marshall III tells of a black beetle who took up residence in
his family's home. "He wanders seemingly aimlessly about, but I'm sure
he knows where he's going... We named him Bailey and we allow him the
run of the place...." [Marshall(2002)][51] Marshall is not advocating that we
allow beetles to take over our homes. But Bailey's presence in the Marshall
home was causing no harm, so they let him enjoy his life however beetles do.
The Marshall family's response to Bailey illustrates Schweitzer's Reverence
for Life. If a person's ethical principles prevent them from squashing even
a black beetle, that person will not be susceptible to the charms and lies of
those who would sell us on racism or ethnic cleansing. A person who will
not, as a matter of conscience, whack off the head of a flower or trample
a beetle is not likely to heap any form of contempt on anything that lives.
Luke W. wrote, "I have never thought about the idea of an insect jumping,
flying, or running away from me as an attempt to save his life. I've viewed
it as the bug just toying with me to see if it can annoy me & then escape...
Have you ever asked yourself if a bug's value of his life is greater than your
desire to end it?" Gabrielle L. added,

When looking at how small and insignificant the human race
is, and how small the size of our planet is vs. the
universe, it makes me consider the smallest organisms of life
with value and awe. The smallest insect is striving to live
and has the desire to exist just like all other living
beings. Yesterday I saw a trail of red ants coming and going
very quickly. I followed the path of red ants.... After
about 10--15 yards I found an underground civilization of
ants that was so vast and intricate. All the ants were
swarming with determination, each having purpose and meaning
in its small civilization. How or why does the human race,
which is much smaller than ants in comparison to the universe,
seem to think we are so much more superior and more valuable
than the creation around us?

Gabrielle's question underlies the ones we have been discussing: Before we bring in the chainsaws and diesel-powered scrapers, might we ask what counts as "necessity?"

Besides matters of acceptance of diverse peoples and respect for other species, several other settings arise where the opportunity to practice Reverence for Life intersects with our society's technology, economy, lifestyle and politics. These include how we treat the animals we raise for food; what values guide hunting and fishing; legal policies and social attitudes regarding abortion, capital punishment and euthanasia; and our response to the promises and perils of genetic technologies such as cloning and stem cell therapies. We seldom have sufficient time in class to discuss all of these loaded issues. But each class usually pursues two or three of them.

Raising animals for food: Livestock animals have life in the first place because we brought them into the world to be eaten by us. But whatever their cognitive and emotional capabilities, any pain and terror they suffer is real. This implies for us an ethical responsibility. While the Humane Slaughter Act of 1958 specified that all livestock had to be "rendered insensible to pain...before being shackled, hoisted, thrown, cast, or cut," workers with hidden cameras show that technologies of efficiency and economies of scale still spawn industrialized cruelty behind windowless slaughterhouse walls.[152] A New Zealand government official wisely observed over a century ago,

Virtues are perfectly possessed when we don't know we have them, and much the same may be said of not a few of our commonest vices.... The more widely prevalent a practice the less notice we take of it, either in ourselves or others... The old fishwife, when rebuked for skinning eels alive, replied that they had got used to it, for she had skinned them that self-same way for fifty years. [Findlay(1908)][5–6]

---

[152]Randy Ehrich, a former vice president of a major meat packing corporation, has visited our class as a guest speaker. He hired Temple Grandin as a consultant and made sure her specifications were met in the plants where he had authority. Grandin, of Colorado State University, researches animal psychology. She helps her human clients be aware of what the animals experience and fear, and how to treat the animals with respect. For ranchers and slaughterhouses, she designs equipment and procedures so the animals will not be terrorized or in agony throughout their lives, including their last moments. Dr. Grandin was recognized by the People for the Ethical Treatment of Animals with the 2005 PETA Award for her work on behalf of livestock welfare.

Hunting: Many STS students are hunters. My brother-in-law Ron, who lives in Colorado, has been a serious hunter from his youth. Depending on the season, he hunts with rifle, black-powder muzzle-loader, or bow, but mostly with the bow. I have never hunted with Ron, but I have accompanied him on scouting expeditions during the off-season, as he continues his education in learning to think like the animals he hunts. During hunting season, Ron will not take a shot unless he has worked himself close enough to his quarry to be confident that he can drop the creature with one shot, for in the role of predator Ron does not want any animal to suffer at *his* hand. Not all hunters are as conscientious as Ron. But in the long view, the population of hunters keeps the population of big-game animals viable. The millions of dollars spent annually in Colorado by hunters, many from out of state, provide the economic incentive for keeping vast tracts of wildlife habitat from being turned into resorts and condominiums.

Abortion, capital punishment, end-of-life issues: During Oklahoma elections, candidates feel obliged to conspicuously proclaim their "pro-life" credentials during campaigns. A discussion of this topic in STS, with the hope of generating less heat and more light, seems warranted.

We start with specific questions. How many of you have at least one close friend or family member who seriously considered having an abortion, or actually had one? About half of the hands go up. Next question: What labels are used in society's discussions about abortion? This everyone knows: Pro-Life and Pro-Choice. What is Pro-Life? Pro-Life proponents oppose abortion, most considering it murder, although some Pro-Lifers reluctantly allow it for pregnancies resulting from rape or to save the life of the mother. What is Pro-Choice? Pro-Choice proponents believe that every pregnant woman has the right to decide what she will do about her pregnancy.

As a practical matter, another question comes up: if abortions were outlawed today, would they stop? No, they would continue in unregulated basements. Of course there is more at stake here than medical safety and constitutional rights. It's about the sanctity of human life.

22 April, 2015
Dear Professor Dyson,
On behalf of the Spring 2015 STS class, I bring you greetings, with good wishes to you and all your family. Please give my regards to Imme as well.
...The students in this semester's class discussed several candidate questions last night, and I have narrowed the field to five.

If you have a few moments to answer one or two of them we would be much obliged...

Your mother ran a family-planning clinic in Winchester, before such clinics were as abundant as they are today. In this role how was she, her clinic and her clients received by the local community? As part of our discussions about genetics last night we also talked about the abortion debate that has gone on so long in society. Picketing abortion clinics is not unheard of in this region. We are not quite sure if your mother's clinic was involved in abortion services, but discussions about abortion led to our wanting to know more about her work with family planning. Your mother was a pioneer in this field. Was Alice's work with single mums related to your mother's work with families?

...Warm regards, on behalf of the students, Dwight

1 May 2015

Dear Dwight,

This has been a busy week. The main event [was] a big celebration for our friend Oliver Sacks in New York.[153] *You may have read some of his books. He learned a few weeks ago that he has a spreading melanoma that will kill him in a few months. So he threw a big party for his friends to celebrate his life. It was a wonderful and joyful gathering. Oliver was in great spirits, and we were too.*

Now I must try to answer the students' five questions....

I know very little of the details of my mother's birth-control clinic. The only episode that I remember vividly is when I was six or seven years old, I picked up some paper from her desk to write my school home-work. On the back of the paper was printed, "Winchester Birth-control Clinic." As I was walking out of the house to school with the home-work, my mother happened to see the back of the paper, and she told me fiercely that I must not use that paper. Being involved with birth-control in those days was not socially acceptable.

I do not know whether the clinic was arranging abortions. I would guess that it was not. My mother was a lawyer and not a physician. I would guess that the clinic was mostly concerned with educating young girls about the facts of life, and arranging adoptions of unwanted babies. I remember my mother telling us about one of her clients who had a baby with bright red hair. My mother asked her whether the father also had red hair. The mother replied, "I couldn't rightly tell you, Ma'am, he had his

---

[153]Oliver Sacks is a professor of nuerology at the New York University School of Medicine, and a best-selling author. His books include *Awakenings*; *Hallucinations*; *Musicophilia: Tales of Music and the Brain*; *The Man Who Mistook His Wife for a Hat*; and his autobiography *On the Move* whose cover shows Sacks on a motorcycle.

hat on." My mother was an upper-class English lady. She saw her clients as children who needed to be helped and guided, but not as equals.
My sister became a medical social worker during World War II when every young person had to do some kind of national service. I do not know whether my mother had anything to do with her choice of service. My sister was a trained professional. She loved the work and stayed with it all her life. She worked in a hospital and dealt with all kinds of patients with all kinds of problems, not only unmarried mums.
...With all my good wishes and thanks to all of you, yours ever, Freeman Dyson.

My sister vehemently opposes abortion. She has participated in political activism on the Pro-Life side of the debate. In my view she has earned the right to do so. Twenty-five years ago a woman living in my sister's community let it be known that she would have an abortion unless someone signed on as adoptive parents. My sister and brother-in-law adopted the baby. They stood in the gap at a crucial moment. One wants to ask the protesters picketing the abortion clinics: How many babies have *you* adopted?

Several students delicately share similar stories, all of them deeply personal. Now comes a pivotal question: Is it possible to be opposed to abortion-on-demand *and* be pro-choice? After a pause, a few heads nod "yes," others are not sure. Most of our students are opposed to abortion, some passionately so with deep conviction. But with few exceptions even the passionate opponents seem to seriously ponder the follow-up question: What gives me license say that *you* have no choice because of what *I* believe, *when I am not the person who must live with the consequences?*

We could go on, and sometimes do—for example, we notice that some of the most vocal opponents of abortion are the loudest advocates of capital punishment. To their credit, they draw a crucial distinction between murder and due process. But is the distinction equally clear between justice and revenge? Although we do not make Colosseum-type spectacles of modern executions, do we still cheer?

As of this writing, four states have legalized physician-assisted suicide. Many people see this as a slippery slope towards policies of euthanasia by less than informed consent. When my mother was in her last months of Alzheimer's disease, we had to feed her, holding the fork to her mouth. At the end of a meal she would say "I'm through." During her last month, this routine changed. At the beginning of each meal she clamped her jaws

shut and said through clenched teeth, "I'm through." After three weeks the
doctors offered us the option of a feeding tube. We talked it over. As she
sat in the nursing home dining room gazing at the pitiful people slumped
in wheelchairs all around her, perhaps Mom realized she had become one
of them. We came to the conclusion that when she said "I'm through" she
was not talking about a particular meal. She was *through*. We decided,
and told the nurses: No, we will not use the feeding tube. Have food here,
and we will offer it to her. But the choice to eat or not eat will be hers. A
week later she was gone. During her last hours, my father held her right
hand and I held her left hand—those lovely hands that played Chopin and
Beethoven and tenderly held my infant children.

Did we do the right thing? We did not proactively end her life, but
we did decide it was time to let nature take its course. The feeding tube
would have only prolonged the inevitable, and so far as we could tell (and
the doctors assured us) Mom was not in pain. She stopped being Evonne
long before the feeding tube became an issue. Had we kept her alive with
this technology, we would have been doing it for ourselves, not for her.

Thankfully, no law or bureaucracy or judge intervened to tell us we
had no choice. We took responsibility for the choice and we accept the
consequences. The values guiding our decision were respect and reverence
and caring.

Genetic manipulation: If there had been a way to restore Mom to her
old self, the pianist, the loving mother and grandmother, the hostess of
wonderful dinners who always had coffee and cherry pie standing by when
we came to visit—of course we would have fixed her, without hesitation.
In the forseeable future, stem cell therapies may offer such an option. Does
Reverence for Life allow genetic technologies such as cloning and using
embryonic stem cells for research and clinical therapies? These are such
emotionally charged topics that they need an entire class meeting time of
their own.

Before going on, it's instructive to take a backward glance and reflect on
how our intellectual companions have articulated themes similar to Freeman
Dyson's youthful Cosmic Unity. In Cosmic Unity we are all connected:

*Cosmic Unity said: There is only one of us. We are all the same person.
I am you and I am Winston Churchill and Hitler and Gandhi and everybody.
There is no problem of injustice because your sufferings are also mine. There*

will be no problem of war as soon as you understand that in killing me you are only killing yourself. [Dyson(1979a)][17]

Albert Schweitzer's philosophy of ethics was based on the principle of reverence for *all* life. [Schweitzer and Campion(1949)]

Lakota ethical philosophy for earlier generations was summarized by Luther Standing Bear: "Kinship with all creatures of the earth, sky and water was a real and active principle... The old Lakota was wise. He knew that man's heart away from nature becomes hard; he knew that lack of respect for growing, living things soon led to lack of respect for humans too." [Standing Bear(1933)]193,197] The contemporary Lakota writer Joseph Marshall III lives that ethic out to this day.

Henry David Thoreau wrote in *Walden* that "No humane being, past the thoughtless age of boyhood, will wantonly murder any creature, which holds its life by the same tenure that he does." [Thoreau(1960)][146]

Robert Pirsig articulated the principle "respect the wholeness and one-ness of life." [Pirsig(1999)][377]

In his letter to us of 1 May 2000, Professor Dyson said "Now I think of cosmic unity as a hope rather than a fact. It still makes sense as a foundation for ethics. It is an ideal toward which we should strive."

On topics where science and technology intersect deeply personal ethical issues, it seems that the fewer personal encounters one has with the issue, the more firmly held are the opinions and the more loudly are they vocalized. But when these issues hit close to home and become personal, black-and-white issues have a way of turning gray. In such discussions the phrase "playing God" often gets thrown around. When someone has an abortion, are they playing God? Does civil authority play God when executing a prisoner convicted of murder? When we did not use the feeding tube on Mom, were we playing God? If I could have injected into her some stem cells that would have reversed her Alzheimer's and restored to us the Evonne we knew, I would have done it in a microsecond. At that moment would I have been guilty of playing God? What does "playing God" really mean?

14 Playing God

Letters on Genetic Engineering

> *"Wells raises the question that must ultimately be faced by all believers in scientific progress. Can man play God and still stay sane?... The character of Doctor Moreau answers it with a resounding No."* –Freeman Dyson[154]

***

Three weeks after I turned 40, on Christmas Day I woke up at 5 am with severe abdominal pain. I could eat no breakfast or Christmas dinner that day, not even Mom's cherry pie, and that is saying something. That evening, a Friday, I was driven to a hospital and arrived with a dangerously high fever. The emergency room nurses and doctors quickly got my symptoms under control, but the cause was ambiguous. On Sunday morning the physician brought out the big guns and ordered a CT scan. Within moments he understood the problem, and within the hour I was headed into surgery. My appendix was leaking and I had a fine case of peritonitis.[155] On that weekend I was thankful for advanced technologies and the nurses and the surgeon who knew how to use them. Had I stayed home and done nothing, almost certainly I would not have lived through the following week. Every day since then is an extra one to which I am not entitled. When you would have died at age 40 had nature been allowed to run its course, you see growing older as a privilege.

There was a time, and there are still communities, where having surgery would be considered usurping God's role. Who are you to change what God made? Who are you to interfere with God's purposes that are beyond our understanding? On the other hand, computer-assisted tomography equipment does not appear spontaneously in nature. But a CT scan works because of nature's laws, the result of minds putting materials and nature's laws together in new combinations. If we accept the technologies of engineering metal and silicon into medical instruments, why not accept technologies that could heal, upgrade, and enhance our bodies and genes?

---

[154][Dyson(1979a)][168–169]

[155]Appendicitis famously produces pain on the right side of the abdomen. Should the appendix get twisted around, the pain radiates from the center, a symptom with multiple possible causes.

If we engineer with gray technology, why not engineer with the green? Such questions have been important to every section of STS.

When someone says "That action is playing God" we know roughly what they mean, even though we cannot articulate it precisely. In the chapter called "The Island of Doctor Moreau" Professor Dyson raises issues that often go under the flag of "playing God." The chapter's title comes from a novel by H.G. Wells. Doctor Moreau isolates himself on a remote island where he surgically carves beasts into human shape, and tries to humanize their behavior through their incessant chanting of his Law. The novel's protagonist, who finds himself stuck for some time on Moreau's island, will never again, even after he escapes, be sure that those around him are truly human. Recent developments in genetics, such as mapping the human genome, place more sophisticated versions of Doctor Moreau's tools within our grasp:

Whoever can read the DNA language can also learn to write it. Whoever learns to write the language will in time learn to design living creatures according to his whim. God's technology for creating species will then be in our hands....

Want a kitten with purple fur? Merely design it into Kitty's genes! Want your child to be a super-genius, or immune to cancer?...

...Then Wells's question will have to be answered, not in a science fiction story but in our real world of people and governments. Can man play God and still stay sane? In our real world, as on [Doctor Moreau's] island, the answer must inevitably be no. [Dyson(1979a)][169]

In the same chapter Professor Dyson recalls the 1924 novel *Daedalus, or Science and the Future* by J.B.S. Haldane, which envisions a world of test-tube babies and free access to psychotropic drugs, as humans engineer their evolution through controlled mutation by universal *in vitreo* fertilization. Haldane's iconic scientist figure was modeled on the Greek myth of Daedalus who hybridized a woman and a bull to produce the Minotaur. Haldane was pessimistic about progress in science unless it was accompanied by similar progress in ethics. He wrote, "There is no great invention, from fire to flying, which has not been hailed as an insult to some god." [Haldane(1924)], [Dyson(1979a)][170]

What does "playing God" really mean? Whatever it means, is it always bad? If deciding to have a baby by artificial methods is playing God, wouldn't having a baby the old-fashioned way, or choosing to not have a baby at all, also be playing God? Either way, someone will live—or not live—when it would have been otherwise. If that's not playing God, what is?

> *12 November 2007*
> *Dear Professor Dyson,*
> *...When discussing ground-breaking genetic technologies, what do you think it means when people assert that we should not pursue a certain course of action any further because we would be "playing God"?*

> *23 November 2007*
> *Dear Dwight,*
> *...Every medical doctor who advises a patient making a life-or-death decision is playing God. So is a minister who advises a parishioner. I have two daughters who are medical doctors and one who is a Presbyterian minister, and they all do this from time to time. In my opinion, the ethical problems are the same,... whether the doctor or the minister is using old-fashioned professional judgment or new-fashioned high technology. The patient or the parishioner comes to you confused and scared, and you try to help the patient or the parishioner to look at the problem objectively and calmly. I would say that is playing God, and the best doctors and ministers are those who can do it well. It is useful to remember that God also has a sense of humor.*

If we *were* granted license to assume God's role for a day, what would we do with it?

> *22 April, 2015*
> *Dear Professor Dyson,*
> *On behalf of the Spring 2015 STS class, I bring you greetings, with good wishes to you and all your family.... If you were granted the privilege of being God for a day, what would you do during that day? The students who proposed this question said to assume the properties usually attributed to God, such as omnipotence, omnipresence, and so on....*
> *Warm regards, on behalf of the students, Dwight.*

> *1 May 2015*
> *Dear Dwight,*
> *...If I were God, I would do what God has been doing for the last few centuries at least, watching the show and not actively interfering. Any quick or hasty actions would probably do more*

harm than good. God has given us the freedom to make mistakes and learn from our mistakes. I would continue with the same wise policy.

...With all my good wishes and thanks to all of you, yours ever, Freeman Dyson.

25 April 1995
Dear Professor Dyson,
...What is the most important scientific discovery of the 20th century?...
Thank you, Professor Dyson, for all your communications with us, from "Disturbing the Universe," to your speeches and papers, to your personal correspondence....
Warm regards, DEN and students

26 April 1995
Dear Dwight Neuenschwander,
...To me the most important discovery was the double helix structure of DNA, showing that the basic processes of biology are understandable in terms of ordinary chemistry. This does not mean that life is "reduced" to nothing more than a sequence of chemical reactions. It means that life is approachable using the methods of science. Life can be studied and sculpted using the tools of chemistry. Compared with this, relativity and quantum mechanics are of minor importance.
... I will be back from Jerusalem in May 25 and look forward to reading any more comments and reactions from the students then. Meanwhile, I wish them a happy final exam and thank them for their questions.
Yours sincerely,
Freeman Dyson

Concerns and accusations about "playing God" become especially poignant in regard to the bodies and genes of human beings. "The hydrogen bomb is almost a simple problem," wrote Professor Dyson, "compared with the problems posed by a deliberate distortion or mutilation of the genetic apparatus of human beings." [Dyson(1979a)][169–170]

1 May 1998
Dear Professor Dyson,
...How far can we go and ethically conduct research in genetic engineering on humans?

2 May 1998
Dear Dwight and Class,
Here I recommend the book "Remaking Eden," by my friend

Lee Silver who is a professor of biology here in Princeton. The book is mostly about fertility clinics and the things people will do in order to have babies that they can call their own. Before you can write laws to regulate genetic engineering applied to humans, you must look at it from the point of view of the parents. Obviously the laws should prohibit practices that carry higher risk than natural conception of giving birth to defective babies. But it is not possible to require the informed consent of a baby before it is allowed to be born. In my opinion, the laws should be written slowly, in response to real problems as they arise. It would be a big mistake to write laws in a hurry in response to political or ideological pressures.
Yours ever, Freeman

3 December 1998
Dear Professor Dyson,
...What comments do you have on current developments in genetic manipulation? Have we already gone too far to turn back?

5 December 1998
Dear Dwight,
I am delighted with the progress in genetic manipulation, because it can help enormously to feed hungry people (when applied to crop-plants) and to cure diseases (when applied to viruses and humans). I would certainly not wish to turn back, even if it were possible. It is impossible to turn back, because sick people and parents of sick children have needs that cannot be denied. Of course applications of genetic manipulation must be carefully regulated so that they do not do harm. Regulations already exist and can be strengthened if necessary, but that does not mean that the useful applications of genetic manipulation can be stopped.
...Happy Christmas and New Year to you all.
Yours sincerely,
Freeman Dyson

When Princeton University wanted to conduct recombinant DNA research, permission had to be granted by city officials. So that all concerns could be fairly heard, a Princeton Citizens' Committee was formed. Professor Dyson was one of its eleven members. After four months of deliberations, the committee said Yes to Princeton by a vote of eight to three. The minority three were Wallace Alston, a Presbyterian minister; Susanna Waterman, an undersea photographer; and Emma Epps, a retiree and leader of the local black community. "But in spite of our difference of opinion, or rather because of our differences of opinion, my service on the

Citizens' Committee was one of the happiest and most rewarding experiences of my life. We were struggling with deep problems and we became firm friends." [Dyson(1979a)][179] For the minority of three, the issues went beyond public health, deep into matters of conscience. Professor Dyson recalls, "Even though I accepted the wisdom of the various philosophical misgivings that caused Alston, Waterman and Epps to vote no, I cannot accept the notion that the Borough of Princeton should have the power to impose their philosophical views upon Princeton University by municipal ordinance." [Dyson(1979a)][181]

Had he been in the Citizens' Committee, Drew S. would have voted No. While he did not want to play God through genetic manipulation—"to approach human study from this angle is dangerous, in my opinion..."—he also realized that he did not have a God's-eye view:

```
    ...Sometimes it's hard to know if a scientific decision
lines up with our morals or not...  This all leads back to
the problem Dyson faced at Princeton.  I cannot, simply
because of my beliefs, limit other people, with different
beliefs, in their endeavors.  Yes I do believe this is wrong
and dangerous, but there are others who believe it is
dangerous not to....  I can't give specific examples of what
will go wrong.  This research could lead to healing of
paralytics and curing of diseases and here people like me
stand in the way saying that it is wrong.  This class is
teaching me how hard it is to approach science with moral
questions, because the answers aren't always obvious.
```

12 November 2007
Dear Professor Dyson,
...With the advent of genetic engineering, should we attempt in any way to alter the human genome?...

23 November 2007
Dear Dwight,...
...There are two main reasons for parents to want to alter the genetic endowment of their babies. The first reason is to get rid of genes that are known to cause fatal or incapacitating diseases such as Tay-Sachs or Huntington's or cystic fibrosis. The second reason is to give the baby a better chance to compete in life by having genes for superior intelligence or superior ability to play football. The first reason is a cheap and effective treatment for otherwise incurable diseases. The second reason is a cheap and effective entrance ticket to high-income professions. The

two reasons raise very different ethical problems. Many people would like to allow the first and forbid the second. I would prefer to allow the parents freedom to make genetic changes for both reasons, if and only if the procedure is medically safe and is equally available to rich and poor. I don't expect all of you to agree with this.

Matter, Life, Personhood

When does genetic material go from being *matter* to being a *person*? "Personhood" is not a quantity that can be scientifically measured like blood pressure.

Recent attempts were made in Colorado, Oklahoma, North Dakota and South Carolina to pass legislation that would have granted "personhood" status to microscopic embryos, legally making abortion into murder.[156] While everyone may *persuade* to their heart's content, the proponents of these proposals tried to *impose* their definition of personhood on everyone else by making it the law of the land. As of this writing, none of these proposals have become law.[157]

International student Niall B. watched these developments with bewilderment:

Last week I came out of the lecture wanting to debate
anything to do with stem cell research, abortion, and
especially the idea of when life begins.... The way I see it
is that ''life'' and ''person'' have two different
meanings... Life is a cell, an organism...so in this debate
you can say life does begin at conception. However, a
''person'' is something so much more complex than just a
''life.''...
The reason that this gets to me the most is that Oklahoma
just passed a bill ending the debate [its passage in the
House] and telling us that personhood begins at conception.
Now I believe that this infringes on people's rights and

---

[156]Attempts are currently underway on other states; see "Personhood Legislation" in the Resolve website, http://www.resolve.org/get-involved/the-center-for-infertility-justice/personhood-legislation/#OK.

[157]Oklahoma's proposal passed the House but was killed in a Senate committee. The Oklahoma Supreme Court would probably have declared the bill unconstitutional had it become law.

liberties as Americans, and I am not even American. It is
obvious to me that the people in the Oklahoma capitol mix
their religious beliefs too much with politics, they are
basing their opinion on faith... In my eyes this is mixing of
Church and State and needs to be fixed.

The same year that he served on the Princeton Citizens' Committee,
Professor Dyson testified before the House Subcommittee on Science, Research, and Technology of the US Congress. Representative Ray Thornton
of Arkansas "wanted to take a longer view, to examine what the recombinant DNA debate might portend for the future relationship between science
and government." [Dyson(1979a)][182] Professor Dyson drew an analogy to
John Milton's *Aeropagitica*. Milton published this pamphlet in 1644 to argue for freedom of the press. He made four points in favor of unlicensed
printing, from which Professor Dyson drew analogies to DNA experiments:

(1) Demonstrably dangerous books (or experiments) should be suppressed, but only after they have done some damage. Books and experiments should not be condemned in advance on ideological grounds.

(2) In suppressing evil, good will also be suppressed.

(3) Intellectual life itself will be suppressed. For instance, silencing
Galileo led to a general decline of intellectual life in seventeenth-century
Italy.

(4) The people can handle it.

> *6 April 1999*
> *Dear Professor Dyson,*
> *...In "Aeropagitica" you describe how genetic research could be
> encouraged yet society protected, provided that strict rules about
> applications are observed. We would appreciate your commen-
> tary concerning recent dramatic developments in bio-technology
> that could lead to especially wrenching ethical choices, such as
> "designer babies," organ cloning, etc.*

When Professor Dyson received our letter, he was a guest lecturer at
Gustavus Adolphus College in Minnesota.

> *10 April 1999*
> *Dear Dwight,*
> *Thanks for your message, and thanks to the class for their good
> questions. It is a wet Saturday in Minnesota, with rain blowing
> horizontally all day long, a good day for staying indoors and an-
> swering letters. This morning I have been composing my homily
> for the chapel service on Monday morning. Whatever I have to*

say has to be said in seven minutes. That is good discipline. I
send you the text of the homily as I wrote it this morning. As
always, your comments and criticisms will be welcomed....

Evidently Professor Dyson was asked to speak in chapel on the Old
Testament story of "Jonah and the whale."[158]   I enjoy sharing Professor
Dyson's homily with the STS students because of the way he handled his
assignment to speak on Jonah:

*I don't know why you gave me the text of Jonah and the whale to preach
from. I am a visitor here, enjoying the hospitality of the College, but I don't
feel like Jonah. I am certainly not responsible for last year's tornado, and you
people are not like the people on the ship going to Tarshish. Instead of finding
a Jonah to blame for the tornado, you stood together and repaired the damage
and got on with your lives. I am deeply impressed by the way you came through
the disaster and took care of one another. You didn't need to find a Jonah to
throw into the sea. That's all I have to say about Jonah...*

Having dispensed with Jonah, Professor Dyson redirected his homily to
the topic on which he writes and preaches often, always with passion: two
visions of the future. One vision he witnessed being expressed among CEOs
at a software convention. The other vision finds expression in Octavia
Butler's *The Parable of the Sower*, a novel about environmental collapse
and social chaos where the rich withdraw into armed fortresses and the
desperate poor are left to fend for themselves.

*Which of these two futures will be yours? The future of the Yuppies,
dreaming that they can bring wealth and enlightenment to the world with
high-bandwidth networks and a global market economy. Or the future of the
street people, left behind by deteriorating public services and inaccessible technology. The choice is up to you. Your generation will have the power and the
responsibility to decide which way you will go. It's fine to get rich, but it's not
fine to build fortresses to keep out the poor...*

Returning to Professor Dyson's letter of 10 April 1999,

...Now it's time to turn to your questions.
What should we do to protect society from the harmful effects
of recent developments in genetic engineering? The main thing
I am doing here at Gustavus Adolphus is to run a seminar with

---
[158]See the *Book of Jonah* in the Old Testament.

twenty students studying precisely this question. We are using
as our text the book: "Remaking Eden" by Lee Silver....

We interrupt the letter again to sample Silver's book. As noted above,
a deep philosophical question asks when personhood begins. At birth?
With the first heartbeat? At conception? Regarding the last option Silvers
points out an important detail about the first cloned mammal, Dolly the
sheep. When Dolly was born on February 23, 1997, cloning human beings
became a real possibility. But the cloning procedure that brought Dolly
into the world has no conception. If personhood begins at conception, then
cloned human beings will not be persons. [Silver(2002)][51] Returning again
to Professor Dyson's letter,

> *...The [Gustavus Adolphus seminar] students just finished read-*
> *ing the book. It is an excellent book, with detailed information*
> *about the fertility clinics where the technology of genetic engi-*
> *neering is applied to humans. The main facts are these: the*
> *fertility clinics are the most rapidly growing branch of medicine,*
> *they are not confined to rich countries but are growing rapidly*
> *in poor countries too, they are funded by private money and not*
> *by governments, and the driving force behind their growth is*
> *the desire of parents to have babies that they can call their own.*
> *The main danger to society is that, if the technology is available*
> *to rich parents and not to poor parents, it will widen the gap*
> *between rich and poor in a permanent and disastrous way, so*
> *that the children of the rich will become a hereditary caste with*
> *a monopoly of genetic advantages. The "designer babies" could*
> *become a hereditary upper class with the rest of the population*
> *condemned to inferior status.*
> *At the Thursday meeting of the seminar we arranged a debate*
> *with the students arguing for and against three possible poli-*
> *cies. (1) Continue the present US policy, with a free mar-*
> *ket in genetic technology, unregulated except for the legal re-*
> *quirements of informed consent and FDA approval that apply*
> *to all medical treatments. (2) Allow genetic manipulation of*
> *embryos only for the purpose of eliminating genetic deformities*
> *and life-threatening diseases, prohibiting manipulation for other*
> *purposes. So parents would be forbidden to use genetic manip-*
> *ulation to give their babies any advantages other than freedom*
> *from hereditary disease. (3) Allow genetic manipulation of em-*
> *bryos for any purpose, but only when the resources exist to make*
> *it available to everybody. This means that genetic manipulation*
> *should become part of a public health service, like the polio vac-*
> *cine that was distributed free to rich and poor alike as soon as*
> *it was available in quantity.*

The division among the students was roughly, ten for policy (1), seven for (2), and three for (3). I am myself strongly in favor of (3), but this is clearly a loser in the eyes of the students. (3) only makes sense if the US has a national health insurance system, which most of our students do not consider a serious possibility. So long as the basic distribution of medical services is unfair, you cannot deal with genetic services in a fair way.

To summarize, the choice between the three policies is a choice of priorities. If you choose (1) you put personal freedom first. If you choose (3) you put fairness first. If you choose (2) you put tradition first. The students who supported (2) were mostly religious believers who consider genetic manipulation of embryos to be usurping the role of God. They would grudgingly allow it for the purpose of preventing disease, but no further.

I will be very much interested to hear how your students divide on this question. Although this is a Lutheran college, the majority of the students seem to be libertarian, believing the religion of the free market. For them the fertility clinic industry is just another example demonstrating the virtues of the free market. The freedom of parents to buy advantages for their children should apply to genes just as it applies to university education and day-care. The students who argued for (1) were the most articulate. The debate was mostly a battle between (1) and (3), with (1) prevailing. The students who supported (2) did not say much, and did not need to say much. Their beliefs are firm and do not need to be defended.

My discussion so far deals with designer babies. You also ask about organ cloning. We have talked about organ cloning but did not find that it raises any big ethical problems. In fact, if organ cloning becomes practical, it will alleviate the severe ethical problems that arise in the obtaining of organ transplants under present conditions....

When our class read this letter, we realized that, on second thought, Professor Dyson's chapel homily (the part after Jonah) and his response to our question really are about the same thing, namely, making medical technology equally accessible to everyone, poor or rich. We discussed the three options and voted. Out of the 42 students, seven voted for option (1), the free market; thirty-five voted for option (2) for health issues only; zero voted for option (3) that allows use for any purpose if equally available to all. Two years later the Fall 2001 class took a turn:

5 December 2001
Dear Professor Dyson,
[Most semesters] I share with the students the three questions

that your class at Gustavus Adolphus discussed, regarding models of US policy towards genetic manipulation of embryos... In this semester's class of 46 students, among those who voted on these three options, the result was 9 for No. 1, 26 for No. 2, and 0 for No. 3. Upon further discussion, the students said they could not vote for 3, not for putting tradition first, but because they saw such ready availability of genetic manipulation as undermining diversity. For them, they saw their support for 2 over 3 not as a choice between tradition and fairness (although this is a pretty traditional population of students), but as using the benefits of genetic technology while preserving diversity. The underlying assumption was evidently that all parents would want the same features in their children. I thought you might find this discussion interesting.

Best wishes to you and your family.

Warm regards,

Dwight (on behalf of the STS class)

8 December 2001

Dear Dwight,

Thank you for the very interesting information about the student voting. It is interesting that they see genetic engineering as undesirable because it would promote uniformity of human populations, while I see it as dangerous because it would promote too much diversity. Perhaps they are right. But we will never know, unless we let the parents try it and see what they choose to do with it.

...Happy Christmas and New Year to you all, yours ever, Freeman.

In a two-week class in the January 2004 "mini-term," and the spring 2005 semester, we did the survey again:

13 January 2004

Dear Professor Dyson,

I am glad that you received our card (selected by the students themselves)...I will pass along to them your greetings and thanks...

Today I presented the three scenarios that came up in your Gustavus Adolphus seminar on genetic technology... Out of a class of 39 students, the class voted 7 for option 1, 31 for option 2, and 1 person for option 3. When I then revealed how your class voted they were surprised, but agreed with your assessment that option 1 represents freedom, option 2 tradition, and option 3 fairness....

22 January 2004
Dear Dwight,
Thank you for another long message which I found waiting when I returned from California yesterday. I guess your miniterm is now over and it is too late to say Hi to the students.... I am impressed with how much you and they managed to do in two weeks.... Yours, Freeman.

A year later:

12 January 2005
Dear Professor Dyson,
We're finishing up a two-week 'miniterm' section of Science, Technology, and Society...
...In our class today we voted on them [genetic policy options] at (3, 37, and 2), which is pretty typical for the STS sections at SNU. After the voting and further discussion, one student suggested a fourth category, "No genetic manipulations at all." 13 students then changed their vote to this option, all of them from the group that voted for No. 2. I thought you might find these numbers interesting. We'll be discussing it some more....

Fast forward almost a decade:

April 24, 2014
Dear Professor Dyson,
A few years ago you led a seminar on genetic technologies at Gustavus Adolphus College.... Our class this semester revisited these options and voted (1,33,0) with three abstentions. Your characterization of the students in your seminar who voted for (2) are a good fit of the student population here....

Here are selected results that represent several STS class responses to Professor Dyson's three scenarios. The entries (x, y, z) means that x students voted for option 1 (free market), y students voted for option 2 (limited to preventing diseases and birth defects), and z voted for option 3 (any reason when equally accessible to all):

Professor Dyson's seminar: (10, 7, 3)
STS classes:
Spring 1999   (7, 35, 0)
Fall 2001   (9, 26, 0)
January 2004   (7, 31, 1)
January 2005   (3, 37, 2)
Spring 2005   (1, 17, 5)
Spring 2013   (3, 37, 2)
Spring 2014   (1, 33, 0)
Spring 2015   (0, 24, 3)

One begins to see a pattern in our student population.

> *14 September 2013*
> *Dear Dwight,*
> *This is just to say thank you for the package of correspondence*
> *with your students that arrived yesterday...*
> *...I was very much interested in the result (3, 37, 2) of your vote*
> *on genetic manipulation of babies... There is a real difference*
> *between Oklahoma and Minnesota...*
> *As always, I shall be glad to hear from the students. Yours ever,*
> *Freeman.*

We engaged Professor Dyson in further conversation about these options.

> *6 May 2005*
> *Dear Professor Dyson,*
> *...In your letter of 10 April 1999 you said you were "strongly*
> *in favor" of Option 3, "Allow genetic manipulation of embryos*
> *for any purpose, but only when the genetic resources exist to*
> *make it available to everybody." In exercising this option, would*
> *you make a policy distinction between somatic gene therapy and*
> *germline genetic engineering? Along with your chapters "The*
> *Island of Dr. Moreau" and "Aeropagitica" we brought in pas-*
> *sages from the recent books "Enough" by Bill McKibben, and*
> *"Our Posthuman Future" by Francis Fukuyama. We also had*
> *some of our biologists come as guest speakers and tell us about*
> *cloning and stem cell research.*

In describing our "posthuman future," Francis Fukuyama tries to prepare us for what could play out when we understand the molecular pathways between genes and personality traits such as aggression, criminality, alcoholism, depression, sexual identity and so on. Genetic manipulation will present not only ethical dilemmas, but political and social and legal ones too. "If wealthy parents suddenly have open to them the opportunity to increase the intelligence of their children as well as that of all their subsequent descendants, then we have the makings not just of a moral dilemma but of a full-scale class war." [Fukuyama(2002)][15]

Bill McKibben presents scenarios such as the impact of genetic manipulation on personal identity. A concert pianist wants to endow her daughter with even greater talent, and buys for her a set of enhanced genes. If the daughter does not have to struggle to achieve world-class excellence, what becomes of the satisfaction of accomplishment that was so important in her mother's life?

And the piano player's daughter? A player piano as much as a human... her music soured before it is made. Because the point was never the music itself; the inclination and then the effort were what created the meaning for her mother. [McKibben(2003)][48–49]

> *7 May 2005*
> *Dear Dwight,*
> *...I had not considered somatic gene therapy when I was discussing the regulation of genetic manipulation of embryos. I was talking about germline genetic engineering. That is what one is doing when one adds or subtracts genes from an embryo before it becomes a baby. Whatever changes you produce in the baby will be inherited by the baby's offspring. Somatic gene therapy is a different procedure altogether, done after a child is born, raising problems of safety and efficacy but not affecting the child's offspring. I would see no ethical objections to somatic gene therapy if the problems of safety and efficacy were solved. On the other hand, with genetic manipulation of embryos there are ethical problems even if the procedure is safe and effective.*

Our guest microbiologist, Nancy Halliday, has visited our classes multiple semesters to tell us about the cellular biology behind genetic technologies. She told us how upon fertilization the first cells are "totipotent"—all their genetic information is "switched on." As the cells replicate, some of the genetic options are "switched off," making the cell "pluripotent" (or "multipotent"). For example, some pluripotent cell lines could turn into pancreas or liver cells but can no longer turn into brain or nerve cells. When cells are fully "differentiated" all the genetic possibilities have been switched off except the one that specializes the cell as, say, a retina cell.

As a strategy for the survival of life, diversity is essential (recall the Irish potato famine of the mid-nineteenth century). Professor Dyson wrote, "Clades are the stuff of which great leaps forward in evolution are made. Clones are evolutionary dead ends, slow to adapt and slow to evolve...." [Dyson(1979a)][233]

> *5 December 2001*
> *Dear Professor Dyson,...*
> *In chapter 20, "Clades and Clones," you say that a clone is a dead end, while a clade is a promise of immortality. Does that mean that present research in that field [cloning] is directed towards a "dead end?"...*
>
> *8 December 2001*
> *Dear Dwight,...*
> *Is research on cloning a dead end? The answer is no. The word "clone" can be either a noun or a verb, and the noun and the verb have different meanings. As a noun, a clone is a population of animals or plants that all have the same genes. As a verb, to clone means to produce an offspring, bacterium or animal or plant, that has the same genes as the parent. When I said a clone is a dead end, clone is a noun, and I meant that a population with the same genes cannot evolve into something different. But when you ask about cloning, clone is a verb, and cloning is a tool that can be used for many useful and important kinds of research. For example, Ian Wilmut who bred Dolly is interested in using cloning to breed sheep or goats that can manufacture various drugs that are difficult to make by other methods. Other people are using cloning to understand basic questions about the development of an egg into an adult animal. So research using cloning is certainly not a dead end.*

To get the genetic material to make the cloned sheep Dolly, the genes in a fully differentiated cell from a donor Finn Dorset sheep were switched back on to totipotency. To replicate the Finn Dorset genetic material while guaranteeing that the resulting embryo came from the donor genes and not from an accidental pregnancy of a Finn Dorset mother, an unfertilized egg was extracted from a second breed of sheep—a Blackface ewe. The Blackface egg's nucleus was removed and replaced with the reactivated Finn Dorset genetic material. Once sufficient cell division occurred, the embryo was implanted into a second Blackface ewe who served as the surrogate mother. After the usual gestation period the surrogate mother gave birth to Dolly, a Finn Dorset lamb, genetically identical to the donor Finn Dorset, identical twins of different ages. The breakthrough, after 276 unsuccessful attempts, was finding the chemical stimulation that enabled the donor genes to be switched back on to totipotency.

In ordinary human reproduction, within five to seven days after fertilization, the fertilized egg turns into a spherical structure called a "blastocyst." Its diameter is about the same as the diameter of a human hair. Inside the blastocyst lies the "inner cell mass," a clump pluripotent stem cells. These are the so-called embryonic stem cells (ESC). For ESC clinical therapy (first done in 1999) these cells are cultured in a petri dish, stimulated with chemicals to turn into the specialized cells the patient needs, and transplanted into the patient. Rejection issues must be addressed.

Opponents of stem cell procedures frequently base their opposition on the assumption that ESCs come from abortion clinics. This is a misconception. Cells in a recognizably human fetus are already differentiated "adult" cells, no longer able to be used as stem cells even if someone wanted to.

So where *do* clinics get donor ESCs? They come from *in vitro* fertilization clinics. When a couple tries to produce a pregnancy through the clinic's services, fertilized eggs are typically left over after the procedures are finished. They are frozen and stored, and remain viable for a fixed shelf life. If that deadline passes, the leftover fertilized eggs must be discarded. As the deadline approaches, the family is given the option of donating them for research or clinical use.

More recently, somatic cell nuclear transfer (SCNT) has become increasingly reliable. The cloning of Dolly pioneered the SCNT process in mammals. In human clinical use, a differentiated donor cell is taken from the patient, the cell's genetic material extracted and placed inside a denucleated egg. With chemical stimulation the donor genes revert to pluripotency, the blastocyst's inner cell mass is removed, stimulated to differentiate into the desired cell line, and inserted into the patient's body. There are no transplant rejection issues because the patient receives stem cells from their own body.

As with all technologies, genetic applications hold out promises and perils. Cells that become cancerous have reversed from differentiated to pluripotent. If we can learn how to turn genes back on, we can also learn how to turn them off. Diseases such as Parkinson's and Alzheimer's might succumb to genetic treatment. Stem cells directed to become new nerves might restore mobility to those paralyzed by spinal cord injuries.

With this background, in a letter of 7 May 2002 our class asked Professor Dyson a broad question:

20 May 2002

Dear Dwight and students,...

What is my take on stem-cell research? Here I have a simple answer. I think the British law on stem-cell research is reasonable and wise. The British law says that human embryos left over from treatment of patients in fertility clinics may be used freely for research until they are fourteen days old. As soon as they are fourteen days old they must be destroyed. This law was worked out after a long and public discussion involving religious leaders, politicians, scientists and concerned citizens. The fourteen-day limit means that the embryo is still a little bag of undifferentiated cells without anything resembling a human body-plan. These embryos would in any case have been destroyed if they had not been used for research. The law allows a great deal of useful science to be done and is acceptable to all except a minority of religious believers.

In contrast, the US law says that research may be done using cell-lines that were derived from human embryos several years ago but may not be done using new embryos discarded by fertility clinics. This is a stupid law, the result of a political process carried on without much public discussion. The old cell-lines are of dubious quality and certainly not adequate in the long run for the needs of science. The distinction between old cell-lines and new cell-lines makes no sense in terms of religious principles. So the US law impedes science without any logical basis in religious principles.

We still do not know how important the knowledge derived from stem-cells will be. That is the nature of science, you can never predict which way it will lead. Certainly we cannot claim that stem-cell research will lead directly to cures for human diseases. All we can claim is that understanding the process of development that turns a single cell into a human baby will provide new insight into the causes of hereditary diseases. Understanding the causes may allow us to avoid the human tragedies that hereditary diseases bring with them.

On March 9, 2009, President Barack Obama issued an executive order that revoked the 2001 Presidential order[159] and called for a review of stem cell policies, making many more stem cell lines available for clinical and research use. STS student Marcus P. wrote in 2009,

```
I think in this instance those against stem cell
research--like our former president--do not have all of their
```

---

[159]Thought by many to be a sop thrown to an ultra-conservative minority, the 2001 order shut down most stem cell research in the USA.

facts.... As a diabetic, I take the issue of stem cell
research personally. It angers me that with a flick of a
pen, millions and millions of dollars were taken away from
this incredibly lucrative research field, wasted on fueling
the war or bailing out big business. I am offended that
human life can be so disregarded and disrespected, even by
those who claim to respect it above all else. There is so
much potential behind stem cell research, beyond curing the
disease that will ultimately kill me.

About the same time the Princeton Citizens' Committee was hearing
arguments for and against recombinant DNA research being conducted in
their community, Harvard biologist Matthew Meselson was encountering
similar resistance in Cambridge, Massachusetts. A Cambridge Citizens'
Committee was formed to weigh the arguments. Professor Dyson writes
that as the committee members listened to Meselson they "trusted his
quiet uncertainty more than they trusted the loud certainty of his opponents." [Dyson(1979a)][177] The Cambridge Citizens' Committee ruled that
Meselson could go back to work, given that the usual safeguards were in
place.

A 1975 international meeting of biologists drew up guidelines to ban
DNA work that could cause immediate dangers to public health. The motivation for such an agreement came from a statement of those dangers,
published by molecular biologist Maxine Singer.

*Why, then, is the public still scared? The public is scared because the
public sees farther into the future and is concerned with larger issues than
immediate health hazards... The public sees, behind the honest faces of
Matthew Meselson and Maxine Singer, the sinister figures of Doctor Moreau
and Daedalus.* [Dyson(1979a)][178]

Professor Dyson writes that from H.G. Wells with his Doctor Moreau,
and from J.B.S. Haldane with his Daedalus, we can come to two conclusions.
First, we cannot play God and remain sane. Second, progress in biology
is inescapably placing within our hands the ability to play God. However,
these two premises do not necessary spell doom. All we need to do, says
Professor Dyson, is place the *applications* of such knowledge under strict
public control. [Dyson(1979a)][172] Maintain freedom for basic research to
deepen our understanding of how the world works; impose restrictions as

necessary on how, to whom and by whom that knowledge may be applied. Matthew Meselson's biology and his ethics were of a piece. Besides performing cutting-edge research on recombinant DNA, more than any other single person, Meselson was instrumental in getting biological weapons removed from the US arsenal. [Dyson(1979a)][173–176] For Mesleson, ethics was a beacon and a conscience for biology applications.

It seems that all STS issues ultimately come back to ethics. Professor Dyson concludes "The Island of Doctor Moreau" by looking back at Meselson, and looking forward to the future: "Matthew Meselson's purpose as a biologist and as a citizen is to build an ethos for the future, one that says a deep knowledge of life processes must be used only to reinforce what is essentially human in us." [Dyson(1979a)][178]

Depending on how it is used, technology can be dehumanizing, or it can be uplifting. To reinforce what is essentially human in us, technology should be used to strengthen bonds of kinship.

15   Bonds of Kinship

Thoughts on Relationships

"There really is no such thing as Art. There are only artists."
–E.H. Gombrich[160]

***

Science and art share a common set of fundamental values: Your search for what's *right* is guided by your sense of what's *good*. When confronted with a puzzle in nature, one can think of more hypotheses than can possibly be tested. Selecting the ones to test requires value judgements, such as elegance and simplicity. Science, like art, requires aesthetic values.

Individual scientists are passionate about their work. It is hard, if not impossible, to be completely objective when you care. The rebar that gives science the strength of objectivity is peer review. Science is done in community.

> *6 December 2005*
> *Dear Professor Dyson,*
> *We hope 2005 has been good to you and your family....*
> *1. What was the greatest intellectual community with which you have been connected?*
> *2. At what time in your life did your greatest intellectual growth occur?*
>
> *6 December 2005*
> *Dear Dwight,*
> *Thanks to you and the students for another thought-provoking lot of questions. 2005 has indeed been a good year for us and our tribe of fourteen grandchildren. We have much to be thankful for. Since time is short, I give you answers to your questions without much reflection....*
> *1. The greatest intellectual community I have known was the physics department at Cornell University when I came there as a student in 1947. It was full of brilliant people, starting with Hans Bethe and Richard Feynman, and it was a real community with old and young people helping each other out. It was a small enough group so that we all knew each other personally and felt like a big family. Also we had theorists and experimenters and engineers all working together. The isolated situation and harsh*

---

[160][Gombrich(1995)][15]

winter climate helped to bring out people's best qualities. You could not survive without help, and so everybody helped.
2. My greatest intellectual growth was...when I was a graduate student at Cornell aged 24 to 25. That was when I learned from Bethe and Feynman how to solve serious problems in physics, and I was also for the first time outside England and making friends with people from many countries.

To supplement meeting Richard Feynman through *Disturbing the Universe* we watch the documentary *Richard Feynman: Last Journey of a Genius.* [Sykes(1989)] It tells Feynman's and Ralph Leighton's passion to visit Tannu Tuva, once an independent country, now a part of Russia near Mongolia. Feynman's philosophy of life comes through in sparkling style. "Sometimes its better to do things at a lower level. There's more to life than traveling on the freeway and staying at the Holiday Inn...The whole point is to have *adventure.*" In the spring of 1948, young Freeman Dyson hitched a ride with Feynman from Ithaca, New York to Albuquerque, New Mexico. They would have driven by our campus, which sits on Route 66, had a flooded highway not forced them to detour to the north. Instead of staying in our town that night, they turned around and found lodging in Vinita, Oklahoma, talking through the night, sharing personal stories and arguing about quantum electrodynamics. [Dyson(1979a)][59] One of Professor Dyson's readers, sitting in a classroom on Route 66 sixty-five years later, wrote in her weekly letter,

``A Ride to Albuquerque'' really stuck out to me from the reading--particularly Dyson and [Feynman's] discussion on science. Although they disagreed and argued with each other on so many aspects, they were still willing to talk to each other, and, most importantly, to listen to each other. There are far too many people in the world that do just the talking and no listening.

While Freeman was at Cornell on a Commonwealth Fund Fellowship, Hans Bethe was his mentor. Professor Dyson's recollections in "A Scientific Apprenticeship" offers most STS students their introduction to Bethe. Amber M. remarked "I found it so interesting that within just a short time [Bethe] could discover someone's gifts and give them situations to help with enhancing them. This part really stuck out to me because lately I have been wondering if I have been using the gifts and abilities I have been given..." Bethe passed away during our Spring 2005 semester.

6 May 2005
Dear Professor Dyson,
*...This spring saw the passing of Hans Bethe. Besides being the
physicist who taught everyone the nuclear reactions that make
the stars shine,[161] and a voice for arms control that "Administrations ignore at their peril" (line from an AJP review of "The
Road From Los Alamos"), he was also your friend and mentor.
Not only has the world lost a great mind that was coupled to a
compassionate heart, but you have lost a personal friend. What
would you have us remember about Hans Bethe? (Our class
"met" him in the documentary "The Day After Trinity" in addition to your book.)*
*Thank you Professor Dyson for sharing your life, your insights,
and—through your letters and books—your family with us as
well. Thank you for explaining to us mostly "unscientific people the nature of the beast we are trying to control."...[162]*
The Spring 2005 Science, Technology, and Society class.

7 May 2005
Dear Dwight,...
*...What would I like you to remember about Hans Bethe? The
main thing was his delight in sharing whatever he was doing
with anyone who was around. He loved solving scientific problems, whether they were important or unimportant. He loved
exercising his skills as a calculator, but he kept his door open
while he was calculating so that students and colleagues could
come in and talk. At lunchtime he would always collect a bunch
of students and go with us to the cafeteria. At lunch he talked
a lot about the latest news in science and in the world outside.
He was also a good listener and did not mind when somebody
contradicted him and even occasionally proved him wrong. The
thing I remember best from those days is that everyone called
him Hans.*
*...With greetings and good wishes to you all from the Dyson
family.*

Professor Dyson's engagement with students has been similar to Bethe's.
In the spring of 2014 Jacob J. wrote:

We are continuing to read more about Freeman Dyson and his
life experience.... From his work at Cornell to his work
with nuclear energy he constantly brings to me a sense of
purpose, love, and compassion that has started me perceiving

[161]In 1938, Bethe worked out the carbon-nitrogen-oxygen cycle of nuclear fusion that
powers some of the larger stars.
[162][Dyson(1979a)][5]

him as a new personal hero. His humility and respect for all
those around him have made science--something that has been
taught to me as cold, methodical, and uncaring--as something
that is to encourage understanding and free thinking to bring
us together and not apart. He has encouraged my pursuit into
science and even literature to better understand myself and
mankind...

April 4, 1995
Dear Professor Dyson,
Enclosed is an essay written for a course in the English De-
partment by Shawn W., a literature major. One of his English
professors...forwarded it to me with Shawn's permission. When
I read it I thought I should forward it to you as well, and have
secured Shawn's permission to do so.
Shawn is a very bright young man who writes a column which he
calls the "IrReverend" in our campus newspaper. He is the kind
of person from which activists are made. Very idealistic, cheer-
fully curious, quite cynical, but eager to learn as much as he
can, he will freely speak out in class and resume the discussion
with the professor afterwards. In the journey of constructing
his own philosophy of life, Shawn is somewhere analogous to
the place you described when the bright days of Cosmic Unity
came to grips with the brutal realities of Bomber Command. I
believe your book has been very influential in Shawn's life. He
in turn may represent many of the less outspoken students who
are also struggling to figure out what life is all about. Working
with these young people is its own reward.
As you see from Shawn's letter, the class was also captivated by
Richard Feynman. Before they were assigned to read "A Sci-
entific Apprenticeship" and "A Ride to Albuquerque," I showed
the film, "Richard Feynman: Last Journey of a Genius," so
they could visualize Feynman as they read about him. In see-
ing this film, and others such as "The Day After Trinity," the
students' stereotypes of scientists were shattered, and replaced
with lively personalities....
It has been a joy to teach from your writings, and to develop
them into a course that for me has been a wonderful adventure,
and one of the most satisfying teaching experiences of my ca-
reer.
Warm regards,
Dwight E. Neuenschwander

Shawn's essay carried a perceptive title.

Science 101: Human Relations

Although there are definite distinctions between the paradigms of literature and science, the boundaries separating the two are becoming increasingly blurred... Until recently, this year in fact, I was under the assumption that the arts and the sciences were two conflicting intellectual arenas. I always respected the accomplishments of those of a scientific persuasion, but I found the introspection into human nature of literature far more fascinating and important than the former. Stephen Bonnycastle[163] summed up my feelings quite well: "Science has nothing to say about some of the most important problems in our lives, because those problems depend on feelings and values, and because they are a matter of choosing to be connected with other human beings..."

However,... I was introduced to two men through Dr. N's class who profoundly affected my perception of not only the science/literature dichotomy, but also of life: Freeman Dyson, a mathematician, and Richard Feynman, a theoretical physicist. Dyson, in his book *Disturbing the Universe*, accomplished what he had set out to do: to show the human side of science. Dyson served as an artist, painting a clear and oftentimes disturbing picture of the ethical dilemmas which all scientists must face. And in doing so, he quoted and made multiple allusions to a number of authors and poets, including Chaucer and Milton. Richard Feynman was proof of Dyson's claims. He became much more than that to me, however. He honestly changed my whole perspective on life. To see this Nobel Prize-receiving physicist, one of the most brilliant men in the country during his lifetime, laugh and carry on as he did, telling of his many pranks and ultimate quest for "adventure" taught me a lesson: It did me no good to get caught up in this pseudo-intellectual struggle if I lost touch of the things that truly mattered—our human relationships.

So you see, scientists could learn a lot from literary theorists, and vice-versa; I learned this first hand. After all, a scientist showed me more about human nature than any work of literature ever did.

We received a handwritten note on IAS stationary:

> *April 19 1995*
> *Dear Dwight,*
> *Thank you for your friendly letter, and for the delightful piece by Shawn W., and also for the comments by the students... My thanks and best wishes to all of them.*

---

[163] Author of *In Search of Authority* (1991).

Robert Oppenheimer, Edward Teller, and Freeman Dyson:
Kinship Across a Schism

When Freeman Dyson left Cornell University at the conclusion of his fellowship in 1948, he spent a year as a visiting scholar at the Institute for Advanced Study (IAS) in Princeton, then returned to England for a year and taught at the University of Birmingham. Cornell invited him back in 1951, and the IAS offered him a permanent post in 1953. By that time Robert Oppenheimer was the new IAS director. Oppenheimer wanted to rein in the growing deployment of nuclear weapons that he helped create. But as the Cold War gained momentum his position was unpopular among politicians.

Oppenheimer was driven to build atomic bombs by the fear that if he did not seize this power, Hitler would seize it first. Teller was driven to build hydrogen bombs by the fear that Stalin would use this power to rule the world.... In the end each of them was irrevocably committed to exercises of the human will in the political as well as the technical sphere. And so each of them in his own way came to grief. [Dyson(1979a)][91]

In a letter of 1 May 2000, the STS class quoted this passage then asked Professor Dyson "Do you feel that a person's drive to seize power always comes from fear?" We received his reply the same day:

> *No, I don't think that fear is usually the main reason for seizing power. You might say that Oppenheimer and Teller were both unsuccessful in seizing power, because they were driven by fear more than by a natural love of power. The power they seized did not last. The people who seize power successfully are usually charismatic leaders who love power and are not afraid of anybody. Examples we have seen in the last century were Lenin, Hitler, Castro. They believed that they were fulfilling a higher destiny and therefore did not need to be afraid. Not only the evil leaders had this unafraid quality. Good leaders like Joan of Arc, George Washington, Gandhi, had it too. They also believed in a higher destiny and were not afraid when they seized power.*

In 1954, Robert Oppenheimer was hauled before a hearing of the Atomic Energy Commission and accused of being a security risk. The hearing took place in the environment of McCarthyism, and was painfully polarizing within the physics community. Edward Teller's testimony was damaging to Oppenheimer. The year after Oppenheimer's security clearance was revoked, most physicists refused to shake Teller's hand. It was within that environment that I want my students to understand what it meant for Freeman Dyson to respond favorably to Teller's overtures of friendship in 1955— "I decided that no matter what the judgment of history upon this man might be, I had no cause to consider him my enemy." [Dyson(1979a)][92]

Six months after Edward Teller passed away, I wrote to Professor Dyson, partly in my STS role, and partly as the editor of a magazine for physics students. I inquired if Professor Dyson could suggest a suitable obituary for Teller that I could share with my students and the magazine's readers.

> *13 January 2004*
> *Dear Professor Dyson,*
> *I am glad that you received our card (selected by the students themselves)... Indeed I will pass along to them your greetings and thanks.*
> *I visited West Point in the early 90's, and my hosts said, "We had Edward Teller here a couple of months ago, and guess what—he's very nice!" That they felt it necessary to talk about their surprise at Teller's human kindness suggested to me that he was never able to entirely shake off the stigma that was attached to him after Robert Oppenheimer's security clearance hearing. I never met Teller personally but it seems to me that the stigma attached to him was unjust. The significance of your accepting him as your friend so soon after the Oppenheimer trial is a point that I wish I knew how to impress more effectively on students. If you know of some tribute to him that would be a fitting memorial, I would be delighted to publish it in "Radiations"....*
> *Happy New Year. I'm glad your family had a great trip to California. I doubt that the trip included a visit to George's tree house...*
> *Warm regards, Dwight*
>
> *22 January 2004*
> *...You ask whether I know of an obituary of Teller that you could publish in "Radiations." I send you as an attachment an appraisal of Teller that I wrote myself. It is not an obituary but a review of his memoirs, written shortly before his death. It was published in American Journal of Physics... I agree with your remarks about Teller, and I think my review describes him honestly and fairly....*

We leave Professor Dyson's letter and delve into an excerpt from his review of Edward Teller's autobiography, *Memoirs: A Twentieth-Century Journey in Science and Politics.* [Dyson(2002a)]

...The second half of this book contains a detailed account of Teller's in-volvement with weaponry... But here too, even when Teller is most heavily engaged in political battles, he portrays his opponents as human beings and describes their concerns fairly. There is sadness in his account but no bitter-ness....

The worst period of Teller's life began in 1954 when he testified against Oppen-heimer in the hearing conducted by the Atomic Energy Commission to decide whether Oppenheimer was a security risk.... One result of Teller's testimony was that a large number of his friends ceased to be friends. The community of physicists that Teller loved was split apart.... Oppenheimer and Teller both suffered grievously from the quarrel, but the damage to Teller was greater....

Almost two years later, we asked Professor Dyson more questions about his bonds of friendship with Edward Teller and Emma Epps. Even when Professor Dyson disagrees with you, he remains your friend.

> *6 December 2005*
> *Dear Professor Dyson,*
> *We hope 2005 has been good to you and your family. During this fall semester of 2005, 44 more students have walked down the path of your experiences, and from your experiences have expanded their own....*
> *Your friendship with Edward Teller is all the more remarkable because you and he became firm friends in 1955, about a year after the infamous Oppenheimer security risk hearings. We know that at that time and thereafter, many physicists refused to shake Teller's hand. Yet you were able to rise above the situa-tion, and become Teller's friend while remaining Oppenheimer's friend also. And while on the Princeton Citizens' Committee, you and Emma Epps became good friends even though you dis-agreed on your recommendations as Committee members. How were egos disarmed when you became a good friend with people with whom you disagreed?*

> *6 December 2005*
> *Dear Dwight,*
> *Thanks to you and the students for another thought-provoking lot of questions. 2005 has indeed been a good year for us and our tribe of fourteen grandchildren. We have much to be thank-ful for....*
> *I never had any difficulty in making friends with people that I disagreed with. Life would be very dull if we could only have friends who agreed with us about everything. Actually I dis-agreed more strongly with Emma Epps than I did with Edward*

*Teller, but that made no difference to our friendships. I liked
and respected both of them equally. Emma was hostile to science because she identified science with Princeton University
and Princeton University had been treating black people badly
for two hundred years.*[164] *She just did not trust scientists to
use their power wisely. That was understandable and maybe
she was right. Whether she was right or wrong, her presence as
a spokesman for the opposition made our meetings much more
meaningful. The whole point of the meetings of our citizens'
committee was to give all sides of the debate a chance to be
heard. Emma's presence made it clear that the opposition was
not only heard but also treated with respect.*

*With Teller my disagreements were more superficial, about de-
tails of the work we were doing together on nuclear reactors.
I did not disagree with him about his testimony at the Oppenheimer security hearing. What he said at the hearing was an
honest statement of his opinion. I was at that time still British
and not involved in American security problems. I thought the
main issue in the Oppenheimer hearing was whether the same
rules should apply to the famous people at the top as to the little people at the bottom. If anyone who was not famous had
behaved as Oppenheimer behaved, telling lies to security officers
and making up stories to confuse them, he would certainly have
been refused clearance. So to me the question was, should the
rules be applied fairly to big shots and little shots alike? If the
rules were applied fairly, Oppenheimer certainly should lose his
clearance. It seemed to me reasonable for Teller to say what he
thought about this. Anyhow, Teller was a likeable character and
remained a close friend of Leo Szilard who disagreed with him
much more fiercely than I did.*

Some historical background to Professor Dyson's reply may be necessary. The lies that Oppenheimer told the security officers occurred after
George Eltenton, an engineer, asked Oppenheimer's close friend Haakon
Chavalier, a professor of French literature at Berkeley, to approach Oppenheimer about sharing atomic bomb information with the Soviets. Eltenton
had worked in Russia before the war and saw the Russians as allies. Chavalier delivered the message at the Oppenheimer home in Berkeley during the
winter of 1942–43. Oppenheimer wanted nothing to do with Eltenton's suggestion. He and Chavalier agreed that any such exchanges would have to
originate from the highest levels of government. Both men put the conver-

---

[164]See Chapter 3, "The Other Princeton," in *Einstein on Race and Racism* by Fred
Jerome and Rodger Taylor. [Jerome and Taylor(2006)] Emma Epps, "one of the principal
and long-term leaders of Princeton's black community," first appears on p. 32.

sation out of mind. But when Oppenheimer was questioned by FBI agents about it six months later in a secretly taped conversation, at a meeting he thought would be about something else, he told the Eltenton story in such an ambiguous way that, when later ordered by General Groves to name the intermediary messenger, the agents had the impression that Chavalier was involved in a spy ring of such seriousness that, had their suspicions been true, could have seen Chavalier sentenced to a long prison term. [Bird and Sherwin(2005)][Chs. 14, 17]; [Else(1981)] These fabrications cost Chavalier his job and were the most damaging evidence against Oppenheimer at his 1954 security clearance hearing.

Throughout the rest of their lives, Professor Dyson remained close friends with Robert Oppenheimer, Edward Teller, and Emma Epps.

Losing with Dignity

In competitive events, while the victors are interviewed and collect the trophy, the losers walk off the field and are not heard from again. But to maintain the bonds of kinship that are necessary for the long-term continuation of the sport, the losers carry the most important role.

> *26 November 2014*
> *Dear Professor Dyson,*
> *On behalf of the Fall 2014 Science, Technology & Society class I bring you warm greetings. Once again we have journeyed with you through the landscapes and personalities and issues we find in "Disturbing the Universe"...*
> *...It has often been observed that we learn more from failure than we do from success. What have you learned from failure?*

I suppose we thought Professor Dyson would give us the kind of advice we would expect from a tennis coach—how to go from being a loser to being a winner. But here again, his advice went deeper than superficial interests. This advice came originally from his mother.

> *3 December 2014*
> *Dear Dwight and students,...*
> *...My biggest professional failure was in 1952. I was then a young professor with an army of graduate students working on a theory of the nuclear forces, the strong forces that hold the nuclei of atoms together. We used our theory to fit the experiments*

of Enrico Fermi, a famous physicist who measured the nuclear forces in Chicago. This was a big deal. If Fermi accepted our theory, we would have solved the most important problem in nuclear physics.

We thought we had a good fit to Fermi's experiments, and so I took a Greyhound bus from Cornell to Chicago to show our results to the great man. Fermi received me politely but was not impressed by our results. He said "There are two ways of doing calculations in physics. One way, which I prefer, is to have a clear physical picture. The other way is to have a consistent mathematical formalism. You have neither." Fermi was of course right. He had the insight to see that our theory was no good. I sadly took the bus back to Cornell to tell the students that all our hard work was worthless.

I learned from this failure what my mother had told me long before. To enjoy any sport or any competitive occupation, whether it is football or science, the most important thing is to be a good loser. It is the good losers who make the enterprise enjoyable for everybody. This is especially true in science, which is an international game that everybody is free to play. By being good losers, my students and I were able to stay in the game and find useful things to do. Twenty years later, we could share the joy of the next generation of winners, when they finally solved the mystery of nuclear forces.

Thank you once more for a good set of questions....

Happy Christmas to you and the class! Yours ever, Freeman.

We have always appreciated how Professor Dyson takes our little questions and unfolds them into larger issues. Incidentally, we have always observed him to be a gracious winner too.

Distant Closeness

Freeman Dyson grew up in Winchester, England, and attended a 600-year-old school. Rather than becoming obsessed with the past, he became obsessed with the future. In *Disturbing the Universe* he wrote "The people of six hundred years back and of six hundred years ahead are people like ourselves. They are our neighbors in this universe...." [Dyson(1979a)][193] The rest of this paragraph from *Disturbing the Universe* was quoted in a letter sent by the Spring 2004 class:

May 6, 2004

Dear Professor Dyson,

...In "A Distant Mirror" you note, "Technology has caused, and

will cause, profound changes in style of life and thought, sepa-
rating us from our neighbors. All the more precious, then are
the bonds of kinship that tie us together." One of our students
wrote...how she saw a family in a shopping mall, and each fam-
ily member was talking on a cell phone to someone who was not
there. Thus while the family was physically together, they were
apart. Do you see the "separation" of technology happening on
the short time scale as well as long timescales?
Thank you Professor Dyson for sharing your experiences and
insights with us.
Warm regards,
DEN and the 38 students in the Spring 2004 STS class

6 May 2003
Dear Dwight,...
I agree with your student that cell-phones are a wonderful exam-
ple of the way technology separates us from our neighbors. The
picture of the family at the shopping mall is a picture of the way
we are all going. I am not yet addicted to cell-phones but I am
already addicted to E-mail. I notice that as a result of E-mail I
have many more friendships all over the world, and many fewer
here at home. Instead of inviting our neighbors over for supper,
I sit here in the office writing E-mail to you. I cannot regret my
addiction to E-mail. After all, my own large family is scattered
over thousands of miles, and it is E-mail that has brought us
closer together. But we pay a price for this distant closeness.
The price is the family next door that we don't really know. So
the answer to your question is yes. Technology is separating us
on the short as well as the long time-scale....
That's all for today. Now I end by wishing you all a good
and peaceful summer, especially those who are going to Costa
Rica....
With thanks and good wishes to all of you,
Yours ever, Freeman.

This response prompted Todd B. to reflect on the new separateness driven
by technology:

```
    The journey through the text has now officially collided
with today's society, and Dyson nailed, almost 30 years in
advance, what is happening....  Perhaps more than the dangers
of cloning or stem cell research, or even artificial
intelligence, are the dangers [of] losing our sense of
brotherhood and becoming hypo-individualized....  Each person
in my family has a cell phone, each person a TV, each person
```

a computer, and we fail to spend a lot of time physically
together. For my family that is because my parents live
overseas, but for most that is because they don't know how to
be with each other and lack social skills. Yet, there are
good reasons for searching for the future, reasons to hope,
and reasons to try to come together and be <u>us</u>...

In the first chapter of *Zen and the Art of Motorcycle Maintenance*
Robert Pirsig writes "We want to make good time, but for us the emphasis
is on 'good' and not 'time'..." [Pirsig(1999)][13]

> *7 May 2002*
> *Dear Professor Dyson,...*
> *Another voice we are reading this semester is Robert Pirsig's*
> *"Zen and the Art of Motorcycle Maintenance." Among many*
> *other things Pirsig emphasizes the importance of living in the*
> *present moment, and spends much of the narrative describing*
> *the details of what's around him at a given time. It's like he em-*
> *phasizes "being" besides "doing." How do you link your passion*
> *for the future with the here-and-now of the present moment?*

> *20 May 2002*
> *Dear Dwight and students,...*
> *How do I link my passion for the future with Pirsig's emphasis*
> *on the present moment? The best answer I can come up with*
> *is to say that I admire Pirsig but do not try to be like him.*
> *He and I have many different interests. We agree about the*
> *importance of tools and of taking care of young people. But he is*
> *intensely interested in philosophy and I am not. I am intensely*
> *interested in the long-range future and he is not. I am glad*
> *you are reading his book, which contains a lot of wisdom and is*
> *beautifully written. But it would be boring if Pirsig and I agreed*
> *about everything.*

Kinship with Extraterrestrials?

The famous "blue dot" photo of the Earth taken by *Voyager 1* from four
billion miles away dramatically re-emphasizes the question of whether we
are alone in the black vastness of the universe. Is there any hope for kinship
with aliens?

One attempt to estimate the number of technologically communicative civilizations per galaxy comes from Frank Drake, a co-founder of

SETI, the Search for Extra-Terrestrial Intelligence. [Comins and Kauf-mann(2000)][420–423] The Drake equation starts with the number of stars per galaxy, then makes cuts. A reasonable estimate suggests about 200 billion stars per galaxy, or 2×10^{11}. Take the fraction of them that have planets within their star's life zone. Of all the planets within a star's life zone, take the fraction of them on which life begins. Of all the planets where life begins, take the fraction of them where life evolves to intelligence. Now imagine an intelligent civilization that can communicate by radio contin-uously for, say, a thousand years. Their broadcasts make a radio wave a thousand light-years long, moving outward at the speed of light. If that wave sweeps over the Earth, to hear it we must be tuned in during the thousand-year interval when the wave goes by. It's not enough to be good; we also have to be lucky.

For all of the factors in the Drake equation except the number of stars per galaxy, we have so little data that we can only speculate. A pessimist might guess that only one percent of all stars have planets, one percent of planets lie within a life zone, and so on. An optimist might guess that all stars have at least one planet and half the stars have a planet in their life zones, that life develops on half the planets that orbit within life zones, and so on. The fraction of a star's life that communicative intelligence exists, is anyone's guess. The optimist might hope the human race can enjoy radio communication for a million years (10^6 yr), one-ten-thousandth of the Sun's ten-billion-year (10^{10} yr) lifetime. A pessimist might say that because civilizations learn about radio and nuclear weapons about the same time, we will be lucky to avoid blowing ourselves up for a century (10^2 yr), opening a window of radio communication for only one percent of one millionth of the Sun's lifetime.

Thus the Drake equation yields numbers that range from the pessimist's value of one or two technological civilizations per one hundred thousand galaxies, to the optimist's estimate of tens of millions of civilizations per galaxy! We have *no idea* how many technological, communicative civiliza-tions exist.

In addition, life elsewhere may bear little resemblance to life as we know it here. Life elsewhere might be based on the chemistry of silicon. The capability to make decisions, retain memory, reproduce, and exhibit other hallmarks of life might be expressed in clouds of polarized molecules. Professor Dyson commented,

I reject as worthless all attempts to calculate from theoretical principles the frequency of occurrences of intelligent life forms in the universe. Our ignorance of the chemical processes by which life arose on earth makes such calculations meaningless. [Dyson(1979a)][209]

The *Kepler* satellite, launched in March 2009, searches for extrasolar planets by taking pictures of stars at different times and subtracting the images to see if anything changed. *Kepler* has surveyed hundreds of stars. So far every star surveyed has revealed at least one planet. Score one for Drake equation optimists, although *Kepler* also shows that most of those planets do not lie within their star's life zone and few of them resemble Earth. However, in 2014, *Kepler* found an intriguing planet called Kepler 186f, orbiting a star 500 light-years away. Kepler 186f is about the same size as the Earth and orbits within the life zone of its star. [Quintana *et al.*(2014)] This does not mean the optimists are right. But it does mean that it's not futile to be an optimist.

> *4 December 2013*
> *Dear Professor Dyson,*
> *On behalf of the Fall 2013 semester Science, Technology, & Society class, we thank you once again for being part of our lives....*
> *For estimating the number of communicative civilizations per galaxy, the numbers that go into the Drake equation are so uncertain as to make any conclusions meaningless. You made this point in the chapter "Extraterrestrials" when you wrote "I reject as worthless all attempts to calculate from theoretical principles the frequency of occurrence of intelligent life forms in the universe." That said, what does your intuition tell you? Given that the Kepler satellite has found at least one planet around every star it has surveyed so far, which outcome would be more difficult to understand: That life and intelligence are rare and perhaps unique in the universe, or that life and intelligence occur with a non-negligible frequency? In other words, if you were going to bet on the existence of other intelligent life in our part of the galaxy close enough that we could exchange radio signals on a timescale within the scope of a civilization's lifetime, how would you bet?*
>
> *6 December 2013*
> *Dear Dwight,...*
> *There are two possibilities about the origin of life. Either the origin of life is a lucky chance with very low probability. Or it is a routine event with reasonable probability. So long as we do not understand the details of the process of originating life, both*

*possibilities are open and it does not make sense to guess which
is more likely. If I had to bet on finding evidence of life, I would
certainly bet on the positive side, because a bet on the negative
side could never win. That does not mean that a positive result
is more likely.*

Professor Dyson is definitely an optimist. Perhaps that is why he has lived
a long and interesting life.

Several times in our STS discussions we have asked what it means for
a society to be civilized. The only hallmark of civilization that could be
detected at interstellar distances would be electromagnetic signals. In 1964,
Nikolai Kardashev suggested a classification scheme for civilizations based
on the extent of their technology. [Kardashev(1964)] Type 1 civilizations
command the resources of their planet; Type 2 controls the resources of an
entire star system, and a Type 3 civilization controls the resources of an
entire galaxy.

When a Type 1 civilization's need for energy outstrips the resources
of its planet, it could move towards a Type 2 civilization by constructing
a fleet of solar panels orbiting around the star to collect more of its light
energy. That concept forms the basis of the so-called "Dyson sphere." In
1960 Professor Dyson described how a Type 2 civilization in possession
of such a fleet might be detected. [Dyson(1960)][165] The notion of a Dyson
sphere has entered popular culture, helped along by a *Star Trek* episode
that envisioned a Dyson sphere as a rigid shell completely surrounding a
star, with its inner surface inhabited.[166] However, that design is not what
Professor Dyson proposed, for such a shell would be mechanically unstable.
We wondered how realistic it would be to anticipate the construction of
such an array by human beings.

> *29 April 2011*
> *Dear Professor Dyson,*
> *We trust that 2011 so far has been a splendid year for you and
> your extended family.... Do you think we humans will ever be
> able to come up with enough resources to build a Dyson Sphere?*

> *29 April 2011*
> *Dear Dwight,...*
> *The "Dyson sphere" is a total misunderstanding of what I had
> in mind, but we will probably develop big settlements and indus-
> tries in space, which will make grand-scale engineering projects*

---

[165] Professor Dyson credits the original concept to Olaf Stapleton's 1937 novel *Star Maker*.
[166] See http://www.youtube.com/watch?v=ECLvFLkvY7Y.

*feasible. The question is not whether these are technically pos-
sible, but whether we will have the motivation to carry them
through. If you look at the Solar System as a whole, there is
no lack of resources to do all kinds of crazy stuff. And some of
the big enterprises may make sense. It all depends on human
choices which we cannot predict.*

Stretching our imaginations further, given the vast distances between
stars we tried to envision humanity someday becoming a Type 3 civilization.

*April 6, 1999
Dear Professor Dyson,
...Given the fact that our lifetimes are so short compared to the
time to traverse interstellar distances, do you think we will ever
develop a Type 3 civilization? What would motivate people to
begin such a migration knowing that only their descendants so
many generations removed would finish it?
Thank you.
The STS Class*

*10 April 1999
Dear Dwight,
Thanks for your message, and thanks to the class for their good
questions....
Type 3 civilizations. These necessarily take hundreds of thousands of years to grow, since it takes almost a hundred thousand
years for light to travel from one side of a galaxy to the other.
When you are talking about things that take hundreds of thousands of years to do, the present human lifetime is not relevant.
Long before we are in a position to evolve a Type 3 civilization,
we will probably know how to control our life processes so that
we can live as long as we like. Many of us might prefer not to
be immortal, but there will be a variety of kinds of people with
a variety of lifetimes. People who want to travel long distances
will be able to choose appropriate lifetimes. Of course it is impossible to guess what their motivations might be. Why did the
paleo-native Americans travel all the way from Alaska to Tierra
del Fuego in less than a thousand years?*

He summarized this mind-blowing vision in his "Extraterrestrials" chapter:

*Given plenty of time, there are few limits to what a technological society
can do. Take first the question of colonization. Interstellar distances look
forbiddingly large to human colonists, since we think in terms of our short
human lifetime.... But a long-lived society will not be limited by a human*

lifetime. If we assume only a modest speed of travel, say one hundredth of the speed of light, an entire galaxy can be colonized from end to end within ten million years.... [I]nterstellar distances are no barrier to a species which has millions of years at its disposal. If we assume... that advances in physical technology will allow ships to reach one half of light velocity, then inter-galactic distances are no barrier either. [Dyson(1979a)][210]

If life learns to travel between the stars, so that life does not end when any particular star dies, and if the universe lasts forever, would it be possible, in principle, for life to go on indefinitely? By addressing this question in an invited 1979 article called "Time Without End: Physics and Biology in an Open Universe," [Dyson(1979b)] Professor Dyson helped start the astrophysical sub-discipline of cosmological eschatology. The article raises meaningful scenarios about what life could do, limited only by the laws of nature, if time has no end.[167] For example, on a timescale of a hundred trillion (10^{14}) years, all the long-lived, low-mass red dwarf stars burn out; on a timescale of 10^{1500} years all nuclei besides iron are radioactive, and so on. Within such mind-stretching timescales, all physical processes, all civilizations, would have ample time to play themselves out to whatever their ends will be.

> *25 April 1995*
> *Dear Professor Dyson,...*
> *What do you think will become of our civilization?*
> *Having read "Disturbing the Universe" and having studied at the level of a popular lecture not only the big bang cosmology but also [been shown the results of] your 1979 paper "Time Without End: Physics and Biology in an Open Universe," the students have confronted some implications that are both disturbing and challenging. It seems most of them had never pondered before the question of the long-term fate of civilization and the universe.*
> *Warm regards, DEN*
>
> *26 April 1995*
> *Dear Dwight Neuenschwander,*
> *...What do you think will become of our civilization? I tried*

---

[167]In the forward of the 2004 printing of *Infinite in All Directions*, Professor Dyson explains that, with the 1998 discovery of the accelerating universe, the answer is not as simple now as it was when he first investigated the question of whether life and intelligence can continue forever in a cold expanding universe. However, the 1979 paper is still valid for asking about the limitations, due only to matters of principle in physics and biology, on life and intelligence across the long-term future.

*to answer this question as best I could in the last chapter of
"Infinite in All Directions." Of course nobody is wise enough
to foresee the march of history. Fate will play us all kinds of
unexpected tricks, good and bad. But the future is still largely in
our own hands. History gives us opportunities to make choices,
to take advantage of Fate's tricks in one way or another. My
firmest belief about the future is that within a few hundred years
life will be streaming out from the earth all over the solar system
and beyond. Once the expansion of the domain of life is started,
we will be powerless to stop it even if we wanted to. If we are
wise, we will go along with it and adapt ourselves to whatever
opportunities we find. Then our civilization will have chances
to grow and diversify in ways we cannot imagine.*
Yours sincerely,
Freeman Dyson

In the last chapter of *Infinite in All Directions*, we are given the image of
humanity on this planet to be like a worm in a cocoon, about to transform
itself into a butterfly and take flight: [Dyson(1988)][298–299]

*The expansion of life and of mankind into the universe will lead to a vast
diversification of ecologies and of cultures.... It is useless to try to imagine
the varieties of experience, physical and intellectual and religious, to which
mankind may attain. To describe the metamorphis of mankind as we embark
on our immense journey into the universe, I return to the humble image of the
butterfly. All that can be said was said long ago by Dante in Canto 10 of the
Purgatorio:*

> *O you proud Christians, wretched souls and small,*
> *Who by the dim lights of your twisted minds*
> *Believe you prosper even as you fall,*
> *Can you not see that we are worms, each one*
> *Born to become the angelic butterfly*
> *That flies defenseless to the Judgment Throne?*

The Greening of the Galaxy

So far in human history, we have used gray technology, from mud bricks to
air conditioned houses, to help the human body cope with the environment.
But we are now reaching the capability of genetically engineering the human

body to fit the environment.[168] Not only might we learn to program the metabolism of a tree so that its sap produces octane or alcohol, we might also program our DNA so that our descendants can walk bare-faced on Mars.

The question that will decide our destiny is not whether we shall expand into space. It is: shall we be one species or a million? A million species will not exhaust the ecological niches that are awaiting the arrival of intelligence.
...When we are a million species spreading through the galaxy, the question "Can man play God and still stay sane?" will lose some of its terrors. We shall be playing God, but only as local deities and not as lords of the universe.... But in the long run, the sane will adapt and survive better than the insane.... Sanity is, in its essence, nothing more than the ability to live in harmony with nature's laws.
...At the same time as life is extending its habitat quantitatively, it will also be changing and evolving qualitatively into new dimensions of mind and spirit that we cannot imagine. [Dyson(1979a)][236–237]

5 December 2001
Dear Professor Dyson,...
In chapter 21, "The Greening of the Galaxy," you remark that "we shall be playing God, but only as local deities and not as lords of the universe." Are you implying that acting as "local deities" is justifiable, and where do you draw the line between being a local deity and trying to be a lord of the universe? You also ask in chapter 15 ("The Island of Doctor Moreau") whether we can play God and still stay sane, and your answer is no. If we are local deities, are we insane?...

8 December 2001
Dear Dwight,...
...You are right in pointing out an inconsistency between the Doctor Moreau chapter and the Greening of the Galaxy chapter of my book. In the Doctor Moreau chapter I am using Wells's powerful myth of Doctor Moreau as an image of a mad scientist playing God with the animals that he has in his power. In the Greening chapter I am imagining a group of people, far away from the rest of human society, who have the right to use genetic engineering to determine their own future. These two

---

[168]These mind-stretching topics are discussed in chapters such as "Thought Experiments," "Clades and Clones" and "The Greening of the Galaxy" in the last third of *Disturbing the Universe.*

images of genetic engineering, one insane and the other sane,
are both possible. Where you draw the line is a question for in-
dividual judgment. You must look at each situation and decide
for yourself whether the use of genetic engineering is justified.
I do not try to draw a line that would apply to all situations. In
my view, one of the important factors in forming a judgment
is whether the use of genetic engineering is imposed by some
political authority or freely chosen by the parents. The danger
of insanity is generally less, but is not entirely removed, if the
parents have freedom of choice.

Genetic diversity may be necessary before the human race can expand very far beyond Earth. Cultural diversity will expand even more as our descendants fan out across the galaxy. In the meantime, cultural and language diversity closer to home expands the mind and makes life interesting. I like to ask my students, most of whom are twenty-something years old, "After graduating you are going to tour Europe on a bicycle, or join the Peace Corps and teach in Malaysia, or take a motorcycle trip to Alaska— right? If not then, when *will* you do it?" The looks I get—and the stories we exchange—are priceless....

...We are sitting in a century-old Maori meeting house next to Lake Rotorua in New Zealand, attending a concert of traditional Maori songs and dances. The evening twilight turns the blue lake to soft grey as the Southern Cross emerges in lovely benediction to a wonderful day. The Maori carvings—the ancestors around us—gaze upon us with bright paua-shell eyes that catch the last rays of deepening twilight, as the young Maori men and women sing a tender lullaby....[169]

E tangi ana koe,	*Softly the moon has ascended*
Hine e hine.	*little girl, darling girl.*
Kua ngenge ana koe	*Sleep till the long night has ended,*
Hine e hine....	*little girl, darling girl....*

...Walking on a Saturday night up the narrow cobblestone streets of old Coimbra, Portugal, I hear the rich baritone of a man's voice coming from

---

[169] *Hine e hine*, pronounced *hee'-nay eh hee-nay'*, written in 1907 by contralto Fannie Rose Howie of Maori and European parents. She performed under the name Te Rangi Pai. Like most Maori music created after European contact, this lovely song is a mix of European and traditional Maori styles. Translation from [Freedman *et al.*(1974)Freedman, Siers and Ngata][66].

somewhere up the hill among the ancient multi-story houses. All along the way, a silent crowd of local people line the narrow streets, sitting on steps and standing in doorways. Everyone listens in rapt attention. I stop and listen too. I catch a glimpse of the singer, a gentleman dressed in a long black overcoat, wearing a black top hat.... Ah, this must be *Fado*, signature Portuguese music of longing and melancholy... When the singing concludes everyone lingers to let the music sink in. After several moments a man sitting on the step next to me slowly stands up, smiles, releases a deep sigh, and softly says to me "Ah, agora que é Portugal," "Ah, now *that* is Portugal."

...We are a dozen high school students visiting Ramah Navajo Reservation in New Mexico, spending several days as volunteers who have come to help build a utility building. One evening we are guests in a Navajo hogan.[170] Our group leader begins introducing us. After introducing two people he pauses. The teenage translator says nothing but looks steadily at him. Our leader continues, pauses again to polite silence, resumes again and eventually makes all the introductions with unbroken silence from the translator. When it is clear that our leader has finished, the teenage girl begins speaking in Navajo. We visitors are given a lesson in the phenomenal memory skill that comes with an oral tradition, as our translator goes on for several minutes, reciting back to her attentive listeners all that she just heard about us. Oh how we wish we had learned a few Navajo phrases before we came! Even if we could only say "hello" (*yá' át' ééh*) and "thank you" (*ahé heé*) and "good-bye" (*há go óneé*) that would have laid a foundation for bonds of kinship....

Jean H., who plans to do missionary work, pondered, "Dyson also taught me about the power of language when he told the story of how he got caught, due to an injury, in an all-Welsh-speaking community in Wales. I am taking this thought with me as I go forth into the many mission fields of life...How much have we stripped away from people by trying to Westernize them?"

> 1 May 2000
> Dear Professor Dyson,...
> In Ch. 20 (Clades and Clones) you discussed languages, and how some are dying off. What do you feel about we Americans?
> — here we are, the most influential country yet we do not put emphasis on learning other languages besides English.

---

[170] "Hogan," from the Navajo *hooghan* for house, is the only Navajo word adopted into English.

1 May 2000
Dear Dwight,
Luckily I have a few short days left before your term ends...
Yes, it is a great shame that Americans generally do not take the
trouble to learn other peoples' languages. But I have to admit
that the English are even worse. I grew up in England and
never learned to speak any other language decently. I admire the
Mormons, because they spend two years abroad as missionaries
and take the trouble to learn the language of the country they
are sent to. When I visited Brigham Young University in Utah,
I was delighted to find a crowd of students who all knew a second
language and were familiar with other cultures. But you don't
have to be a Mormon to spend two years in a different culture.
You can also join the Peace Corps. My Peace Corps daughter
perfected her French in francophone Cameroon.
Of course the best time to learn a second language is when you
are two or three. But you lose it if you do not keep on speaking
it as you grow up. I wish the schools in the US would allow (not
compel) children to be immersed in a second language as soon
and as long as possible. This would be easy in regions where
Spanish speakers are a big fraction of the population, as they
are in New York or California. It is a terrible waste to bring
up children surrounded by Spanish-speakers and not speaking
Spanish.

As a schoolboy Freeman Dyson taught himself Russian. At the Arms
Control and Disarmament Agency he studied Russian-language documents.
In Singapore, I asked Professor Dyson if he was fluent in Russian. He said
no. Imme, whose first language was German, clarified that his standard of
fluency is very high.

The scarcity of American students who learn a second language continues to bother STS students. In the spring of 2003 they brought it up
again.

8 May 2003
Dear Professor Dyson,...
Against the background of "Clades and Clones," we are curious
about your thoughts on our country's increasing measures to-
ward monolingualism. We noted in our discussions that many
languages are projected to go extinct in this century, and that
one can travel abroad and expect to find English almost every-
where.

21 May 2003
Dear Dwight,...
Good to hear from you again. For the last few days I have been
enjoying writing a review of a new biography of Newton. I send
you the review as an attachment. ...The life of Newton is a
wonderful example of the unpredictability of human nature. A
weird mixture of mathematics, magic, theology and politics, and
out of it came modern physics!
I find it encouraging that Spanish is gaining ground in this coun-
try rather than disappearing. Recently some cousins of Imme
from Argentina came to visit. They speak only German and
Spanish, and we were anxious when they decided to spend a day
in New York on their own. When they came back to Princeton
at the end of the day, they said they had had no trouble at all,
because everybody in New York speaks Spanish. It is true of
course that most of the rare languages become extinct, but the
major languages, those that have a homeland with more than a
million people, seem to be surviving well. The fact that English
is a second language for much of the world does not mean that
the local languages are disappearing. Of course I still deplore
the fact that Americans and Brits don't take the trouble, as ed-
ucated people everywhere else must do, to learn to be fluent in a
second language. It would have been much better if we had kept
Latin as the second language for international communication,
as we did in the time of Newton. But I am not advocating the
revival of Latin. It is too late for that.
Now it is time to go home to Imme and supper... As always,
thanks to the students for their questions and all good wishes
for the summer. Yours ever, Freeman.

Having struggled myself to learn German and Spanish, a day with Imme's
Argentine cousins would have been instructive. Although a common language would make the world easier for bureaucrats to manage and marketers
to steer, the variety of human experience, expressed through our diverse languages, customs, and cultures, enhances interestingness and gives us more
to live for.

Are we to be a clade or a clone? This is perhaps the central problem
in humanity's future. In other words, how are we to make our social insti-
tutions flexible enough to preserve our precious biological and cultural diver-
sity? [Dyson(1979a)][223]

After our class discussed Professor Dyson's chapter "Clades and
Clones," Nigerian student Larry A. wrote:

This week I realized that I was making a great mistake by
not trying my best to have a conversation in my own language.
I read Dyson's ''Clades and Clones'' and I could not help but
agree with some of the points he made concerning languages,
as well as disagree in some other ways. It seems to me now
that I have traded my language for dollars, the language that
my great-grandfathers fought their colonial masters to keep.
Not only have I lost the ability to speak my natural language
fluently but I have also lost the ability to write a single
complete sentence in my own language.... During the British
colonial rule in Nigeria, the country was forced to give up
its languages for British English.... The inability of the
British to turn the country into a clone lead to the failure
of their colonialism. Nigeria today has more than 256
languages... but they are bound together with the universal
English language.... Having a common language has its own
advantages and disadvantages...

A 22 May 2003 letter to Professor Dyson contained more lines about
another nation's language:

> *My mother's side of the family has a small amount of*
> *Potawatomi in our genes (Grandpa knew the dances) and the*
> *Potawatomi tribe members are struggling to keep their language*
> *alive. It's an uphill battle, there are few fluent speakers. Lan-*
> *guage diversity gives all of us some insights into other peoples'*
> *view of the human condition....*

The Potawatomi are struggling valiantly to keep their language alive.
The nation has a Language Department that offers classes and literature.
Over the decade since the preceding letter was written, the number of fluent
Potawatomi speakers is still small, but interest seems to be growing. The
People of the Fire have not given up.[171]

Bozho nikan!	*Greetings, friend!*
Ahaw nciwénmoyan ewabmlnan.	*I am glad to see you.*
Iwgwien ébyayen mṡoté.	*Thank you for your visit here.*

---

[171]Potawatomi phrases from http://www.kansasheritage.org/PBP/homepage.html and
http://www.potawatomi.org/lang.

16 Two Windows

Letters on Science and Religion

> *"Science without religion is lame, religion without science is blind."* –Albert Einstein[172]

***

This evening the students enter the classroom to *All Night Vigil*, Op. 37, by Sergi Rachmaninov (1873–1943). Even though Rachmaninov was not deeply pious, *All Night Vigil* forms one of the most beautiful liturgies of the Orthodox Church. A section of Vigil No. 2 comes from Psalm 103:

> *Blessed art Thou, O Lord...*
> *Is wisdom hast Thou made all things.*
> *Glory to Thee, O Lord, who hast made them all.*

On the whiteboard are today's STS questions *du jour:*

> *What kinds of questions are best approached with the tools of science?*
> *What kinds of questions are best approached with the tools of religion?*
> *Is it irrational to allow the possibility of some sort of Cosmic Mind?*
> *What is faith? What is its relationship to doubt?*
> *Which is more important: What you believe, or how you behave?*

Here in our small faith-based denomination-sponsored university located in Oklahoma, a discussion of science, technology, society, and life would leave unaddressed some of the largest questions in students' minds if we did not include science and religion. This is an important topic for two reasons.

One reason comes from the history of Western civilization. The connection between science and religion in this tradition was eloquently described by Professor Dyson in 1998, in his review of two books, both written by physicists: *The Meaning of it All* by Richard Feynman, and *Belief in God in an Age of Science* by John Polkinghorne.[173] Before turning to the books,

---

[172][Einstein(1956)][26]

[173]R. P. Feynman, *The Meaning of It All* (1998); J. Polkinghorne, *Belief in God in an Age of Science* (2001); Polkinghorne is also an ordained minister in the Church of England.

Professor Dyson sketched some historical background. Theology is the intellectual study of God. "The idea that God may be approached and understood through intellectual analysis is uniquely Christian... The prominence of theology in the Christian world has two important consequences for the history of science." On the one hand, "Western science grew out of Christian theology.... A thousand years of theological disputes nurtured the habit of analytical thinking that could also be applied to the analysis of natural phenomena." But on the other hand, "the close historical relations between theology and science have caused conflicts between science and Christianity that do not exist between science and other religions...." The common soil from which both Christianity and science grew was Greek philosophy. "The historical accident that caused the Christian religion to become heavily theological was the fact that Jesus was born in the eastern part of the Roman Empire at a time when the prevailing culture was profoundly Greek." [Dyson(1998)]

The second reason for including science and religion in an Oklahoma classroom comes from regional culture. As a Territory and later as a state (statehood came in 1907), Oklahoma was awash in the conservative religious fervor that became entrenched in the American South after the Civil War. The defeated Confederacy found in religion a way to maintain a distinctive cultural identity. [Phillips(2005)][Ch. 5] In a religious secession from Northern mainline denominations, much of the southern gospel leaned towards fundamentalism.

Oklahoma is often described by its residents as "the buckle of the Bible Belt." Despite the state's numerous public and private universities, despite its leading meteorological expertise, despite its world-class research hospitals and efforts to build a spaceport, Oklahomans find themselves embedded in a cultural environment that sometimes sees science as a threat to religion. It came as no surprise that in our very first STS batch of questions, sent to Professor Dyson on 6 April 1993, he was bluntly asked "What effect does science have on your religion?" His reply of April 9 has echoed throughout all our classes and beyond it across the years:

> *I am not an orthodox Christian, but I am loosely attached to Christianity and value the serenity and community that the Church provides. There is no conflict at all between my science and my religion. I consider science and religion to be two windows through which we look out at the world. Neither window by itself gives a complete view. The windows are different*

but the world outside is the same. Our job as scientists is to explore as much as we can through one window while recognizing that this window gives only a one-sided view. In the talk with the title "Science and Religion" I discuss this question a little more deeply. That talk was also expanded into a book, "Infinite in All Directions."

Professor Dyson's "two windows" metaphor has given us a vivid mental picture on which to build. Science and religion can be what they are, and both treated with respect. While the two windows cannot be looked through simultaneously, how *are* they to be reconciled after looking through both of them?

In 1985, Professor Dyson delivered the Gifford Lectures in Aberdeen, Scotland. The next year he addressed the Conference of Catholic Bishops on the same subject. The Gifford Lectures and the talk to the bishops were published afterwards as *Infinite in All Directions.* [Dyson(1988)]

The 1989 Gifford Lectures were delivered by Ian Barbour, and published as *Religion in an Age of Science.* [Barbour(1990)] Barbour slices the relationships between science and religion into four dimensions: integration, independence, dialogue, and irreconcilable conflict. Barbour does not claim his categories are exhaustive or mutually exclusive. But for discussion they offer a useful partitioning.

Integration

A model of integration that hits close to home for many STS students is "natural theology." In his Gifford Lectures, Professor Dyson began,

Adam Gifford in his will establishing the Gifford Lectures ordained that the subject should be "Natural Theology." The words "Natural Theology" have a technical meaning. According to Christian doctrine, God gave us two books in which his actions are recorded. One book is the Bible, the other is the Book of Nature.... Natural Theology is the reading of God's mind as expressed in the works of Nature. [Dyson(1988)][3–4]

A precedent exists for seeing God in nature through science, as Professor Dyson reminds us in "The Argument from Design" chapter of *Disturbing the Universe.* For instance, Thomas Wright waxed theological in 1750 when announcing the discovery of galaxies: "Since as the Creation is, so is the Creator also magnified..." [Dyson(1979a)][245]

Some parents send their children to denomination-sponsored universities on the assumption that this is how they teach science. However, the ambiguity inherent in trying to deduce God's attributes from observations of nature places natural theology in an awkward situation. Gazing at glorious sunsets and snow-capped mountains may lead to uplifting conclusions about the nature of God. But watching an orca bite a sea turtle in half could lead with equal logical justification to an opposite conclusion about God's attributes. Nature is beautiful and awesome, and she is also violent and cruel. When integrating religion and science by natural theology it's too easy to cherry-pick images to support a foregone position. Professor Dyson's Gifford Lecture introduction continued, "I do not claim to be reading the Book of Nature when I do a scientific calculation..." [Dyson(1988)][4]

> *1 May 1998*
> *Dear Professor Dyson,*
> *...From [your chapter] "The Argument from Design"– How would you integrate science and religion?*
>
> *2 May 1998*
> *Dear Dwight and class,*
> *Thank you for your message and the questions. Since time is short I give you some quick answers. Since I am retired I am busier than ever before. Traveling too much and pontificating wherever I go. Luckily your message arrived during a brief visit home between two trips.*
> *The quick answer is, I don't integrate science and religion. Science and religion are two windows that give us different views of the world outside. Both are valid, but we can't look through both windows at the same time. I attach to this message a chapter with the title "The Two Windows" explaining what this means. The chapter belongs to a book "How Large is God?" edited by John Templeton and published a few months ago.*
> *Yours ever, Freeman*

In the attached draft of his Templeton chapter, "Two Windows," Professor Dyson further developed the two windows metaphor:

> *Science and religion give us views of the universe which are both illuminating and both, to some degree, true. But they cannot be seen simultaneously. They are an example of the situation which Niels Bohr called complementarity,... when a single point of view cannot give you a complete description of things. The most famous example of complementarity is the first thing God created, light...* [Templeton(1997)][47–68]

Professor Dyson offers a brief description of wave-particle duality, then continues with another reason why the two windows are distinct:

Another reason why you cannot look through the two windows simultaneously is because they require different ways of looking. To look through the religion window you have to be quiet. You have to meditate or pray or think or listen or read or write, opening your mind or your soul to the still small voice that you hope to hear. To look through the science window you need only learn to handle a few technical tools then hammer away to your hearts content. Science is gregarious and noisy. It is mostly done by groups rather than by individuals. The joy of doing good science is like the joy of helping to put a solid roof on a house. Science has more in common with house-building than with philosophy.

As understood by its practitioners today, science tries to explain nature in terms of mechanisms that operate exclusively *within* nature. Whenever someone invokes supernatural events or personalities they are no longer doing science, but something else. That something else may be worthy of respect—it might even be true—but it's not *science*. Richard Feynman said in his lectures to undergraduates, "If we say that something is not a science, that does not mean that there is anything wrong with it. It just means that it is not a science. Love, for instance, is not a science." [Feynman *et al.*(1963)Feynman, Leighton and Sands][3–1]

Edwin Grant Conklin (1863–1952) was a distinguished embryonic biologist and zoologist who spent most of his long career at Princeton University. Before landing at Princeton, as a young professor he was invited to join the faculty at Ohio Wesleyan University. He was well acquainted with the culture of such universities. As a young man, before settling on a career in biology, Conklin considered entering the ministry. But when offered a biology faculty position at Ohio Wesleyan he expressed a concern.

Before I accepted President Bashford's invitation to the professorship of biology I told him that I must have freedom to teach the truth as I saw it, and in particular that I could not teach biology without teaching evolution. He assured me that I should have such freedom... Thanks to his vision and courage and to the broadmindedness of his successors there has never since been any serious attempt to interfere with the teaching of evolution at Ohio Wesleyan University. [Harvey(1958)][68]

I understand Conklin's concern, having felt it myself. When invited to interview for my present position, I was asked to present a colloquium. I talked about recent developments in big bang cosmology, first because it is interesting, and second to gauge the intellectual climate at SNU. Like Conklin at Ohio Wesleyan, so far at SNU I have encountered no attempts by administrators, trustees, or other faculty to interfere with the teaching of evolution or big bang cosmology. So far both windows have always been open during my time here.

Independence

Keeping science and religion in separate compartments of the mind offers an extreme form of independence between them. But instead of being seen as highly reactive reagents that must be isolated from each other like sparks from gasoline, a more honest form of independence occurs when science and religion are seen as complementary, asking different kinds of questions that require different sets of tools. As I understand it, this forms the essence of Professor Dyson's "two windows" metaphor.

Dialogue

The *Dialogues* of Plato are significant in the history of thought. But the Dialogue we would find even more intriguing has only been imagined:

> *13 April 2009*
> *Dear Professor Dyson,*
> *...If you could select one individual from history for a face-to-face conversation, who would you select and why, and what might you ask them?*
> *Thank you again Professor Dyson for all you have contributed to our lives....*
> *On behalf of the students, Warm regards, DEN*
>
> *17 April 2009*
> *Dear Dwight,*
> *...The obvious choice would be Jesus of Nazareth, the person who had the most profound effect on our history and about whom we know very little. I would like to listen to him talk rather than asking him questions. If you insist on a question, I would ask whether he would consider it good or bad for the religion that he founded to become the official religion of the Roman Empire....*
> *Yours ever, Freeman.*

On important matters of human dignity, social justice, and respecting the environment, science and religion share many overlapping goals. Through dialogue and working together they can accomplish more than either one will separately. Science sees through its window something that religion does not: an understanding of how the physical world works. Religion sees through its window something that science does not: a sense of the sacred. An instructive instance of dialogue in action appeared in a 1990 manifesto written by Carl Sagan, "Preserving and Cherishing the Earth: An Appeal for Joint Commitment in Science and Religion:" [Sagan(1990)][174]

As scientists, many of us have had profound experiences of awe and reverence before the universe. We understand that what is regarded as sacred is more likely to be treated with care and respect. Our planetary home should be so regarded. Efforts to safeguard and cherish the environment need to be infused with a vision of the sacred. At the same time, a much wider and deeper understanding of science and technology is needed. If we do not understand the problem, it is unlikely we will be able to fix it. Thus, there is a vital role for religion and science.

The list of distinguished signatories included Hans Bethe and Freeman Dyson.

Irreconcilable conflict

This is the one that sells books and DVDs and makes headlines. When real or perceived conflict between science and religion flares up, it typically arises over one of three issues: teleology, free will, or origins. Teleology asks whether the universe has a purpose. Debates about free will ask if we are truly free to make autonomous choices. The stakes on questions of origins go deeper than natural history, reaching into human identity and the meaning of life.

In a 1996 address to the Pontifical Academy of Sciences, Pope John Paul II officially declared that no conflict exists between the Darwanian evolution and Roman Catholic teachings, stating "Today... new knowledge leads to

---

[174]It was presented in January 1990 at the Global Forum for National Religious Partnership for the Environment in Moscow.

recognition of the theory of evolution as more than a hypothesis." [Pope John Paul II(1997)][175]

The pope's statement and responses to it generated a lively article in *USA Today*. [Marklein(1996)] Leonard DeFlore, the president of the National Catholic Educational Association, supported the papal statement by saying "We start from the premise that all creation came from God. Beyond that its a scientific issue." The article's title exhibits perceptive journalistic marketing: "Pope accepts evolution, creates furor." The furor was introduced in the subtitle: "Creationists denounce pontiff's 'compromise.'" Mike Zovath of the Christian fundamentalist organization Answers in Genesis of Florence, Kentucky, set the pope straight with adamant certainty: "It's a complete compromise of God's word. It directly contradicts the Bible. It can't be compatible with the Christian position based on biblical principles and biblical understanding." William Hoesch of the Institute for Creation Research in San Diego, California (now of Dallas, Texas) added: "Because he [the pope] believes this, he's going to cause a lot of others to believe it, just because people want to believe stories like this, not because its scientifically valid. I think its pretty sad."[176]

The journalist mentioned that "supporters of creationism fear the effects of the pope's statement." The word choice was insightful: Fundamentalism is driven by *fear*. To a person immersed in a religious fundamentalist culture, the Science Book and the Sacred Book are opposing authorities and one must choose between them—with grave consequences if you get it wrong!

Scientific fundamentalists also see science and religion as mutually exclusive; to allow interpretations other than scientific ones is to admit irrational nonsense. Such certainty seems to assume the human mind to be capable of comprehending all things. But given that the human brain is part of nature, how can a *part* of nature hope to comprehend *all* of nature? John Dryden asked this question in 1682: [Dryden(1958)]

> *In this wilde Maze their vain Endeavours end:*
> *How can the less the Greater comprehend?*
> *Or finite reason reach Infinity?*

---

[175]Ever since the publication of *The Origin of Species* in 1859, the Catholic Church has never officially opposed evolution by natural selection; indeed, the 1996 statement of John Paul II updated a similar 1950 statement by Pope Pius XII.

[176]One wonders if the same criticism might apply to ICR's literal interpretation of *Genesis 1*. "Just because the ICR believes this..."

13 April 2009
Dear Professor Dyson,
I bring you greetings from the Spring 2009 section of the Science, Technology, and Society class...
Is there anything for which science does not have the answer?

17 April 2009
Dear Dwight,
...Here I can answer simply "almost everything." Science is a bag of tools which are spectacularly effective in answering questions for which the tools are designed, but quite ineffective for answering questions outside that area. Examples of questions outside the scope of science are: Which is the best form of government? Which is the best way to distribute wealth among humans? Do animals have rights equal to human rights? Is there such a thing as a just war? Is Sharia, the Islamic system of law, acceptable as the basis for Islamic civic societies? And so on, and so on. All questions about values rather than quantities.

Very few people become passionate about, say, semiconductor physics, even though the technologies it spawns have indelible effects on our daily lives. However, on topics such as the age of the Earth or the origin of species, which have zero practical effect on life's daily routines—but deep impact on how we see and value ourselves—many people become passionate to the point of withdrawing their children from public school and writing agitated letters to university presidents. Some of the faithful evidently assume big bang cosmology was dreamed up by heathen sorcerers for the expressed purpose of leading impressionable youth astray. But the history of this topic shows that its greatest skeptics were the scientists themselves, until they were compelled by the weight of evidence to take the paradigm seriously. A brief overview seems appropriate. Let us set religion aside for a few moments and put a question of origins directly to nature, in particular, a survey of big bang cosmology.

The Origin of the Universe as Seen Through the Window of Physics

At least five major evidence-based reasons justify our taking seriously the big bang cosmology. They are: (1) the dark night sky; (2) the observed expansion of the universe; (3) the relative abundances of the elements; (4) the existence and temperature of the big bang's afterglow (the cosmic background radiation, or CBR); and (5) correlations between temperature fluctuations in the CBR and the distribution of galaxies. Because science is evidence-based reasoning and its claims do not come from authority, we review these points and the evidence for them.[177]

(1) Dark sky: Since gravity attracts all matter together, why doesn't the universe collapse? A symmetry argument offered a candidate resolution. If the universe were filled with eternal stars distributed uniformly to infinity, the sum of gravitational forces on any one star due to all the others would cancel out. However, this arrangement would be highly unstable, like a knife balanced on its sharp tip—the slightest perturbation from perfect symmetry would trigger a collapse.

Furthermore, for any observer, every line of sight would eventually terminate on a star. The stars farther away would appear fainter, but there are more of them. In such a universe the sky could not be dark at night. The cosmos could not be infinite *and* its stars be static *and* eternal.

(2) Expansion of the universe: If the volume of the universe were finite then the instability and dark-sky problems of the infinite universe go away. In 1917, Albert Einstein applied his new General Theory of Relativity to the entire universe. General Relativity sees gravitation as geometry. Like a bowling ball curving a trampoline when placed on it, a star curves the space around it. The trampoline's curvature determines the trajectory of a marble rolling across it, similar to the curvature of space determining the motion of orbiting bodies.[178] Einstein made this mental picture mathematically precise. When applied to the entire cosmos, Einstein reasoned that perhaps all the matter in the universe curves space so much that the space closes back on itself. In other words, the three-dimensional space that stars move through, said Einstein, is the *surface* of a sphere in four spatial dimensions

---

[177]In class I feel it necessary to go into these points at the level of a public lecture, to address "How do we know?" concerns. The big bang can sound so outlandish to initiates that I feel it's important for students to realize that scientists do not make this stuff up. Many students come to class with misconceptions and skepticism about the big bang. For more technical detail see cosmology or astronomy textbooks, popularizations such as Steven Weinberg's *The First Three Minutes*, or the author's pedagogical "History of Big Bang Cosmology," written in parts for *The SPS Observer* and *Radiations* between their respective Fall 2007 and Spring 2010 issues (both magazines published by the American Institute of Physics).

[178]Technically, it's the curvature of four-dimensional spacetime. As Charles Misner, Kip Thorne, and John Wheeler wrote in *Gravitation* (Freeman, 1973), matter tells spacetime how to curve, and spacetime tells matter how to move.

(a "hypersphere"). While difficult to visualize, the notion can be put self-consistently into mathematics.[179]

Einstein assumed the universe to be static, because astronomical data at the time gave no reason to suppose the stars appreciably moved. The Russian mathematician Alexander Friedmann wondered what would happen if rates of change were allowed to be non-zero in Einstein's cosmological model. In 1922, Friedmann published a paper showing that, according to Einstein's equations, the surface of the hypersphere—in other words the observable universe—would expand or contract! In a second paper, Friedmann showed that other types of curvatures were consistent with Einstein—space could also break open like an infinite saddle-surface, or be infinite but have no curvature at all—and still expand.[180]

The expansion would stretch space analogous to how a photocopy machine enlarges an image. If you enlarge an image by 10%, two points A and B originally 10 centimeters apart become 11 cm apart; if point C was originally 20 cm from A, then after stretching, C and A are 22 cm apart. Suppose the stretching takes one second. The speed of B relative to A is 1 cm/s, but the speed of C relative to A is 2 cm/s. C was twice as far from A as was B, and as seen from A, C moves at twice the speed of B. Graphing the relative velocity of pairs of points vs. their separation yields a sloped straight line.

An observer on A might be tempted to assume that she resides at the center of the universe. But an observer at C would see all other points receding from him, such as A receding from C at 2 cm/s. No matter where you are, when space stretches uniformly in all directions, every other point recedes from *you*. The universe is not expanding *into* a pre-existing space; rather, *space itself* stretches, carrying matter (such as galaxies) along with it. The expansion of space does not mean that galaxies themselves or the Earth or our bodies are expanding. Those structures are held together by their own internal, non-gravitational forces. Like pennies on a stretching rubber sheet, the pennies are carried apart but not enlarged themselves.

In 1929, Edwin Hubble first published data that plotted velocity vs. distance for galaxies. [Hubble(1929)] The data had a lot of scatter in it, but in 1931, Hubble and Milton Humason published a larger data set that probed galaxies to greater distances. [Hubble and Humason(1931)] Their data showed the universe to be expanding according to Friedmann's pre-

---

[179][Einstein *et al.*(1952)Einstein, Lorentz, Weyl and Minkowski][175–188]
[180][Tropp *et al.*(1993)Tropp, Frenkel and Chermin]

diction. A graph of relative velocity vs. separation gives a sloped straight line.[181]

(3) Element abundances: The expansion of the universe does not *prove* the big bang; it only *suggests* it. Draw a coordinate grid on the rubber sheet. Now run the expansion backwards, making the universe contract. At earlier and earlier times in cosmic history, any two addresses on a coordinate grid draw closer and closer together. The *addresses* do not change, but the *distance* between them does. No matter how far apart any two coordinate addresses might be today, by going back to a sufficiently early time in cosmic history, the distances between those two addresses become as close to zero as you want. Significantly, all pairs of addresses come infinitesimally close together at the same moment—call it time zero—when the universe was microscopic.

While running the movie backwards towards time zero, the galaxies eventually crash together and break apart. With further contraction, the stars and planets collide; earlier still, atoms collide and break apart into nuclei and electrons. Going farther back, even the nuclei eventually collide and break apart into separate protons and neutrons. The temperature increases without bound as the distance between any pair of points approaches zero. At less than a hundredth of a second after time zero, the universe would be an incredibly hot dense gas of elementary particles, consisting of quarks (constituents of protons and neutrons), electrons, photons (particles of light) and a few exotic particles (which we leave to the aficionados). The infinite temperature and zero size at time zero is called the "initial singularity."

Now start the movie at time zero and let it run forward. As the universe expands, we can use the laws of physics to predict what events should occur, and what structures should form. We don't *know* that the laws of physics in the very early universe were the same as they are today, but with one exception we have no reason to throw them out, and no better assumptions with which to replace them even if we wanted to. The one exception is the so-called Planck time, the incredibly short epoch between time zero and 10^{-43} seconds. During this ultra-diminuitive interval, the temperature was so high that our laws of physics cannot be trusted.[182] But after the

---

[181] Speeds are measured from the shift in wavelength of light emitted by a moving source; distances are measured with the received brightness of "standard candles," such as the Cepheid variable stars or specific types of supernovas.

[182] More specifically, we need laws of microscopic gravity that we do not yet possess.

Planck time, the temperatures drop into ranges where physics principles have shown themselves to be trustworthy, even in extreme environments such as the interiors of stars. Thus we assume the venerable laws that describe gravity, heat, light, nuclei and atoms have held throughout cosmic history from the Planck time to the present moment. Applied to the early universe environment, these laws predict specific fossils of the big bang that should be observable today. Astronomers search for them in the present universe. Cosmology is a forensic science.

One of the first people to take the initial singularity seriously was a Catholic priest from Belgium, Georges Lemîatre, who also was an astrophysicist with a PhD from Cambridge University. In 1927 Lemîatre independently rediscovered the velocity-distance relation, and went on to think seriously about events right after the initial singularity, which he called the "cosmic egg."

Let us begin the story of the cosmic egg at a hundredth of a second after the initial singularity.[183] By this time the temperature has dropped to about 10 billion degrees.[184] For about the next three minutes the universe is a gas of protons, neutrons, electrons, and photons.[185] After expanding and cooling for three minutes the temperature drops to a balmy 800 million degrees, cool enough for protons and neutrons to stick together and form the first helium nuclei.

The challenge of predicting the element abundances coming out of primordial fireball was first addressed by Ralph Alpher and George Gamow in 1948. [Alpher and Herman(2001)][186] By the end of the 1960s such calculations had become an industry among a community of specialists, which continues with ever-finer refinements today. The calculations say that about three-fourths by mass of nuclear matter emerges as hydrogen nuclei, and about one-quarter as helium.[187] This prediction can be compared to the measured abundances of these elements in the universe today because the

---

[183] A lot happens during that first 0.01 s, such as the mechanism leading to the dominance of matter over anti-matter, but this we also leave to the aficionados.

[184] At these temperatures we need not distinguish degrees Celsius from the absolute Kelvin scale; they differ by an additive 273 degrees, which is a negligible difference until we come to the story of the cosmic background radiation.

[185] Since this presentation is delivered in the spirit of a popular lecture, antiparticles, neutrinos, gauge bosons other than the photon, and (regrettably) the accelerating universe, are not discussed unless someone asks about them. So many topics, so little time.

[186] This was the topic of Alpher's PhD dissertation at George Washington University; Gamow was Alpher's PhD advisor.

[187] Other elements, such as lithium or carbon, are predicted to be present in the promordial fireball in trace amounts, such as parts per trillion.

chemical composition of stars can be assayed by analyzing the light they emit. Taking those post-primordial contributions into account by working out fusion reaction rates in stars, the primordial nucleosynthesis predictions are found to match observations to about one part out of a thousand—*if* for every proton or neutron (collectively, the "baryons") there are a billion photons. This billion-to-one photon-to-baryon requirement leads to an observable prediction unique to the big bang: This photon afterglow, or "cosmic background radiation," *must* exist in the universe today if the big bang scenario describes the real universe.

(4) Cosmic background radiation (CBR): For a few thousand years, it was too hot for atoms to hold together; the universe was a gas of electrically charged particles (bare nuclei and electrons) and photons. Collisions between photons and all those freely moving charged particles scattered the photons about in random directions—the same mechanism that keeps us from seeing *into* the Sun. About 380,000 years after time zero, when the temperature dropped to around 3,000 degrees, the violence of these collisions diminished to where the negatively charged electrons could stay attached in orbits about the positively charged nuclei, to form electrically neutral atoms. At that time and temperature, matter and light became "decoupled;" the photons were no longer scattered and could move freely. The universe became transparent to light.

In 1948, Alpher and Robert Herman were the first to realize that the CBR must exist in a big-bang universe, and that its present-day temperature could be estimated. From the physics of stars it was known that the oldest ones are between ten and twenty billion years old. Taking time zero to be about fifteen billion years ago, Alpher and Herman estimated that the universe had expanded by a factor of about a thousand since then; therefore, they predicted that today's temperature of the CBR should be around one-thousandth the temperature at decoupling, around 5 degrees (Kelvin) above absolute zero. Light at that temperature produces its strongest signal in microwave wavelengths. For the next fifteen years, Alpher and Hermann tried to convince radio astronomers to search for it, but nobody was interested, thinking the CBR would not be detectable. [Alpher(2012)]

Also in 1948, Fred Hoyle, Thomas Gold, and Herman Bondi proposed an alternative cosmology which they called the "steady state" model. They disliked the notion of an initial singularity. Their alternative model postulated that as the universe expands, new matter is spontaneously created between receding galaxies, such that the average number of galaxies per volume remains constant throughout cosmic history. No initial singularity, no primordial fireball, no CBR. A mechanism for creating the postulated new matter was unknown, but so was the mechanism for triggering the big bang.[188] One mystery was merely being swapped for another. Both models had their proponents and critics; consensus was not forthcoming, more data was needed, and Alpher and Herman continued to be ignored. In the meantime, in a 1950 radio program, a discussion about cosmology took place between Hoyle and Gamow. There the term "big bang" was introduced by Hoyle while mocking the idea of the initial singularity. Somehow the name stuck. Bring back Lemîatre's "cosmic egg!"

The CBR was eventually stumbled upon accidentally by Bell Lab scientists Arno Penzias and Robert Wilson in 1964. They could not find the source of persistent static in a microwave antenna they were calibrating to track the Echo satellite. Someone put them in touch with Robert Dicke at Princeton University. His group had been gearing up to look for the CBR themselves, and they provided the cosmological interpretation of the Penzias-Wilson data. Alpher and Herman had estimated a CBR temperature around 5 degrees; the Penzias and Wilson measurement gave about 3.5. The steady state model was dead. From that moment, everyone serious about cosmology had to pay attention to the big bang.

In the mathematics that describes the big bang scenario, aside from small local statistical fluctuations, the gas of elementary particles is assumed to have uniform density and temperature throughout all space at a given time. The validity of that assumption can be tested, because it predicts the CBR temperature to be the same, out to four significant figures, across the entire sky (we will return to the small fluctuations). This uniformity in the CBR at this level of precision would be an important test for its cosmic egg nativity. In November 1989 the Cosmic Background Explorer satellite, or COBE, was launched, with instruments dedicated to studying the CBR with fine resolution.

---

[188]A hypothetical scenario for the big bang's genesis has since been proposed. Called "vacuum genesis," it violates no known laws of physics: In the beginning was nothing, with zero energy. But according to quantum mechanics and its uncertainty principle, "zero" means the *average* energy was zero; the energy was $0 \pm \epsilon$ where ϵ fluctuates randomly. Perhaps ϵ became large enough for a *very* short time to give that fluctuation enough zip to blossom into the entire universe. It would be unlikely, but only had to happen once. This idea raises the question of where the principles came from that would tell the universe about the uncertainty principle and what to do with the energy from this stupendous fluctuation. It seems that no matter the perspective from which you come, you always encounter a mystery: Why is there something rather than nothing?

The instrument of one group led by John Mather measured the temperature of the CBR across the sky to high precision. Within nine minutes of taking calibrated data, Mather's group could see it was going to be good. At a meeting of the American Physical Society in January 1990, Mather presented a graph that showed *all* the COBE measurements across the sky could be fit, to within about half a percent, by *one* temperature. That temperature was 2.735 degrees above absolute zero. This was one of the closest agreements between theory and experiment in the history of science. Dr. Mather received a standing ovation. Now let's return to those matter density fluctuations.

(5) Temperature fluctuations in the cosmic background radiation:

Galaxies today appear in clusters, and clusters come in superclusters with vast voids between them. Therefore, the matter density must have had fluctuations early in cosmic history, before the expansion amplified those differences into the present galaxy distribution of today. If the matter distribution had fluctuations, then the temperature of the CBR must have fluctuations also. Let us see how this works.

For matter to evolve into galaxies and voids out of the big bang's fireball, regions whose matter density was slightly higher than average were needed to seed gravitational accretion. Such seeds would be available in the form of statistical fluctuations in the early spatial distribution of matter. A region with slightly more matter than average would pull nearby matter to it, draining matter from the surroundings. Because this would be ongoing in the very early universe while matter and radiation were still in thermal equilibrium, those extra-dense regions of matter would squeeze on the radiation and elevate its pressure and temperature ever so slightly, and radiation in regions drained of matter would be under less pressure and have its temperature slightly lowered. When matter and radiation fell out of thermal contact after neutral atoms formed, the imprint of temperature differences would still exist in the radiation. Thus, for the big bang model to be consistent with theories of galaxy formation, those imprints *must* exist in the CBR today. The matter flucutations in the early universe grew with the expansion into the clusters and superclusters of galaxies we see today, and detailed calculations predict that fluctuations in the radiation's temperature should show up at the millionth-of-a-degree level—the sixth decimal place.

Measuring these fluctuations was the job of a second group directed by George Smoot. At the April 1993 APS meeting, Smoot reported the results. The measured temperature fluctuations agreed with theory out to the sixth decimal place. The big bang is consistent with our understanding of galaxy formation. It was Smoot's turn to receive a standing ovation.

With these results from the Mather and Smoot teams—and with data from their even more precise successors[189]—the big bang stands today as affirmed as any sophisticated scientific model can reasonably be. We have entered the era of precision cosmology, so now the problem can be turned around. Having found that the CBR validates the big bang to high precision, analysis of the CBR's fine details enables astronomers to observe the state of affairs in the very early universe, analogous to how an electrocardiogram enables a physician to indirectly observe the heart.

Back to Science and Religion

It will be noticed that big bang cosmology says nothing either for or against a God or gods. A skeptic may say the big bang makes God *unnecessary* for the creation of the universe. A believer may say the big bang shows *how* God created the universe. On this question the universe itself gives no measurement or signal that compels all reasonable observers to agree. One might say it's a matter of faith. What is faith? How is it related to knowledge? How is faith related to doubt?

> *"Faith" is a fine invention*
> *When Gentlemen can see—*
> *But Microscopes are prudent*
> *In an Emergency.*
> –Emily Dickenson[190]

---

[189]These include the balloon-borne Boomerang observations, WMAP (Wilkerson Microwave Anisotropy Probe satellite), DASI (Degree Angular Scale Interferometer at the South Pole); and the Planck satellite.
[190][Dickinson and Franklin(1999)]

17 Doubt and Faith

More Letters on Science, Religion, and Honesty

"There lives more faith in honest doubt,
Believe me, than in half the creeds."
–Alfred, Lord Tennyson[191]

***

The Irreproachable Inspector Javert

A pantheon of tragic figures in literature would surely include Inspector Javert, the officer of the police who relentlessly pursued the convict Jean Valjean throughout Victor Hugo's unsurpassed novel *Les Misérables*. The Inspector "had nothing but disdain, aversion, and disgust for all who had once overstepped the bounds of the law. He was absolute, and admitted no exceptions." [Hugo and Wilbor(1943)][59]

Javert's unbending legalism was found wanting after Jean Valjean showed him mercy at the barricades. Even though Javert had doggedly pursued Valjean for years, the old convict released the collared Inspector instead of blowing out his brains with a pistol as the revolutionaries had intended. Jean Valjean cut Javert's bonds and said "Go." As the bewildered Javert departed, Jean Valjean fired the pistol into the air, returned to the barricades and said "It is done." [Hugo and Wilbor(1943)][416–417] Late that night Javert arrested Jean Valjean at the latter's residence. Javert allowed Jean Valjean to go upstairs to say his farewells. When Jean Valjean returned, Javert was gone.

We next see Javert standing alone on a bridge over the gurgling black waters of the Seine, in despair over the events of a day that overthrew his rigid certainties. [Hugo and Wilbor(1943)][446–447]

One of his causes of anxiety was, that he was compelled to think. The very violence of all these contradictory emotions forced him to it...
...A single resource remained: to return immediately to the Rue de l' Homme Armé, and have Jean Valjean arrested. It was clear that was what he must do. He could not.
Something barred the way to him on that side.

---

[191]From *In Memoriam*.

328

Something? What? Is there anything else in the world besides tribunals, sentences, police, and authority? Javert's ideas were overturned...
His supreme anguish was the loss of all certainty. He felt that he was uprooted...
To retain his old virtue, that no longer sufficed. An entire order of unexpected facts arose and subjugated him. An entire new world appeared to his soul; favor accepted and returned, devotion, compassion, indulgence,... respect of persons, no more final condemnation, no more damnation, the possibility of a tear in the eye of the law, a mysterious justice according to God going counter to justice according to men....
Javert's ideal was not to be humane, not to be great, not to be sublime; it was to be irreproachable. Now he had just failed...

In matters of law and crime and punishment Javert was a legal fundamentalist. His fate illustrates how the rigid certainties of fundamentalism are intrinsically unstable. The scene on the bridge does not end happily for Inspector Javert.

The term "Fundamentalist" as a proper noun originally came from a set of ninety essays, published in twelve volumes by the Bible Institute of Los Angeles and privately distributed from 1910–1915, called *The Fundamentals: A Testimony to the Truth*. The essays insisted the Bible to be inerrant in all things, and was therefore to be read and lived out literally. In the STS class we use the word "fundamentalist" in a broader sense, to mean someone holding an opinion so solidified as to make them tone deaf to contrary evidence or opinions. If Mr. Stiffnecke is a fundamentalist, there is nothing we can say or do that will make him ponder whether he might be mistaken; he allows no possibility that a contrary view might contain an atom of truth. Fundamentalists claim a monopoly on truth, which appears to them as the sharp contrast between black and white.

As mentioned, our university sits in one of the more conservative regions of the United States, in a state whose wider culture includes a large dollop of Southern gospel fundamentalism.[192] Besides the geographical influence, our university is owned by a conservative Protestant denomination in the Wesleyan tradition, founded in 1895 at a Los Angeles mission by a Methodist Episcopal minister named Phineas Bresee. Bresee preached and practiced a return to John Wesley's original emphasis on ministering to

---

[192]The "Southern" in our university's name refers to geography. The names of our sister institutions elsewhere in the USA include "Northwest," "Mid-America" and "Eastern." We have no connection to the Southern Baptist Convention, one of the more conservative large denominations with Southern roots.

the poor. In 1908, a fateful merger took place with another denomination that had been founded in Texas in the 1890s. The Texas group, under the leadership of a minister named Charles Jernigan, was dominated by the radical legalism and literalism that was soon articulated thereafter in *The Fundamentals.*

I have personal experience with the fundamentalism that dates back to these events. My paternal grandmother was one of the most ardent religious fundamentalists who ever lived. As a child she lost her mother, and as a young woman in the 1920s she became strongly influenced by a boarding house landlady who became the mother figure. The good lady was a committed product of Jernigan's group.

When Grandma stayed with us and I was kept home from school with the flu, about mid-morning she would invite herelf into my room with her big Bible in hand, and proceed to read aloud a lengthy passage of Scripture to her captive audience of one. After the reading she knelt by my bedside and embarked on a lengthy prayer that went around the world and surely reached Heaven by sheer force of lungs.[193] For Grandma, the proposition that God created the world according to a literal reading of *Genesis* was not negotiable. She was stern with herself, too. She always wore long dresses with long sleeves and kept her hair in a bun. Makeup, jewelry, television and coffee were mortal sins. Her ideal was to be irreproachable.

I think Grandma really believed that evolution was diabolical propaganda brewed in the blackened souls of wicked scientists in order to lead innocent lambs astray. For Grandma, *all* the answers—not only about values and morality, but also about the origin of stars and species—were in The Book. Nor was she content to keep her beliefs to herself. I suppose she thought God needed her help to steer other people onto the straight and narrow path. But she was a kind-hearted person who never raised her voice, and she had many admirable qualities—she meant well, she lived humbly, she knew what it meant to believe in something, and she did not care what other people thought about her (my father and uncles declared her "stubborn"). Sadly, she deprived herself of some of life's simple pleasures that would have done her no harm. Tragically, in the name of Doing Good she unwittingly drove wedges deep into countless personal relationships.

---

[193]My father and uncles knew the routine. When they were kids she made them lie down on Sunday afternoons to take a nap. As they settled down she read the Sunday School papers aloud to them, but she was the one who fell asleep. The lads would sneak out of the house, catch a calf and have a rodeo.

Grandma's legalism survives as a vocal minority among the grassroots in our university's sponsoring denomination. Although recent years have seen a growing diversity in our student body, extrapolating from the STS classes, I estimate that about three-quarters of our students were raised in homes where church attendance, prayers and Bible reading were part of life's routine. Institutional data indicates that about forty-five percent of our students come from households that identify with the sponsoring denomination. [Zabel(2014)][10][194] I was raised in such a home, and felt enhanced pressure from the culture to conform, because that home was a parsonage.

As university juniors and seniors, most STS students are in their early twenties and have been away from home for two or three years. Reconciling one's childhood pieties with a growing awareness of the wider world raises large doubts and questions. Engaging doubts and questions are the reason universities exist. Dealing with them honestly, while respecting parents and traditions, presents significant intellectual and emotional challenges. By the time students walk into STS during their junior or senior year, most are heavily engaged in the internal wrestling match that Edgar Lee Masters describes so well in *Silence*: [Masters(1916)]

> *There is the silence of a spiritual crisis,*
> *Through which your soul, exquisitely tortured,*
> *Comes with visions not to be uttered*
> *Into a realm of higher life...*

Reconciling a Platonic world of ideals to our world's gray realities offers a perpetual work in progress.

As our students raised in church-going families grew up, most of them were encouraged to not doubt, but have faith. With forty people in a class, each with their personal identity struggles, we have ample motivation for class discussions about doubt and faith. Science in society includes this dimension of life. The problems presented by technology are simple by comparison.

We start by asking for descriptions of faith. These need not be definitions the students adhere to personally; we also invite recollections of what they were taught or have heard advocated by others. The students are given a few minutes to discuss the question with their neighbors, then the floor opens for suggestions, which are collected on the white board. Faith is

---

[194]This number for 2014 is down from about 60% a decade ago, although the difference has been made up by students from other denominations.

a belief you can't prove. Faith is trust. Faith is an expectation. Faith is a hope. Faith is perseverance in the face of doubt. Faith is an extrapolation from what you know to what you don't know but believe might be possible. Faith is action—committing yourself to something. Inevitably someone recalls the famous passage from the New Testament: "Now faith is being sure of what we hope for and certain of what we do not see."[195] The passage seems contradictory, presenting faith as both a hope and as a certainty!

Follow-up questions explore relationships between faith and doubt. If we *know*, do we need faith? Can intellectual growth occur without doubt? If we suppress doubt, are we being dishonest?—but how could one build a relationship with the Divine on a foundation of dishonesty? What kind of God would smite us for having honest questions? If we never doubt, how can we live authentically with beliefs not truly our own? In one of her weekly STS letters Laura addressed her pastor back home:

Dear pastor,
Remember when you sent me to school at SNU and warned me to guard my heart and mind against things that might harm my beliefs. The thing is, I'm not sure that all those beliefs were actually mine and not just things I believed because you had told me they were true. It has been through many theology classes and others like STS that I've had my eyes opened to new beliefs and concepts... I'm thankful for these classes to grow and stretch things that I believed to be right or wrong. I like that I'm beginning to discover myself and my voice as well as my own opinion about what I believe. You may find that a terrible thing, but I'm becoming me and that's better than being a robot.

Madison B. wrote,

My dad is a pastor and for many years I took the Bible literally.... I then began to realize that my beliefs were those of my family and not my own. I spent a lot of time this semester reflecting on what I have been taught growing up versus what I actually believe. I have realized that the [relationship] of science to religion...is not something to fear, but rather something to dive into and learn more about.

---

[195] *Hebrews* 11:1, NIV

I am not saying that my family's beliefs are wrong.... I am
simply stating that mine do not have to be identical to
theirs, and that's okay.

Science could not function without doubt. To do science is to manage
uncertainty, not suppress it. Science says, "Is that so, eh? What's the
evidence? *How* do you know?"

> *7 December 1999*
> *Dear Professor Dyson,*
> *...In view of the metaphysical possibility of an "ultimate mind,"*
> *do you believe in the possibility of the supernatural, e.g., the*
> *resurrection of Christ?*

> *8 December 1999*
> *Dear Dwight,*
> *...To me, religion is not a matter of belief but a way of life. I go*
> *to church to be part of a community of caring people. I consider*
> *myself a Christian, but I don't believe in the resurrection. I*
> *am not saying dogmatically that the resurrection is impossible.*
> *Obviously there are more things in heaven and earth than we are*
> *capable of understanding, and this may be one of them. Being*
> *a scientist means being comfortable with uncertainty.*

Similarly, are honest doubt and uncertainty necessary for responsible religion?

Positions A and Z

On practically any controversial topic, it seems that most of the shouting
comes from the extremes. Extremists are good at shouting. They are not so
good at listening. In his article "Letter to a Creationist" published in *The
Science Teacher*, [Dickerson(1990)] Michael Dickerson offers a spectrum of
positions, ranging from position A for religious fundamentalists, to position
Z for science fundamentalists.

Position A: A few years ago a student named Leslie, who had been home-
schooled, lent me a copy of the textbook from which she had been instructed
in what her family thought was science. The book was called *Unlocking
the Mysteries of Creation*, [Petersen(1986)] published by the Creation Resource Foundation, an organization founded by the book's author, Dennis
Petersen.

Genesis Chapter 1 says in English translation that God created the heavens and the earth in "six days." On Day 6, Adam and Eve appear. From genealogies cited in the Bible that go back to Adam,[196] Biblical literalists insist that the Earth cannot be more than about six thousand years old. To question the geneaologies would be to challenge Scripture itself, and you know where that puts you—on the slippery slope.

To argue for a young Earth, Petersen presents, among others, the case of atmospheric helium. "The total amount there can be measured. One of the sources for it is the constant measurable decay of uranium on the Earth." So far, so good, if by "constant" decay he means the half-life for the alpha-decay of uranium, and not the number of decays per second. The author continues: "If Earth is billions of years old the atmosphere would be saturated with helium to such a degree that there would be up to a million times more helium there than we have now! Some have suggested that the helium must be escaping into outer space. But actually such escape is impossible." [Petersen(1986)][42] This statement offers no data for the factor of a million, and no reason for helium escape being impossible. I offer my STS colleagues an explanation of why helium escape *is* possible.

The distribution of molecular speeds in a gas at a given temperature—the Maxwell–Boltzmann distribution—is a well established tool of molecular physics.[197] Plot speed on the horizontal axis and the number of molecules on the vertical axis. The distribution shows a curve with a peak, the most probable speed. At speeds greater than the peak the curve falls asymptotically towards zero but never reaches it. Thus at any high but finite speed a small number of molecules are found at even higher speeds. The minimum speed to escape Earth's gravity is about 11 kilometers per second. High in Earth's atmosphere, a small but nonzero fraction of helium atoms have sufficient speed to escape. Thus the statement "such escape is impossible" is false. If Petersen's purpose was to defend truth, doing it with a false statement seems inconsistent with the values being defended.

Petersen correctly notes that the radioactive decay of uranium is a source of helium. Uranium isotopes are alpha-emitters, with the abundant U-238 isotope having a half-life of about 4.5 billion years. *Unlocking*

---

[196] Adam to Noah in *Genesis* 5; Noah to Abraham in *Genesis* 10-11; Abraham to Joseph, the husband of Mary the mother of Jesus, in *Matthew* 1.

[197] An important application of the Maxwell–Boltzmann distribution was its use in the Manhattan Project's gaseous diffusion facility at Oak Ridge, Tennessee, to separate U-235 from U-238. Molecules of uranium hexafluoride with U-235 moved slightly faster than those carrying U-238.

the Mysteries of Creation uses some findings of science when convenient, and ignores others when it's not.

Petersen also asks, "Is there evidence to disprove the big bang theory?... The following problems are observed in our solar system and defy the big bang explanation." [Petersen(1986)][45] He lists nine "problems" with big bang *cosmology* that come from observing the *solar system*. We might pause to critique this strategy. With the observable universe holding something like a billion trillion stars (10^{21}), how could evidence potent enough to shoot down the cosmology of the *entire universe* come from *one* of those stars and its planets that formed some nine billion years *after* the big bang event? But that's where the *Mysteries* author is going. The "problems" concern retrograde motion and the distribution of angular momentum among our sun and planets. These features were understood long ago, and shown to be consistent with the nebula condensation model.[198] But that's beside the point. The point is, these observations of our solar system do indeed "defy big bang explanation" because they are *irrelevant* to the big bang. The author's argument is like saying plate tectonics is suspect because the founding of the United Nations defies a plate tectonics explanation. Such objections are not arguments to satisfy the knowledgeable, but to impress the impressionable.

Petersen warns his readers, "When scientists do say things about origins, supernatural powers and spiritual things, you should be careful to examine and challenge them. Theories are not facts!" [Petersen(1986)][66] Science deals with phenomena that operate strictly *within* nature; therefore "supernatural powers and spiritual things" are not science topics. Perhaps challenges should also be directed to those who judge science without understanding what it's about. Petersen rightly observes what theories are *not*: they are not facts. However, he creates a misleading impression about what theories *are* because he describes the word's meaning in a way contrary to its use in science. He continues, "What is a theory? A theory is a guess or suggestion that spawns inventive and logical research to explain some natural phenomenon." This is opposite to what scientists mean when they say "theory," as in "the theory of relativity" or "nuclear theory." A one-sentence description of what "theory" means among scientists could include the words "organized knowledge with predictive power."

Although he used the word "theory," Petersen instead has described "hypothesis" or "speculation," a convenient move for his purpose. If the

---

[198]Developed by Emanuel Swedenborg, 1734; Immanuel Kant, 1755; Pierre-Simon Laplace, 1796; see [North(1965)].

meaning of "theory" can be shifted to suggest "speculation," a neat trick
has been deftly pulled off to make suspect "Darwin's theory of evolution"
or "big bang theory," without the inconvenience of having to do the hard
work of gathering evidence, thinking through inferences and interpreting
all of it consistently.

As a scientist, I have an obligation to criticize Petersen's statements
about *science*. However, I will not criticize him as a *person*. I doubt that
he set out to *intentionally* deceive anyone. I assume he sincerely intended
to protect young people from what he saw as threats to their souls. The
tragedy is not that Petersen attacks science; scientists attack each other's
ideas all the time. The tragedy is that he allows himself to use incorrect
statements about science to indoctrinate children with the impression that
science is their enemy. Petersen's commitment to young-earth creationism
ideology is not only irrelevant to authentic religious faith, but by not doing
his science homework, to settle for a superficial understanding of science in
order to defend an ideology, he loses credibility outside his own circle and
thereby damages the very faith he tries to defend. As Conklin observed,
"The fundamentalists, rather than the scientists, are helping to make this
an irreligious age." [Conklin(1925)] Long before Conklin, Alexander Pope
(1688–1777) summarized it well in *An Essay on Criticism* (1709):

> *A little learning is a dangerous thing;*
> *Drink deep, or taste not the Pierian spring:*
> *There shallow draughts intoxicate the brain,*
> *And drinking largely sobers us again.*

The biographical notes in the back of his book say that Petersen taught
in a Bible college and pastored churches. [Petersen(1986)][205] Speaking
from those roles, Petersen might have insights about the Beatitudes of Jesus
that I would do well to hear. But will I listen to him if he has squandered his
credibility? To the ministerial students in STS I say: choose your battles
well, and stick to issues where you have authentic expertise. Science is not
your enemy.

> *"Come mothers and fathers throughout the land*
> *And don't criticize what you can't understand..."*
> –Bob Dylan[199]

---

[199]Lyrics from "The Times They Are A-Changin'" by Bob Dylan (Columbia Records,
1964).

Position Z: The October 1996 issue of *The American Journal of Physics* carried an interesting guest editorial, "Hope Springs Eternal—Why People Believe Weird Things." It was written by Michael Shermer, the editor of *Skeptic* magazine. [Shermer(1996)]

Shermer began his editorial by describing how our society is saturated with technologies and outlooks that come from modern science. "But if we are living in the age of science why do so many pseudoscientific and non-scientific traditions abound? Religions, myths, superstitions, mysticisms, cults, New Age beliefs, and nonsense of all sorts have penetrated every nook and cranny of both popular and high culture."

Skeptics and believers are both in awe of the universe; both seek meaning and hope. But they differ in where they find it:

So hope springs eternal not just for spiritualists, religionists, New Agers, and psychics, but for materialists, atheists, scientists, and, yes, even skeptics.... The first group is willing to use the benefits of science and rationality when convenient, and dump them when it is not.

Shermer's editorial both inspired and puzzled me. Using the benefits of science and technology when it's convenient, and dumping them when it's not, is a common behavior among some religious folk that Shermer rightly criticizes. But I also know personally many deeply religious people who take science seriously, who find religious fundamentalism more distasteful than skepticism, and who struggle to formulate a personal philosophy that reconciles their soulful yearnings with the wider view of science. To put Albert Schweitzer and Georges Lemîatre in the same equivalence class as Answers in Genesis and Dennis Petersen seems to paint with an excessively broad brush. A broad sweep of innuendo continues when "religionists" and "psychics" are linked by association into one group and "scientists" and "atheists" are linked into another. Georges Lemîatre and Edwin Grant Conklin were scientists, but they were not atheists. One would expect a self-proclaimed skeptic to be the first to challenge hasty generalizations.

Many skeptics evidently assume with Bertrand Russell that all religious faith resembles that which he describes in his blunt essay "Why I Am Not a Christian." His reasons are clear. Russell describes faith as a "conviction which cannot be shaken by contrary evidence." [Russell(1957)][vi] If Russell's description of faith is a requirement for being Christian, then I would join him at once in having nothing to do with it.

In contrast, in *The Faith of a Heretic* Walter Kaufmann describes faith as an "intense, usually confident, belief that is not based on evidence sufficient to command assent from every reasonable person." [Kaufmann(1963)][2] When the evidence is not sufficient to draw all reasonable observers towards consensus, one has the freedom to *choose* what to believe. Faith is a *choice*.

But the choice is not arbitrary. We can identify two constraints for faith to be honest. First, honest faith must be reconciled to knowledge, not the other way around. This constraint was eloquently described by Conklin. As a genuinely religious person and a distinguished biologist, he delivered hundreds of public lectures supporting evolution by natural selection. In a *Scribner's Magazine* article written for a general audience and published only four months after the 1925 Scopes trial, Conklin explained: [Conklin, Scribners 451–458]

The real problem that confronts us, and it is a great problem, is how to adjust religion to science, faith to knowledge, ideality to reality, for adjustment in the reverse direction will never happen....
We must keep our feet on the ground of fact and science, but lift our heads into the atmosphere of ideals....
...The world never needed a religion of high ideals and aspirations more than it needs it now. But the old religion of literalism and of slavish regard to the authority of church or book, while well suited to some minds, cannot serve the needs of those who have breathed the air of science.

Second, for honest faith to have any operational meaning, it must be lived out. Essentially, I say "This is what I *choose* to believe. Although there's no way to *know* whether I am right, I will live personally *as though* this is true, and accept the consequences." Faith carries the obligation of humility to realize I could be wrong. Doubt and faith are two sides of one coin. When adopting a faith for myself, I do not impose it on my neighbors.

We hear position A individuals condemn science without bothering to learn it. We hear position Z individuals mock religion without getting to know thoughtful religious people and where they are coming from. Joey C. tried to pull it all together:

The development of faith toward maturity, I think, relies heavily on honest doubt.... To blindly accept faith in the Christian God without transparently acknowledging doubt, even serial...

serious doubt, is condescending. It seems to assume that God
cannot handle our honest questions... What fear! How
difficult to wholeheartedly worship one who is threatened by
your questions...

As I grew older and began putting Grandma's world view into a larger
perspective, eventually I came to pity her. She professed to worship a loving
God, but deep down she was terrified of Him.

Fear, and the Principle of Inconsistency

*"Those who 'stick to words' are likely to purchase certainty at
the price of honesty."* –Walter Kaufmann[200]

Why does most of the shouting come from the extremes? If I may, I will
suggest a principle about fundamentalists, "the Principle of Inconsistency,"
in terms of which shouting from the extremes becomes understandable. The
Principle of Inconsistency postulates that it is impossible to be a fundamentalist and always be consistent with one's precepts. [Neuenschwander(2006)]
Narrow inflexibility places one, inevitably, on a collision course with reality;
sooner or later, fundamentalists contradict their own values. Let us consider some empirical obserations that led to the inductive generalization
expressed in the Principle of Inconsistency:

(a) In the name of spreading democracy, political fundamentalists make
preemptive war on dubious pretenses, while demanding their fellow citizens
suspend all judgment and criticism.

(b) Religious fundamentalist textbooks tell falsehoods about science in
the name of defending Truth.

(c) Position A biblical literalists insist that God is the Almighty Creator
of the universe, then tell Him how He had to create it.

(d) Position Z evidence-demanding skeptics draw firm conclusions on
religious matters for which data is ambiguous or subjective.

Such positions would be less corrosive if their proponents did not assume
that having firm opinions of their own entitles them to ridicule the opinions
of others. [Quindlen(2005)], [Will(2005)] Sometimes behaving respectfully is
more important than making everyone acknowledge that I am right. It's
so ironic. Religious fundamentalists unwittingly drive people away from
religion. Science fundamentalists who publicly mock religion drive people

---

[200][Kaufmann(1963)][36]

away from science. By taking extreme positions and being in-your-face militant about it, and not trying to understand where the other person comes from, they damage the very causes they love.

How can the Principle of Inconsistency inform an understanding of fundamentalism? In Position A, I fear that if I deviate from the True Path—even to privately acknowledge an honest doubt—then God will condemn me. In Position Z, I fear that if I allow the possibility that some things do not fit between the microscope slides of science then I will lose my reputation as a hard-core rationalist.

Because of such overhanging fear, the fundamentalist is poised for inconsistency. From Position A, in the struggle to save my skin or my soul, deep fear is more powerful than evidence; conformity to party line or doctrine becomes more important than data or logical consistency (my grandmother repeatedly said she could not "compromise"). From Position Z, being faithful to hard-nosed rationality becomes more important than relating to human anguish; snapping everything into logical arguments becomes more important than weighing the limitations of the human experience and mind. As it was for Inspector Javert, the ideal is not to be humane, but to be irreproachable. From either extreme, I become most defensive about issues on which I feel the least secure. The greater the insecurity, the greater the shouting. We should expect brittle certainty to be shouted from the police states of fundamentalism. Thoughtful uncertainty does not need to shout.

When doubt is suppressed, it does not go away. It remains buried alive, where it festers into the rigid ideologies of fundamentalism. Acknowledged doubt is the precursor to authentic understanding.

> *24 April 2014*
> *Dear Professor Dyson, I hope the first half of your 91st year has been one of joy, time with family, many conversations with grandchildren, interesting work to do, and new adventures.*
> *Once again our STS class risks wearing out our welcome by sending you some questions....*
> *...Since science is evidence-based reasoning, do you think that some scientists deny the existence of God due to the lack of tangible evidence for God's existence?*
> *Another way to word this question might be, do some scientists see all the dimensions of human experience through only the lens of science?... Your letter to us about science and religion being "two windows" for looking at the world continues to be so very helpful. This topic never fails to hit close to home for many*

students here. In class we have discussed the importance and necessity of honest doubt, and how the existence of a Cosmic Mind cannot be proven in a way that will satisfy all reasonable observers. One cannot help but wonder, if God is real and has the attributes claimed by Christianity, why isn't He obvious to everyone? Sometimes the best we can do is to understand the questions; the answers may always remain elusive. Then we have to learn to live within the questions... The majority of our students were raised in devout Christian homes. For many of them, questioning their faith is a significant intellectual challenge, but a necessary one to go through if one is going to be honest....

28 April 2014
Dear Dwight and Students,
Thank you very much for your questions. These are good questions and the discussions that came along with them are very helpful....
Why do some scientists dogmatically deny the existence of God? I make a strong distinction between agnostics, who doubt whether God exists, and atheists, who are sure that God does not exist. I agree with your discussion of science and religion. I consider militant atheists like Richard Dawkins to be just as misguided as militant fundamentalists who consign unbelievers to Hell. I was brought up as a church-going Christian by parents who were agnostics. A good scientist may be a religious believer or an agnostic, but should not be a militant atheist or a militant fundamentalist.
Just two days ago I flew home from a trip to Japan, a marvelously beautiful country full of wonderful people. I spent a day there with a group of students like you, talking about the same problems. The student who talked the best English was Tomone Watanabe, a nursing student who will graduate this year. By a happy coincidence, when I looked at my e-mail after returning home, I found a message from Tomone together with your message, asking similar questions. In spite of her excellent English and French, she has never traveled out of Japan. She belongs to the small minority of native Japanese Christians, and she takes her religion seriously. After she graduates, she will spend a year at the London Institute of Tropical Medicine. From there she will study public health problems in Africa and in Europe. I will not be surprised if she turns out to be another Mother Teresa. She has what it takes.
The answer to your last question is no. The majority of scientists are agnostics, because of the lack of tangible evidence for God's existence. Those who are militant atheists, dogmatically

> *denying the existence of God, have a different motivation. They*
> *are driven by hatred for people whose feelings and ideas they do*
> *not understand.*
> *That is enough for today. In conclusion, thanks again for your*
> *friendship and your questions. Imme was with me in Japan and*
> *enjoyed it as much as I did. Our big family is growing up fast*
> *and enjoying the American Spring.*
> *Yours ever, Freeman*

Although Position Z militants to not share the Position A fear of divine punishment, perhaps the former's insecurities are those of the *prima donna*, intellectually superior with an image to maintain. Casey S. shares an observation along these lines:

```
Since class last week I have been thinking a lot about what
I believe and why I believe it.  I was really bothered by the
Michael Shermer article & the ''creationism'' textbook.
Seeing the errors that both of these authors made helped me
to step back & evaluate my own beliefs.
I've encountered Michael Shermer before in a discussion panel
entitled ''The Question of God.'' [Shermer(2004)] We've
watched clips of these discussions in one of my classes &
I've noticed that Shermer seems to have a certain image he
tries to maintain.  Aside from being very confident of his
opinions, Shermer is always trying to make the most
off-the-wall statements.... It's the same idea we saw in the
creationism textbook:  One cannot embrace certain ideas
because doing so would force him/her to redefine their
identity.
Last week I realized that this is what drives me crazy about
people who are extremely closed-minded.  It's not the fact
that their opinions differ from mine, but that they believe
what they do simply because it's too big of a risk to believe
otherwise.  I really hope that I will have the confidence to
challenge my own beliefs.
```

Some wag has remarked that intelligence is like underwear. It's important to have it, but you don't need to show it off.

In Dickerson's spectrum, Position M denotes a wide middle ground where most people live in quiet, thoughtful uncertainty.

The Thoughtful Uncertainty of Position M

"The most incomprehensible thing about the world is that it is comprehensible." –Albert Einstein[201]

Most religious believers and most scientists are somewhere in the middle ground, away from arrogant extremes. Position M scientists respect religion for teaching morality and social justice, and for the sense of community it provides. Position M religious persons respect science for showing how the universe works, and for its applications that contribute to a better life.

Our university's sponsoring denomination publishes a magazine that has for many years carried a question-and-answer column. In December 1994 a reader wrote: "It is a known fact that many of the teachers in our Nazarene schools don't believe in the Bible creation theory.[*sic*] When are we going to invite those teachers to go elsewhere?" [Tracy(1994)]

The magazine's editor at the time, Wesley Tracy, responded with a measured reply that offers a fine example of Position M. The main body of his response demonstrated that belief in a six-solar-day creation developed only recently in Christendom. He answers the correspondent, "From your letter it is plain that you assume that the truly devout have always understood Genesis 1 to teach that creation was achieved in six solar days. That, however, is simply not the case. The solar day theory is relatively new. The ancient Jews, who gave us Genesis, considered the day divisions to be metaphorical..."

Let us hear from modern Jews on this point. *Gates of Prayer*, published by the Central Conference of American Rabbis, contains in its preface an eloquent prayer:

You have spoken in a thousand tongues for all to hear; In every land and age, we, your children, have heard your voice and recognized you in separate ways. And yet, O God, You are One; though each may see you differently, you are the one God of all humanity. Humble in the face of a spiritual reality whose essence we cannot "know," we speak in metaphor. [Stern(1975)]

If the Jewish people of 600 BCE did not take *Genesis* literally, and if 2700 years later the Jewish rabbis still profess that we must speak of

---

[201][Einstein(1982)][292] As printed in the 1982 reprinting of the 1954 original, Einstein is translated as saying "One may say 'the eternal mystery of the world is its comprehensibility.'" The quote above is the more famous version of the statement.

holy things in metaphor, why should anyone feel obliged to read an English translation of *Genesis* 1 literally?

The professor presses the "play" button on the CD player. A song begins, "The Rose:"[202]

> *Some say love it is a river that drowns the tender reed.*
> *Some say love it is a razor that leaves your soul to bleed.*
> *Some say love it is a hunger; an endless aching need.*
> *I say love—it is a flower and you its only seed.*

As we listen to this song we do not demand to know which of these four descriptions of love is the "true" one. We understand that each one is true *within its own context.* We embrace this ambiguity as the method of poetry. Through metaphor, the poetic lyrics speak to everyone.

In science and religion, as in poetry, whenever we try to wrap our minds around concepts that do not fit within our patterns of previous experience, we have little choice but to resort to analogies and metaphors, despite their limitations. Science has the solar system model of the atom and the liquid drop model of the nucleus; Christianity has the Good Shepherd and the Lamb of God, and so on. When confronting a mystery, we grapple with it in terms of things we already understand. In his essay contributed to *How Large is God?* published by the Templeton Foundation, Professor Dyson wrote,

All our understanding of nature is based on human language. And human language is a tool contingent on the particular history of our species. It would be amazing if human language could comprehend aspects of the universe that no human has seen or experienced. If there are minds in the universe larger than ours, it is unlikely that our language could encompass their thinking. It is unlikely that our science could explain their concepts. [Templeton(1997)]

Since Tracy's questioner self-identifies with our university's sponsoring denomination, Tracy calls as his next witness one of the denomination's revered theologians, "the sainted H. Orton Wiley" who wrote a three-volume systematic theology used for decades in the denomination's seminary. Wiley writes that "The Book of Genesis opens in an inspired Psalm, sometimes known as the 'Hymn of Creation,' and sometimes as the 'Poem of the Dawn.'" [Wiley(1985)][449] *Genesis* offers a *poetic* description of creation. A few pages after the Poem of the Dawn discussion Wiley discusses "The Days of Creation," the passage referenced by Tracy:

---

[202] "The Rose" by Amanda McBroom, Fox Fanfare Music, BMI; the recording played in class is performed by Bette Midler (Atlantic, 1993).

The Genesis account of creation is primarily a religious document. It cannot be considered a scientific statement, and yet it must not be regarded as contradictory to science... The Hebrew word *yom* which is translated "day" occurs no less than 1,480 times in the Old Testament, and is translated by something over fifty different words, including such terms as *time, life, today, age, forever, continually* and *perpetually*.... It is frequently assumed that originally orthodox belief held to a solar day of twenty-four hours....[but] the best Hebrew exegesis has never regarded the days of Genesis as solar days, but as day-periods of indefinite duration. [Wiley(1985)][454–455]

In the faces and essays of so many students I see years of tension melting away. Heidi S. wrote,

Out of all the topics discussed, I feel the topic of the creation of the universe has been personally relevant. Before I came to college, I never really thought of the universe as not being created in six solar days.... I have learned through this class and others... to have an open mind. I now see how the Big Bang could be very true and the story of creation found in Genesis does not have to be literally interpreted as God creating the universe in six 24-hour days. I found it interesting to know that the original Hebrew word that was translated into day actually meant an indefinite period of time. I have learned in this class that science & religion are two separate windows on the world....

Tim A. added,

The discussion of relationships between science and religion, in light of Big Bang cosmology, set my mind into action more than any other topic covered in this course. Prior to this class, I have viewed the Bible as my textbook for the creation of the world, and had dismissed most scientific knowledge (i.e., evolution, Big Bang, etc.) as material contrary to my understanding of God.... By no means are all my questions answered on this point, and I still have difficulty viewing the creation of the universe completely separate from the Biblical account. I suspect, however, that

the more I study the Bible in its original language and
context, the more I will be able to separate religion &
science into two different realms of thought. All in all, I
appreciated the thought-provoking material presented in light
of Dyson's book, and I will no longer disavow the findings of
science as nonsense.

The Templeton Prize

In January 1999 I received a letter on stationary bearing the heading "The
Templeton Prize." The letter said "We wish to consider Dr. Freeman
Dyson for the Templeton Prize and your name has been given to us as
a possible nominator." While I felt honored to be asked, my immediate
reaction, alone in my office with the just-opened letter, was a feeling of
hopeless inadequacy. But the faces floated before me of the STS students
struggling to reconcile science and religion. Professor Dyson's letters in
response to their questions came immediately to mind. This would be a
good way to publicly thank Professor Dyson on their behalf.

   The formal name of the Templeton Prize is the "Templeton Prize for
Progress in Religion." Sir John Templeton wrote that "The Prize celebrates no particular faith tradition or notion of God, but rather the quest
for progress in humanity's efforts to comprehend the many and diverse manifestations of the Divine." One would expect awardees to include philoso-
phers, theologians, and clergy of all traditions, but the Prize has also been
awarded to scientists, writers, and reformers for good works including "research about the fundamental questions of existence, purpose and the origins of the universe." [Templeton(1972)][203] As a nominator I was to explain
my reasons for the nomination. That was easy.

   ...Somewhere between these extremes lies a large middle ground where a
person may embrace religious and scientific perspectives simultaneously, honestly, and with intellectual integrity. Attempts to chart this middle ground
will be taken seriously only if the cartographer commands the respect of the
scientifically literate and the religiously sensitive. Professor Dyson is that cartographer...

---

[203]Templeton Prize recipients have included Mother Teresa (1973), Rev. Billy Graham
(1982), Alexander Solzhenitsyn (1983) and Ian Barbour (1999).

The letter concluded by describing the "two windows" metaphor that Professor Dyson shared with our class.

The Templeton Prize was presented to Professor Dyson in a ceremony at Buckingham Palace on 9 May 2000. His acceptance speech took place in a second ceremony, held in Washington National Cathedral, on May 16th. Following a performance of Johann Sebastian Bach's *Prelude and Fugue in G Major* on the Cathedral's magnificent pipe organ, the acceptance speech proceedings got underway with a stately procession down the cathedral's center aisle.[204] George Dyson's music, performed by the Cathedral Choirs, was featured three times during the evening. Professor Dyson took the podium and addressed the packed cathedral in a ringing voice. [Dyson(2000)] He began by recalling previous Prize winners:

I am amazed to find myself in the company of these great spirits, half of them saints and the other half theologians. I am neither a saint nor a theologian.

To me, good works are more important than theology...

Science and religion are two windows that people look through, trying to understand the big universe outside, trying to understand why we are here... Trouble arises when either science or religion claims universal jurisdiction, when either religious dogma or scientific dogma claims to be infallible. Religious creationists and scientific materialists are equally dogmatic and insensitive. By their arrogance they bring both science and religion into disrepute. The media exaggerate their numbers and importance. The media rarely mention the fact that the great majority of religious people belong to moderate denominations that treat science with respect, or the fact that the great majority of scientists treat religion with respect so long as religion does not claim jurisdiction over scientific questions...

As he did with his homily on Jonah, Professor Dyson took this opportunity to deliver the sermon that comes from within his identity:

The great question for our time is, how to make sure that the continuing scientific revolution brings benefits to everybody rather than widening the gap between rich and poor....

Technology must be guided and driven by ethics if it is to do more than provide new toys for the rich....Science and religion should work together to abolish the

---

[204] As Professor Dyson walked down the aisle in the procession, he was obviously relaxed, as if he had wandered in and happened to fall innocently into the lineup. It was delightful.

gross inequalities that prevail in the modern world. That is my vision, and it is the same vision that inspired Francis Bacon four hundred years ago, when he prayed that through science God would "endow the human family with new mercies."

On the STS final exam the students are asked to describe which topic meant the most to them personally, and why. "Full credit will be given for your genuine, thoughtful response." Lisa S. wrote,

    The topic that has struck me the most was the discussion of
    faith and doubt. I have always questioned my faith in
    everything from religion, to family, to myself. While it was
    only a discussion for roughly one day, it has been on my mind
    my whole life.... I question God's existence continually...
    What I realized recently [was that] the faith I have in God
    reflects on my faith in people... My faith comes from my
    ability to question it.

Sarah W. echoed,

    The topic that meant the most to me was the discussion
    concerning science and religion. I have struggled with
    this..., and thus appreciate the opportunity to hear other
    opinions on the matter. The lecture showing the extremes of
    science and religion as well as the middle ground helped me
    to reconcile the two realms personally. Also, the model of
    two windows into the same world gave me a good analog with
    which to guide my thoughts.

> *19 December 2007*
> *Dear Dwight,*
> *I suppose the students have gone home, but I ask you anyhow to thank them for their two Christmas cards. And thank you to yourself for the latest batch of essays. The latest batch was particularly illuminating. Since these were the last essays of the course, the students were writing more from the heart than they were before. And I found their struggles with fundamentalism very moving...*
> *Happy Christmas to you and the students.*
> *Yours ever, Freeman.*

18 Dreams of Earth and Sky

Thoughts on Meaning

> *"A dream shows us hidden connections between things that our waking minds keep in separate compartments."*
> –Freeman Dyson[205]

> *"Sometimes dreams are wiser than waking."* –Black Elk[206]

***

One of my wise friends once said, "The real tragedy is when you die with the music still inside you."[207] That's a comment you file away, knowing you will come back to it later. Fast forward fifteen years. I am a nervous novice operator of an alto saxophone. To get some experience with real musicians I join the volunteer orchestra of a large church across the street from the university.[208] All the other orchestra members are far more experienced; some are music professors and three play in the Oklahoma City Philharmonic. Thankfully they and the director are generous with advice and encouragement. It was a broadening experience to get a good look into their world, to hear their stories and share with them the joy of making music—not letting it die inside.

During eight consecutive Christmas seasons, for six nights each December the church put on for the public a huge musical performance. Besides the cast of principal characters, the program featured a chorus of 120 voices, superb sets and costumes and lighting, real sheep and a donkey, a horse and two camels. The people who put it together knew what they were doing. Like most Christmas programs, it was the familiar story of Mary and Joseph and Baby Jesus, the Wise Men, Angels and Shepherds. The musical drama that we performed was called *Two From Galilee*.[209] It expands the New Testament account into a heart-wrenching love story as the young engaged couple confronts the social ostracism and personal crises that ensue after teenage Mary receives the angelic visit announcing the stupendous news

---

[205][Dyson(1979a)][258]
[206][Neihardt(1961)][10]
[207]The wise words of my friend Jim Cullumber of Chandler, Arizona.
[208]The orchestra director allowed the alto sax to double French horn parts.
[209]Written by Robert Sterling and Karla Worley, based on the novel of the same title by Marjorie Holmes, published in 1972.

that she will bear the Christ Child. In 2001, as rehearsals were underway near Thanksgiving time, our STS class was discussing the closing chapters of *Disturbing the Universe*. The very last chapter, "Dreams of Earth and Sky," quietly ends in an indelible scene with an infant. Before dashing to rehearsal one evening I sent a quick note to Professor Dyson.

> *20 November 2001*
> *Dear Professor Dyson,*
> *...In honor of the closing chapter of "Disturbing the Universe" I am sending once again the poster [this time] from our 4th annual local presentation of the musical "Two From Galilee." This year I will play in the orchestra! (A new experience for me.) Time to stop being a spectator and help make it happen. Like Faust at the dike. The young lady who sings Mary (Krista Olmsted Miller) took STS from me and read "Disturbing the Universe;" it must have been about five years ago. Most of the year she sings professionally throughout this part of the country.[210] I know that the baby in your book is not necessarily the Christ child; rather, I would turn it around and say that the most beautiful symbol of Christianity is found in the infant, new life and unfathomed promise, and hope for the future, in the arms of his young mother....*

The Madonna and Child motif has been a lovely recurring theme throughout the history of Christian art. From the sixth-century Byzantine icon *Virgin and Child Enthroned between Saints and Angels* (artist unknown)[211] that shows the Christ Child as an minature adult, to High Renaissance works such as *The Virgin of the Rocks* by Leonardo da Vinci (1485) and *La Belle Jardinière* by Raphael (1507) that portray the Christ Child as an adorable infant, His divinity was understood by the faithful.

Scholars have long debated the historical accuracy of the Nativity accounts in the Gospels, and among Christian traditions universal agreement does not obtain on all theological points of the story. But the story itself is a touching one, because it revolves around an Infant as the link between humanity and the divine. Charles Dickens wisely observed, "it is good to be children sometimes, and never better than at Christmas, when its mighty Founder was a child himself." [Dickens(1957)][82] But whatever the facts of history, and whatever one's tradition or the official interpretation, Christmas raises the question: In what sense are all infants a little part of God?

---

[210]Over the years in the productions described here, there were three Marys.

[211]Other paintings of this period have similar titles; the one mentioned here resides at the Monestary of St. Catherine, Mount Sinai, Egypt [Janson and Janson(2001)][237]

The Grace of Tragedy

Before the subject of cosmology recedes farther into our rear-view mirror, we might ask what it says about the ultimate fate of the universe. Will the universe keep expanding forever? The issue reduces to a contest between gravity and speed. If the universe contains enough matter, gravity's brakes will eventually halt the expansion, which will be followed by contraction with the universe collapsing in a "big crunch." Alternatively, the expansion might have speed left over when the galaxies are beyond the reach of each other's gravitation. A scenario on the cusp between the other two would see gravity and speed balance exactly, so that when the galaxies have just escaped each other's gravity they have also practically stopped. These three options are called respectively the "closed," "open," and "flat" universes.[212]

If our understanding of cosmology is correct, then the universe will continue expanding forever in the "flat" scenario.[213] If that is so, the universe will get colder and darker and emptier as each galaxy cluster sees all the other galaxy clusters recede to infinity. Within each galaxy, the stars will eventually run out of fuel. One by one they will go out, leaving a cold, dark universe.

In the final chapter of *Disturbing the Universe*, "Dreams of Earth and Sky," Professor Dyson shares with us some of his dreams. One dream occurs after a long day in an astrophysics conference at the Israel Institute of Technology in Haifa, Israel. All day Professor Dyson has been discussing galaxy dynamics with experts. That night he falls into an exhausted sleep in Haifa's Hotel Dan. In the dream, his son George has just finished building

[212]These options are discussed in terms of a parameter called Ω (Greek capital omega), which stands for the ratio of the actual energy density to the so-called critical energy density. By definition, the critical density is that which results in a flat universe. Thus in the flat universe $\Omega = 1$, in the closed universe $\Omega > 1$, and in an open universe $\Omega < 1$. In 2001 the Degree Angular Scale Interferometer measured $\Omega = 1.00 \pm 0.04$. [Pryke *et al.*(2002)Pryke, Halverson, Leitch, Kovac, Carlstrom, Holzapfel and Dragovan]; in 2007 the Wilkerson Microwave Anisotropy Probe measured $\Omega = 1.0052 \pm 0.0064$. [Spergel *et al.*(2007)Spergel, Bean, Doré, Nolta, Bennett, Dunkley, Hinshaw, Jarosik, Komatsu, Page *et al.*] All the measurements so far are consistent with Ω being 1, the "flat" universe. Theory says that if $\Omega = 1 + x$ then x would grow *rapidly* with time, unless it is exactly zero. To have Ω near 1 now would require extreme "fine-tuning" of the initial conditions. However, a theoretical mechanism, inspired by elementary particle physics, predicts the *very* early universe expands exponentially ("inflation"), driving Ω to 1 independent of its initial value. [Guth(1981)]
[213]Data first gathered in 1998 and reinforced ever since suggest that the expansion is accelerating. It could be that $\Omega = 1$ only in the present cosmic epoch; what Ω will be in the distant future is open to speculation. If the acceleration continues, the universe will darker and emptier even faster.

an elegant little spaceship with an unusual feature. You push a button and pop up at some random place in the universe. George and Freeman play "homing pigeons" where they pop up randomly and have to navigate their way home by recognizing galaxy clusters and nebulae.

After some time they abandon the game and sit quietly in the little ship, adrift in the universe, gazing at the majestic galaxies all around them. Eventually they realize the expansion of the universe is unfolding before their eyes, as the galaxies recede, imperceptibly at first, then faster and faster, growing dimmer and dimmer, eventually leaving them alone in infinite blackness. This, writes Professor Dyson, is the kind of universe that Steven Weinberg had in mind when he wrote "The more the universe seems comprehensible, the more it also seems pointless." [Dyson(1979a)][255–258] Weinberg's famous quotation appears in the closing chapter of his superb popularization of big bang cosmology, *The First Three Minutes*. After describing the possible fates of the universe, Weinberg reflects on what it all means: [Weinberg(1988)][154–155]

However all these problems may be resolved, and whichever cosmological model proves correct, there is not much of comfort in any of this. It is almost irresistible for humans to believe that we have some special relation to the universe, that human life is not just a more-or-less farcical outcome of a chain of accidents reaching back to the first three minutes, but that we were somehow built in from the beginning. As I write this I happen to be in an airplane at 30,000 feet, flying over Wyoming en route home from San Francisco to Boston. Below, the earth looks very soft and comfortable—fluffy clouds here and there, snow turning pink as the sun sets... It is very hard to realize that this all is just a tiny part of an overwhelmingly hostile universe. It is even harder to realize that this present universe has evolved from an unspeakably unfamiliar early condition, and faces a future extinction of endless cold or intolerable heat. The more the universe seems comprehensible, the more it also seems pointless. But if there is no solace in the fruits of our research, there is at least some consolation in the research itself.... The effort to understand the universe is one of the very few things that lifts human life a little above the level of farce, and gives it some of the grace of tragedy.

Weinberg could be right. The Earth has made some four billion laps around the sun, and will make as many more before the Sun swells up to engulf our oasis planet. That repetitive mechanical motion, age after age, only to end in dissolution, seems as pointless as the infinite blackness.

Long ago the author of *Ecclesiastes* was on the same page as Weinberg when writing "Vanity of vanities, all is vanity... One generation passeth away, and another generation cometh... The sun also ariseth, and the sun goeth down... All the rivers run to the sea; yet the sea is not full..."[214] Perhaps our fate is to maintain our dignity by facing tragedy with grace. Perhaps it is only about the journey, not the destination.

Professor Weinberg also shares his dreams with us, in *Dreams of a Final Theory*. Here he describes the aesthetic hope that motivates so much of theoretical elementary particle physics: that the fundamental forces in nature will ultimately be shown to be unified. That would mean the distinct forces we observe today, such as gravity and electromagnetism and the nuclear forces, are different phases of an underlying unity, analogous to how ice and steam are different phases of water. Such a strategy has a rich heritage in physics. In the eighteenth century Isaac Newton unified terrestrial and celestial gravity into universal gravitation. In the nineteenth century, Michael Faraday and James Maxwell unified electricity and magnetism. In the early twentieth century, Albert Einstein unified mass with energy, light with space and time, and spacetime with gravitation. In 1948 Freeman Dyson unified the quantum electrodynamics methods of Richard Feynman, Julian Schwinger, and Sin-itiro Tomonaga, showing their methods were equivalent. In the 1960s Weinberg, Adbus Salam and Sheldon Glashow unified electromagnetism and the weak nuclear force into one, the electroweak interaction. We don't *know* that all the fundamental forces can be unified. But pursuing that dream has, so far, been a fertile strategy for finding something interesting. In sharing with his readers this elegant dream of physics, Weinberg moved on to a question of unity beyond the physical in the chapter "What About God?" There he returned in depth to the deep questions he hinted at in the closing paragraphs of *The First Three Minutes*.

Some people have views of God that are so broad and flexible that it is inevitable that they will find God wherever they look for him...
In this spirit, it seems to me that if the word "God" is to be of any use, it should be taken to mean an interested God, a creator and lawgiver who has established not only the laws of nature and the universe but also standards of good and evil, some personality that is concerned with our actions, something in short that it is appropriate for us to worship. This is the God that has mattered to men and women throughout history. Scientists and others sometimes use the

---

[214] *Ecclesiastes* 1:2,4a,5,7a (KJV).

word "God" to mean something so abstract and unengaged that He is hardly to be distinguished from the laws of nature...but it seems to me that it makes the concept of God not so much wrong as unimportant....

Among today's scientists I am probably somewhat atypical in caring about such things. [Weinberg(1992)][244–245, 256]

I appreciate that Professor Weinberg cares about such things. Whether or not God exists, the question is a serious one. Whether or not the universe is pointless, the two windows of science and religion are not reconciled by redefining God so drastically as to make Him pointless. Professor Weinberg continues:

...At least the conservatives like the scientists tell you that they believe in what they believe because it is true, rather than because it makes them good or happy. Many religious liberals today seem to think that different people can believe in different mutually exclusive things without any of them being wrong, as long as their beliefs "work for them."

Wolfgang Pauli was once asked whether he thought that a particularly ill-conceived physics paper was wrong. He replied that such a description would be too kind—the paper was not even wrong. I happen to think that the religious conservatives are wrong in what they believe, but at least they have not forgotten what it means to really believe something. The religious liberals seem to me to be not even wrong. [Weinberg(1992)][257–258]

Believers need thoughtful skeptics like Weinberg, in order to keep them honest. Skeptics need non-dogmatic religious sympathizers like Professor Dyson, to keep them honest too. Both Professor Dyson and Professor Weinberg know how to maintain respect despite disagreement. It is not surprising to learn that they are old friends.

> *4 December 2006*
> *Dear Professor Dyson,*
> *...Did you and Steven Weinberg ever discuss between yourselves the topics that you address in the final chapter, "Dreams of Earth and Sky" and in your review article, "Physics and Biology in an Open Universe"? Weinberg's position on questions that belong to religion and not to science are described in Chapter 11 ("What About God?") in his 1992 book, "Dreams of a Final Theory." There he beautifully articulates the issues involved, with a clarity we seldom hear from the pulpit.*
> *We are wondering if you and he ever had the opportunity (say,*

*over lunch) to discuss these matters between yourselves, in addi-
tion to the discussions that occurred in public. It is inspiring to
see that you and Steven Weinberg have dreams and are willing
to share them.*

9 December 2006
Dear Dwight and students,
*I just came back from a tour of family in various places, our
minister daughter Mia in Maine, our son George in Bellingham
and our step-daughter Katarina in Vancouver, with their various offspring. A great trip. Came back yesterday to find your
message, luckily just in time....*
*...I am sorry to say that Steven Weinberg and I never sat down
to discuss our disagreements privately. It seems we are both
more comfortable arguing in public than in private. We are
and remain good friends, and don't want to let our disagreements damage our friendship. I think everything we have said
about philosophical and religious questions is out in the open
where you can read it for yourselves.*
*...Thanks again for your thoughtful remarks. I wish all of you
a joyful holiday and safe travel.*
Yours ever, Freeman.

Fair enough. We appreciate that Professor Dyson cares more about
maintaining friendship with Professor Weinberg than he does about scoring
points in an argument. Perhaps those in Positions A and Z could take a
lesson from Steven Weinberg and Freeman Dyson.

Mind and Reality

*"It takes three people to make music: the composer, the per-
former, and the appreciator."* –Evonne Neuenschwander

After ten years of correspondence on behalf of the STS students, I felt I
could risk sharing something personal with Professor Dyson. I wanted to
tell him why *Disturbing the Universe* hits so close to home for me personally. In addition, I would be speaking for many of my students with similar
backgrounds. The result was a long letter of 13 November 2003. It summarized much of what I bring to the "science and religion" discussions in STS.
Someone who articulated the Two Windows metaphor would understand.

In the letter I described how in graduate school I was studying Weinberg's electroweak theory and the Dyson equations. Thus *Disturbing the
Universe* stood out when it appeared in our university bookstore. It came

at a crucial time in my life. I had come to the place where I could be a reluctant atheist. It held a logical appeal for me, and still does—it seems the simplest answer to the problem of meaninglessness that Weinberg articulated in the closing lines of *The First Three Minutes*. But I also had some issues of my own. I grew up in a parsonage. My parents formed a team in all aspects of ministry, and ministry was their life. From the week I was born until the middle of my junior year in high school, I was present in every church event.

We were told by Sunday School teachers that we should not doubt. But I had doubts, plenty of them, and they were not easily dismissed. If a Divine Mind is the ultimate reality, why doesn't it reveal itself openly so everyone would know? As I grew up, I became increasingly uneasy with the loud certainty that permeates much of grassroots church culture. Once you realize that going to Heaven and avoiding Hell are selfish motives for being Christian, you begin digging for deeper reasons to take it seriously.

There is much about my upbringing that I appreciate. Most church teaching forms solid policies for living. Many of my closest friends, including my wife, came through relationships with church people. I am deeply grateful that my parents were not fundamentalists. They were fascinated by what I was learning as a physics major, and showed themselves open to the ideas I brought home.

I have always respected my parents and others like them, because they lived every day of their lives faithful to their principles. They knew what they believed, they believed it because they thought it true, and it was an integral part of who they were. Nevertheless, I felt awkward at being thrust into situations where, as the pastor's son, I was presumed to hold a particular ideology. I was caught between the competing values of striving to be honest while not breaking the hearts of loved ones....

The letter went on like this for an embarrassingly large number of pages. It was an attempt to tell Professor Dyson how *Disturbing the Universe* pulls beautifully together some thoughts that I had carried half-formed for years but could not articulate. I knew that most of my students would share similar backgrounds, questions and doubts. They, too, would wish to live divided no more.

In his penultimate chapter "The Argument from Design" Professor Dyson describes two separate levels where mind enters our awareness of nature.[Dyson(1979a)][249] At the top level, we are consciously aware of our own minds. At the lowest level, the level of single atoms and electrons, modern physics shows that the mind of an observer participates in the unfolding of events; for instance, whether an electron behaves like a wave, or whether it behaves like a particle, depends on what measurement the observer chooses to make. In between the level of self-aware consciousness, and the level of our poking into the doings of sub-microscopic particles, lies levels of nature where mechanical models are adequate and mind appears to be irrelevant, such as planetary orbits, evolution by natural selection, and the expanding universe. Professor Dyson writes that he will propose a hypothesis to bridge the gap between the two displays of mind.

But I, as a physicist, cannot help suspecting that there is a logical connection between the two ways in which mind appears in my universe. I cannot help thinking that our <u>awareness</u> [emphasis added] *of our own brains has something to do with the processes which we call "observation" in atomic physics. That is to say, I think our consciousness... is an active agent forcing the molecular complexes to make choices between one quantum state and another. In other words, mind is already inherent in every electron...* [Dyson(1979a)][249]

The way I understand this passage, if electrons, either inside our heads or outside them, must "choose" whether to be like waves or like particles depending on how we probe them, then somehow the electron is receptive to our mind. If that is so, perhaps "mind" in some sense permeates the universe. Professor Dyson continues:

It is true that we emerged in the universe by chance, but the idea of chance is itself only a cover for our ignorance. I do not feel like an alien in this universe. The more I examine the universe and study the details of its architecture, the more evidence I find that the universe in some sense must have known that we were coming.
There are some striking examples in the laws of nuclear physics of numerical accidents that seem to conspire to make the universe habitable... [Dyson(1979a)][249–250]

If the strong nuclear force was a little stronger, the universe would be a giant nucleus; if it was a little weaker the only element would be hydrogen. The parameters that make life possible as we know it are so narrow in range that the universe could easily have been inhospitable to us, not allowing for us even a little niche like the Earth.

However, the fact that we are here does not prove that the universe was designed for us by a cosmic intelligence. Proponents of "Intelligent

Design" seem to imagine that blueprints for the human species were drafted before everything else, requiring a niche habitat to be custom-built around that design. But that is not how evolution works. Life adapts to the environment. Genetic diversity produces variations, and only the well-adapted ones avoid being filtered out. Only the survivors live long enough to pass their genes on, to make successive generations even better adapted to the niche. If no niche hospitable to life existed in the universe, we would not be here to wonder about it.

But, despite all obstacles, life *is* possible in the universe. *We are here.*

I conclude from the existence of these accidents of physics and astronomy that the universe is an unexpectedly hospitable place for living creatures to make their home in.

It's almost as if the universe *needs* life. We do not *know* this to be so...

Being a scientist,... I do not claim that the architecture of the universe proves the existence of God.

...but it *could* be so without violating any known laws of physics or biology. Thus comes Professor Dyson's hypothesis:

I claim only that the architecture of the universe is consistent with the hypothesis that mind plays an essential role in its functioning. [Dyson(1979a)][251]

How could mind hypothetically play an "essential" role? Consider, as we must, an analogy. We know that temperature differences are necessary for physical processes to proceed. When temperature gradients no longer exist, life will shut down. By analogy, we might hypothesize that the universe needs awareness just as much as it needs temperature gradients. Temperature gradients for processes to proceed; minds for awareness and appreciation. Wind and surf and stars are impossible without temperature gradients. Winds and surf and stars are pointless without appreciators. Life needs habitat for survival; *intelligence* needs the universe to be *interesting*. Like composers and performers, perhaps the universe also needs appreciators. Perhaps it really is about the journey and not the destination.

Now we have found a third level to add to these two. The peculiar harmony between the structure of the universe and the needs of life and intelligence is a third manifestation of the importance of mind in the scheme of things. This is as far as we can go as scientists. We have evidence that mind is important on three levels. We have no evidence for any deeper unifying hypothesis that would tie these three levels together. As individuals, some of us may be willing to go further. Some of us may be willing to entertain the hypothesis that there exists a universal mind or world soul which underlies the manifestations of mind that we observe.... The existence of a world soul is a question that belongs to religion and not to science. [Dyson(1979a)][252]

Begging the reader's indulgence, I must finish the core part of my 13 November 2003 letter to Professor Dyson:

> *...But the existence of God, or a Cosmic Mind, or the Great Spirit, or (as Einstein said) the Old One, remains the great unanswerable question.... Thus your closing three chapters of "Disturbing the Universe" hit me like a ton of bricks during graduate school, when I could have embraced the point of view well expressed by Weinberg. The "deeper unifying hypothesis" that you articulated so beautifully in "The Argument from Design" showed me that I was not being intellectually irresponsible by supposing that the hypothesis of a Cosmic Mind could be taken seriously.... In addition, at that time... I was beginning to appreciate the value of interpersonal relationships as the source of meaning in our existence. The down-to-earth scenes you enjoyed with George, and the closing dream when you and your daughters hold the baby as he smiles at you, expressed what I knew I was missing. Images, like music, reach deeper than words.*
>
> *In those last three chapters of "Disturbing the Universe" you articulated what I had been thinking and feeling for a long time but could not put into words. I thank you for that....*
>
> *...So at that moment in graduate school, I did not throw overboard the concept that there may be, perhaps, a Cosmic Mind, a source of love and meaning larger than ourselves.... The "evidence," such as it is, for the Cosmic Mind, consists not in the majesty of the Universe itself but in the existence of love and caring relationships between minds that could behave otherwise....*
>
> *Thank you for sharing yourself with me and with my students. Warm regards, Dwight*

I did not need assurance that God really exists. For a long time it has been enough for me to suppose that a Cosmic Mind *might* exist, *could* exist. But Professor Dyson's thoughts on Mind offered reassurance that one could entertain such a hypothesis without being intellectually irresponsible.

We return to the student's questions.

> *11 November 2014*
> *Dear Professor Dyson,*
> *...In "The Argument from Design" you discuss three roles for "mind" in the universe. The relation between mind and matter, the brain and consciousness, has been a long-standing philosophical debate. Do the roles for mind in the universe depend on how one answers the mind-body problem?*

> *3 December 2014*
> *Dear Dwight and students,*
> *...My answer to this question is no. I consider the role of mind in the universe to be a religious mystery, while the relation between mind and matter in a human brain is a scientific mystery. The two mysteries are both concerned with the nature of mind, but they are different. The mind-body problem might be solved using the tools of science, but the understanding of the mind-body problem would not give us understanding of the mind-universe problem. The mind-universe problem has nothing to do with the tools of science. To me it is important to keep science and religion separate. The idea that God might be explored by doing scientific experiments is absurd. The idea that the working of the human brain can be explored by scientific experiments is not absurd. That is the essential difference between religion and science.*
> *Thank you once more for a good set of questions....*
> *Happy Christmas to you and the class! Yours ever, Freeman.*

The Honesty of Doubting Thomas

In the 13 November 2003 letter to Professor Dyson I also asked him about some of his neighbors I met. "He gave me his card which I have unfortunately misplaced but they were very nice. He told me what a good friend and neighbor you are, and also mentioned that you could be 'fierce' when it came to sticking up for science...." Included with the letter was the current STS syllabus and a few talks and articles, including a university convocation speech[215] in defense of one of twelve Apostles, the notorious "doubting Thomas."

According to the Bible story,[216] after the Crucifixion, when the other disciples told Thomas they had seen the resurrected Jesus, Thomas didn't buy it. He told them that unless he saw Jesus with his own eyes, he would not believe. Evidently Jesus respected Thomas's doubt and appeared to him, saying, "Here I am, Thomas, look and see." Then Thomas said "My Lord and my God." I take from this story the implication that if there is a God to doubt, that God respects honest doubt and will meet the doubter at the point of his or her need.

After I mailed the November 13 letter I had second thoughts that I might have been too presumptuous. But Professor Dyson's reply was thoughtful and gracious. He continued the conversation, which I have always appreciated:

> *18 November 2003*
> *Dear Dwight,*
> *Thank you for the long letter and the package of papers.... the Thomas is the most thoughtful. Do you know the Gospel of Thomas, one of the gospels that were excluded from the Bible by the enforcers of orthodoxy in the fourth century? Elaine Pagels[217] has written a lot about it. Here is one of the verses: Jesus said to His disciples, "Compare me to someone and tell Me whom I am like." Simon Peter said to him, "You are like a righteous angel." Matthew said to Him, "You are like a wise philosopher." Thomas said to him, "Master, my mouth is wholly incapable of saying whom You are like." I would give the same answer as Thomas.*
> *...You ask who was the neighbor who sat with you at the Cathedral in Washington.... Several of our Princeton friends were there but no immediate neighbors. It might have been Wallace Alston, who is director of the Center of Theological Inquiry, an offshoot of the Princeton Seminary. Before that he was pastor of the Nassau Presbyterian Church, so we have known him well for many years. Just two weeks ago my wife and I had supper with him and I gave a lecture at the Center... After the lecture we had a session with the local theologians. One of them, a man for whom I have a deep respect, attacked me strongly. He said I am an "arrogant agnostic," trying to impose my set of rules on*

---

[215] 20 August 2000.

[216] *The Gospel According to John*, Ch. 20.

[217] E.g., Elaine Pagels, *The Gnostic Gospels* (Vintage, 1989); *Beyond Belief: The Secret Gospel of Thomas* (Pan Macmillan, 2005).

*God, telling God that He is not allowed to reveal Himself to us
even if He wants to. I did not find it necessary to defend myself
but was glad to let him have the last word. Maybe he is right
and I am an arrogant agnostic. I can live with that. Maybe
I impose my rules on God, but that is not so bad as imposing
them on my neighbors....*

Three semesters later, our kindred spirit the Apostle Thomas came up
again.

March 22, 2005
Dear Professor Dyson,
*Thank you for your family's wonderful 2005 New Year letter.
....the students wrote you some notes that I have enclosed. In
addition, for her "STS Museum" project, student Krystal S. designed and made the enclosed T-shirts...*
*I see that George did not move his family into his tree house
in the Douglas fir. The breathtaking picture of Mount Shasta,
taken from the home of Rebecca and Peter, motivates me to
enclose a photo of Mt. Rainier taken last summer during our
family vacation....*
*I have read several times your 2003 Witherspoon Lecture, "The
Varieties of Human Experience." ...In your lecture you said,
"[William] James looked at religion from the inside." This has
been my lot in life as well.... Like [Elaine] Pagels, I find the
church's meaning in the sense of community. For those personal relationships I am grateful....*
*Elaine Pagels' book "Beyond Belief" became quite personal for
me when I saw how it compares to Gospel of John to the Gospel
of Thomas. For many years our denomination sponsored a
Bible quizzing program... I participated during my [high school]
sophomore year. That year we quizzed over the Gospel of John,
King James Version. Reading Pagels' book replayed tapes in
my head of familiar passages in John....*
*Thomas has always been one of my heroes, because he dared to
acknowledge his honest doubt....*
*...Insofar as I have a theology, it would be like this: If a gracious
Cosmic Mind truly exists, then to the person who honestly seeks
to know it, that Mind will reveal itself in terms the individual
can understand...*
Best wishes & warm regards, Dwight

7 May 2005
Dear Dwight,
*Before I answer the students' questions, I take this opportunity
to answer (better late than never) your splendid letter of March*

22 with the picture of [your] family in front of Mount Rainier...
I heard Elaine Pagels recently speak about the gospels of John
and Thomas. One thing struck me forcefully. John is talking
poetry and Thomas prose. Just from an artistic point of view,
John is infinitely superior. Perhaps that is the reason why he
is in the Bible and Thomas is not. The people who chose the
canonical texts in the fourth century, like those who translated
them into English twelve hundred years later, had a deep re-
spect for style and language. Although I am closer in my view
of Jesus to Thomas than to John, I have to admit that I would
rather listen to John than to Thomas....

Since about half of our correspondence over the years occurs near the
Christmas season, Christmas gets a lot of mention. However, there may
be deeper reasons why a Christmas motif keeps recurring. We recall that
Charles Dickens observed "it's mighty Founder was a child." There is nothing more sacred than a child.

13 November 2003
Dear Professor Dyson...
...The symbol I find the most meaningful in the Christian
mythos is the Christ Child of Christmas (another resonance
with "Disturbing the Universe's" final scene, and... reason to
play in the orchestra for our Christmas musical). Many peo-
ple say that the Christmas mythos is secondary, that Easter is
what it's all about. Perhaps for them, but not for me. Death is
not the worst thing that can happen to us; that is not the fate
from which we need redemption. Loneliness and meaningless-
ness are far worse. Viktor Frankl was right when he said that
the strength of his love went beyond the physical presence, or
even the continued existence, of the beloved.[218] Babies are an
inspiration to live, and a hope for the future....

18 November 2003
Dear Dwight,
...I liked especially the remark in your letter that you respond
more to Christmas than to Easter. I believe this is true of the
majority of Christians, but they do not like to admit it. Cer-
tainly it is true of me....
...Did I tell you that we had a grand family reunion in San Diego
in August? This was to celebrate my eightieth birthday which is
actually in December, but it was easier to get the family together

---

[218][Frankl(1963)][60]

in August. All the six children and twelve grandchildren were together for a week. The mothers and fathers took turns cooking great meals for twenty-four people and organizing expeditions to interesting places. The children all enjoyed this chance to get to know their cousins, and for me it was a fore-taste of heaven, to spend a week with nothing to do but carry babies around...

Questions Answered, Not With Words but With a Smile

When Alice and Freeman Dyson were children, they accompanied their parents to the annual Three Choirs Festival that rotated between the cathedrals of Gloucester, Worcester, and Hereford. "Apart from the new works by my father and other young composers, the staple diet of the festivals was Bach, Handel, Mendelssohn and Elgar. The works that the choirs sang with the most genuine gusto were the three old standbys of the English choral tradition, Handel's *Messiah*, Mendelssohn's *Elijah*, and Elgar's *Dream of Gerontius*. Mendelssohn wrote the *Elijah* for the Birmingham festival of 1846 and conducted its first performance there. It was a tremendous success..." [Dyson(1979a)][259]

The story of Elijah comes from the Old Testament. After defeating the prophets of Baal, Elijah wanders depressed in the wilderness. An angel comes to Elijah at Mount Horeb and tells him, "Go forth, and stand upon the mount before the Lord. And behold, the Lord passed by, and a great and strong wind rent the mountains, and brake in pieces the rocks before the Lord; but the Lord was not in the wind: and after the wind an earthquake; but the Lord was not in the earthquake: and after the earthquake a fire; but the Lord was not in the fire: and after the fire a still small voice." [Dyson(1979a)][259][219]

In the homing pigeons dream, the galaxies in all their majesty were magnificently carried apart towards a depressing infinite blackness.

In that dream at Haifa I have seen the greatness and the emptiness of the universe. I have seen the strong wind, and the earthquake, and the fire; but I have not heard the still small voice. I have seen the galaxies pass before me, but the Lord was not in the galaxies... [Dyson(1979a)][259]

There has to be more.

[219] *I Kings* 19: 11–12.

The vision of the universe that I saw in my dream was only one of many possible universes. It was a mindless, mechanical universe.... George and I were traveling through that universe like tourists...not belonging to it and not influencing it. I do not accept this vision.... We are not merely spectators; we are actors in the drama of the universe. I wish I could take another look.... [Dyson(1979a)][258]

The morning after the homing pigeons dream, Professor Dyson embarked on a day of sight-seeing in the Golan Heights, taking lunch by the Sea of Galilee where Jesus taught and ate fish with his disciples. That night Professor Dyson returned to the Hotel Dan. The hotel stands on Mount Horeb, where Elijah came long ago in his despair. Perhaps Elijah's angel came to the Mount a second time, for that night Professor Dyson got his second look, in the form of another dream....

...At lunch with his wife and children, he grumbles about the bureaucracy. His wife says, "Why don't you go straight to the top?" He picks up the telephone to book an appointment with the Authorities. A friendly voice schedules his appointment, in one hour. He asks the children if they want to accompany him to his appointment with God. Two daughters want to go. The three of them slip out of the house and walk to the office, a large building. Its inside looks like a church but has no ceiling. Professor Dyson and the girls hold hands and jump. Up the shaft they go. At the top they step into a great throne room with whitewashed walls and dark heavy oak beams. At the top of some steps sits a wicker throne. It appears to be unoccupied. Perhaps God did not expect them to be so punctual. After a few minutes Professor Dyson ascends the stairs.

The girls are shy and stay at the bottom. I walk up until my eyes are level with the seat. I see then that the throne is not empty after all. There is a three-month-old baby lying on the seat and smiling at me. I pick him up and show him to the girls. They run up the steps and take turns carrying him. After they give him back to me, I stay with him for a few minutes longer, holding him in my arms without saying a word. In the silence I gradually become aware that the questions I had intended to raise with him have been answered. I put him gently back on his throne and say goodbye. The girls hold my hands and we walk down the steps together. [Dyson(1979a)][261]

This scene that closes *Disturbing the Universe* has generated more interest than any other single one.

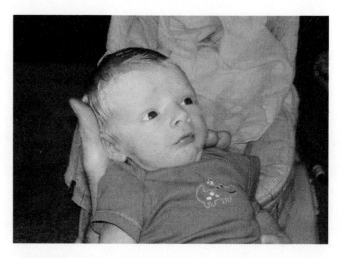

Fig. 18.1   *"There is a three-month-old baby lying on the seat and smiling at me. I pick him up..."* (author photo)

25 April 1995
Dear Professor Dyson,
....Referring to the last chapter, "Dreams of Earth and Sky,"
what does the baby represent—what specifically did you have in
mind? What attributes of God are you trying to represent?
We discussed this question at some length in class. I personally
find it fitting that you did not make more specific the reasons
for the baby on the throne of God, or specify your questions that
had been answered. Like great music or literature, this chapter
describes, through a vivid image and mood, that which words do
not have the power to articulate. By not being overly specific,
the reader can place himself or herself in the dream, with his or
her own questions....

26 April 1995
Dear Dwight Neuenschwander,
It was lucky that you send the letter by FAX, as today is the
last day I have any time to answer it. Tomorrow we start three
full days of astronomy meetings, and then I fly off to Jerusalem
for three weeks of lectures at the Hebrew University. So I give
you my answers to the questions as best I can....
What does the baby represent? What specifically did you have
in mind? What attributes of God are you trying to represent?
(Here I agree with your comment in your letter).... The main
fact concerning the dream is that it was a genuine dream, not
a consciously composed story. I had nothing in mind when I

dreamed it but the dream itself. I did not think about what the dream was supposed to represent until much later.

I should say that the account of the dream in the book is incomplete in one respect. In the actual dream, there was an intense and overwhelming flood of joy that streamed through me while I was holding the baby. It was not that my questions were answered, but my questions were swept away by the power that streamed through me. Afterwards, when I wrote the concluding pages of the book, I decided to leave out this aspect of the dream for artistic reasons. As a writer, I wanted the book to end with a quiet good-bye, not with a flourish of trumpets. So I toned down the ending. I still think it was better to give it a quiet ending. The ending as written is not untrue, only incomplete.

To come back to the question of what the dream means. In my waking life, holding babies is about as close as I ever come to a personal religion. In some sense, holding babies is an act of worship. When I am holding a baby, it often reminds me of the Bergman film "The Seventh Seal," in which the juggler Jof with his young wife and baby sit snug while the storm rages and the angel of death flies over their heads. So for me every baby carries a message of life and hope and survival. It is natural to think of a baby as a little bit of God. But the dream is not an intellectual exercise. It is rather a mystical exercise, or an unconscious work of art. I am not "trying to represent" anything. You might say, God is representing himself in the only way I can understand.

If I try to answer your question by interpreting the dream in intellectual terms, I would say: God is not an end but a beginning, a part of the universe that was only recently born. But that is only an after-thought.

...I will be back from Jerusalem in May 25 and look forward to reading any more comments and reactions from the students then. Meanwhile, I wish them a happy final exam and thank them for their questions.

Yours sincerely, Freeman Dyson

A few semesters later, a new group of students wanted to ask Professor Dyson about the scene with the baby. However, upon reviewing our past correspondence on this question they did not want to be repetitious, and asked something else. However, to their questions I attached this note:

1 May 2000

Dear Professor Dyson,

Eight of the students asked a question about the dream with which you close "Disturbing the Universe." Those questions took the form of asking about the symbolism of the baby, and/or what questions you wanted to ask when you made the appoint-ment.... I thought you might be interested to see how this image continues to capture the imagination of readers.

As a postscript to his replies to our other questions Professor Dyson volunteered another glimpse into his thinking about the throne room scene.

1 May 2000
Dear Dwight,
...About the baby, I don't need to add much to what I said before. The symbolism is obvious. My father who was a musician used to say that music was the closest he ever came to God. And I feel the same way about babies. Recently I was at a party in California and had the luck to hold a baby for two hours while his mother cooked the dinner. His mother was grateful and so was I. Holding a baby is the closest I ever come to God. So the dream made sense. I think of God as coming into existence like a baby, still close to the beginning, no end in sight.
You ask what questions I had in mind to ask him. Just the usual questions, why the world is so full of misery and injustice and evil, why so many people never have a chance of a decent life, why the people who have the power to make things better are mostly viscous and stupid. If God made us, couldn't he have made us better? And of course the questions were answered the same way babies always answer questions, not with words but with a smile....

Other Dreams?

4 June 2001
Dear Professor Dyson,
...Have you had any more dreams, similar to those [described] in your book, since "Disturbing the Universe" was published?

10 June 2001
...Sad to say, I never had any dreams in recent years as vivid as those I wrote about in the book. Perhaps that is a part of growing old. I looked in some more recent papers for interesting dreams, and all I could find was the following item:
January 2, 1995. The most banal conversation ever dreamed. I was in the underworld and met Hitler dressed in his usual Army uniform. I said, "You were not much of a general" and he replied, "You were not much of a general either." I said, "But I was not trying to be one." End of conversation.

> *Sorry, that is the best I can do. Thank you, students, for an-
> other good set of questions. And good wishes to all of you for
> the summer....*

One semester, as part of the science and religion section of the course, we also wrote to Professor Karl Giberson, who wrote an insightful book called *Worlds Apart: The Unholy War Between Religion and Science.*[220] We asked him a few questions, and in his reply he included this note:

> 11 December 2000
> Dear Dwight:
> I am humbled to respond, knowing that Freeman Dyson is also a
> part of your course....

The Faith of a Heretic

"God is an overwhelming responsibility..." –Jethro Tull[221]

We have seen how our students frequently grapple with spiritual struggles alongside their academic ones, trying to reconcile their teachings from childhood with the wider world. In Professor Dyson's contributed chapter for the Templeton Foundation book *How Large is God?* he turned the book's title around: "When we ask the question, 'How Large is God?' we are asking whether God transcends all the concepts and images that human beings have formed of him. Another way to ask the same question is, 'How Small is Human Understanding?'" [Templeton(1997)]

Our students are trying to construct a philosophy of life that is authentically their own. Recognizing that my background resembles many of theirs, sometimes they want to know what I make of all this. That is not what this is about. They must form their own philosophy of science and religion. But as Professor Dyson showed me that one could take seriously the possibility of a Cosmic Mind without being intellectually irresponsible, I should return the favor to my students whenever they ask. I have no answers that would compel all reasonable observers to agree, but have learned to live in the questions.

It seems to me that doubt and faith go together. Faith is a *choice* about which principle to act upon when one cannot *know*. I must confess

---

[220]Beacon Hill Press (1993).
[221]Lyrics from "Thick as a Brick" (Chrysalis, 1972).

it would have been easy for me to be an atheist, taking the simple solution of dismissal to all my doubts and struggles. But an atheist does not say "I choose to not believe in God." An atheist declares "There is no God." I don't *know* that there is no God. Therefore I cannot be an atheist.

I want to embrace the spiritual dimension of being human, even though I don't fully know what that means—I don't think anyone does. In some way I feel but cannot rationalize, an elegant liturgy such as Rachmaninov's *All Night Vigil*, or the beauty and solemnity of a Mass, express a deep need that must be acknowledged. Whether these poetic expressions are merely creations of our own minds and emotions, or whether they are the result of our minds and a Cosmic Mind reaching out towards communion, I have no way of *knowing*. But I can live with the uncertainty. As Tennyson observed, there exists more faith in honest doubt than in half the creeds.

At the intellectual level, the Christian tradition has the Nicene Creed and the Apostle's Creed, fourth-century statements that spell out what Christians are supposed to believe. My creed is much simpler, perhaps simplistic. I express it in what I call the Agnostic's Prayer. It goes like this: "God—if there is a God—reveal yourself to me in a way I will understand." Any Deity that exists and is worthy of respect will surely respond to an Agnostic's Prayer expressed with sincerity. That response may vary from person to person, but it will meet each one at the point of his or her need.

Maybe Steven Weinberg is right and I have so enlarged the concept of God as to render it meaningless. But in the absence of evidence for God that would compel all responsible observers to converge to a more precise description, I do not know what else to do. I think Weinberg would agree that one cannot make a definitive statement that goes beyond the evidence we have, and that deep concepts can be expressed in more than one representation. Given the finiteness of our minds, the concept of God is too important to be flippantly dismissed. I can live with the uncertainty that my response implies. I am walking in all the light that I have, while trying to remain open and receptive to more light. What more can anyone do?

My theology is very simple. The Apostle John has written, "He who does not love does not know God, for God is love."[222] *God is love.* I take that as an operational definition of God. I also take it as a symmetric relation that goes the other way too: "Love is God." By that I mean, if you would seek God, look for love. That is theology enough for my limited mind.

---

[222] *1 John* 4:8

Perhaps I am subjecting myself again to Professor Weinberg's criticism of re-defining God so broadly as to be pointless. [Weinberg(1992)][256] But I don't think so. A world with love is not pointless. Love *is* the point.

The ancient Gregorian hymn "Ubi Caritas" contains all the theology I need. It offers a moving benediction to our class discussions on science and religion, and to the STS course. To the soft accompaniment of piano and flute, we listen as it is sung first in Latin, then in English, by a children's choir:[223]

> *Ubi Caritas, et armour,*
> *Ubi Caritas, Deus ibi est.*
>
> *Where love and caring are,*
> *There is God.*

---

[223] *Ubi Caritas* from the CD *Be Still My Soul*, arranged and performed by Earl Hefley (flute, clarinet, alto sax) and Howard Hanger (piano), and a choir of six children. Jazz Fantasy Records, Asheville, NC (1998).

19 Family First

Letters on Priorities

> *All you need is love,*
> *All you need is love,*
> *All you need is love, love*
> *Love is all you need...*
> –John Lennon and Paul McCartney

***

On the evening when Professor Dyson delivered his acceptance speech for the Templeton Prize in May 2000, prior to the ceremony that took place in Washington's National Cathedral a reception in his honor was held on the Cathedral campus at St. Alban's School. Amid tables covered with elegant linen and o'dourves, many distinguished people stood in a receiving line, patiently waiting their turn to shake Professor Dyson's hand. I was standing off to one side, watching and taking it all in. Suddenly through the door burst half a dozen lively, merry children. Their ages ranged from toddler to about seven. They ran towards Professor Dyson with gleeful shouts that sounded like "Papa! Papa!" He turned from the line of dignitaries and knelt down with outstretched arms, placing himself on eye level with the children. They smothered him with gleeful hugs. Those grandchildren had Professor Dyson's full attention. The line of dignitaries had to wait, but no one seemed to mind. As smiling witnesses of Professor Dyson's priorities we felt privileged to view a heart-warming moment between this grandfather and his grandchildren.

Our class saw this side of Professor Dyson's priorities early in our correspondence with him. Members of a January miniterm class wrote greetings in an oversize card that carried a print of Claude Monet's *Water Lilies*. A cover letter was attached:

> *15 February 1995*
> *Dear Professor Dyson:*
> *...The enclosed card is signed by the students who took the course during the January "mini-term." ... I thought you might enjoy hearing these student's comments.*
> *I have found in all semesters (including mini-terms) that the students genuinely like "Disturbing the Universe," and appreciate how it opens their minds and gets them to think. They say*

372

it transforms the way they think about science, since most of them come into the class with images of the usual stereotypes. They say "Disturbing the Universe" is more approachable than a regular text....

On behalf of the several hundred students at SNU who have examined important issues through "Disturbing the Universe," I thank you for your important contribution to their lives—and to mine.

Warm regards, Dwight E. Neuenschwander

Before mailing the card I photocopied for our memory scrapbook the student's hand-written messages. Thus I can share some of them:

```
Prof Dyson-- Thank you for giving us a ''textbook'' that
was so much more than a textbook.  I think I thought more
about philosophies while reading your book than in my whole
Philosophy course.  I really enjoyed the thought experiments
as well.  Melissa W.
```

```
I enjoyed your book.  I hope I will be one of the pioneers
to Saturn.  Nate C.
```

```
You have shed a new light on some of my long-time beliefs.
I enjoyed reading about your adventures.  What a life!
Meredyth S.
```

We were quickly honored with another reply:

21 February 1995

Dear Dr. Neuenschwander,

What a delight to hear from you again, and this time with such a heart-warming collection of accolades from your students! Please thank the students, and yourself, for the beautiful Monet lily-pond and the messages inside it. It means a great deal to me to receive a response like this from a new generation of young people. I wish every one of the students as challenging and rewarding a life as I have been blessed with.

Now I am a busy grandfather with our three little grandsons living here in Princeton (ages 3, 1, 1). Lucky again! On Sunday we took all three of them to church and they loved it. As I grow older, I spend more time baby-sitting and less time writing books. You never know which job will turn out to be more important!

Please keep in touch!

Yours ever, Freeman Dyson

Fig. 19.1 *Professor Dyson's letter of February 21, 1995.* (author photo)

A letter from the Spring 1995 class carried a postscript:

> *4 April 1995*
> *Dear Professor Dyson,*
> *...P.S. ...Congratulations on your wonderful and relatively new profession of being a grandfather to three young grandsons.... You said in your letter of Feb. 21, "I spend more time baby-sitting and less time writing books. You never know which job will turn out to be the most important!" This is similar to your remark to the survivor of the capsized boat [who was rescued by George],[224] "But it seems to me now the best thing I ever did in Princeton was to raise that boy." I find it significant that the last lines printed in "Disturbing the Universe" ["About the Author," p. 285] tell of your raising five daughters, one son, and one stepdaughter. It is so appropriate and meaningful that the text of "Disturbing" ends in the dream of God's throne, where we find the smiling infant. This profound yet tender image perfectly expresses that which is too deep to be articulated. It has been the source of some of our best discussions in class....*

---

[224][Dyson(1979a)][243]

Fast-forward to August 2013—a conference has been organized by the Institute of Advanced Studies, at Nanyang Technological University in Singapore, to honor Professor Dyson on his ninetieth birthday. At the conference I am to give a talk, describing twenty years of correspondence between STS students and Professor Dyson. Throughout the weeks before the conference, I found myself baby-sitting two of my grandchildren, ages 1 and 4, for a few hours each day, while also trying to prepare the talk. Recalling Professor Dyson's words from the February 1995 letter, I remembered: You never know which job will turn out to be more important. That line was oh so helpful in trying to maintain a proper perspective of family and profession. At the conference I was able to thank Professor Dyson in person for his wise grandfatherly advice to this relatively new grandfather. The months following the conference I am writing this book, and am doing a lot of babysitting still. You never know which job will turn out to be more important! Children and grandchildren grow up so fast! Moments with them are to be savored and cherished. There are very few things that I know for sure, but this is one of them: My grandchildren, like my children before them, do not care how many books I write or how many conferences I attend. But they do care, and they will remember, if I was there for them. Professor Dyson understands. Hopefully I have respected Professor Dyson *and* my family. Let us return to our exchanges with him about family:

> *25 April 1995*
> *Dear Professor Dyson,...*
> *For what do you wish to be the most remembered? The students have learned that you are a mathematician, physicist, father, grandfather, figure in public policy affairs....*

> *26 April 1995*
> *Dear Dwight Neuenschwander,*
> *...I take some pride in doing a number of different things well, and I do not much care which thing will be remembered longest. My children and grandchildren are a source of great pride and joy, but to their grandchildren I will be only a name. My work as a scientist was like putting a few stones into one of the arches during the building of Chartres Cathedral. The science will endure as a thing of majesty and beauty long after my personal contribution is forgotten. At the moment I am best known to the public because of the "Dyson Sphere" that appeared on the Star Trek program. This is a silly joke, but still I enjoy the fame that brings me closer to the Star Trek generation. I suppose in the long run it will probably be the writing of "Disturbing the*

Universe" that has the best chance of leaving a personal trace of me in the memory of future generations. But I am quite satisfied if the book speaks to your generation. Whether it lasts longer than that is not important.

3 December 1998
Dear Professor Dyson,
Would you do anything different, knowing what you know now? On behalf of the class, I thank you for sharing your insights with us...
Warm regards, DEN

5 December 1998
Dear Dwight,
...I have done many stupid things in my life which I would avoid if I had the chance to live my life over again, but they are all personal things like spanking a child harder than necessary or forgetting my wife's birthday. So far as my public and professional life is concerned, I would not want to do anything differently. I think I used my talents as well as I could, as a scientist and as a writer. I think I made the right choice in ordering the priorities of my life, family first, friendships second, work third. Happy Christmas and New Year to you all.
Yours sincerely, Freeman Dyson.

8 December 2003
Dear Professor Dyson,
Thank you once again for your patient willingness to consider our questions....
Scientific work often takes one away from home and family. If you had to choose between being with family and being away from them to cure cancer, how would you find the balance?

9 December 2003
Dear Dwight and students,...
The order of priorities in my life has always been, family first, friends second, and work third. This was easy for me because my work was more like a hobby, to be put aside when more serious problems arose. My work was interesting and challenging but not really important to anybody except me. Now you ask what the priorities would be if my work was curing cancer. My answer is, it all depends. That is not a very satisfactory answer, but I think it is the right answer. If the family is running smoothly and the work is at a crucial turning-point, I would leave the family and take care of the work. If the work is running smoothly and the kids are sick and the wife is exhausted, I would leave the work and take care of the family. If both the

*work and the family are in a crisis simultaneously, I would di-
vide the time between them as best I could. The point is, you
have to use common-sense in making such decisions. Judge
each situation as it happens, and do not try to follow inflexible
rules.*

*17 July 2012
Dear Professor Dyson,
What makes life meaningful? Surely science has provided meaning in your life. But have the most meaningful things in your
life come from science?*

*17 July 2012
Dear Dwight,
Since your students have only three questions, I have time to
answer them right away.
...I have always said that the most important things in my life
are in this order, family first, friends second, work third. And
for me, work includes writing books as well as doing science.
So altogether, science is only a small part of my life and not
the most meaningful. Doing science for me is like playing a
concert for a musician. It is exercising a God-given skill which
I am happy to share with an audience. I do not care whether
the science that I do is important. It gives me the same joy,
whether it is important or not.
Yesterday something happened which is for me more meaningful than science. I spent the day with my 20-year-old grandson
Randall whom I had not seen for two years. In two years, Randall changed from a shy and inarticulate teenager into a self-
assured and thoughtful grown-up. Suddenly he is my friend and
colleague and I enjoy listening to his stories. In spite of my
distrust of higher education, I have to admit that three years
of college have done him a lot of good. He is applying to medical school at UC-San Diego and has a good chance of being
accepted. I am proud to be his grandfather.
...Yours ever, Freeman Dyson*

For Professor Dyson's ninetieth birthday in December 2013, we sent
some birthday cards signed by the students. A copy of the Dyson family's
New Year Letter for 2013 that came in January 2014 bore this hand-written
note:

*Thanks to you and the students for your delightful birthday
cards. Please also share this family chronicle with them. The
best part is the paragraph at the end about our granddaughter*

Clara. We are flying out to California tomorrow to see her. Happy New Year to you and the students! Yours ever, Freeman.

This New Year's letter closed with this story written by granddaughter Clara. By including it here, perhaps we have the honor of carrying her first published work:

> *...A year ago, Rebecca's daughter Clara, then aged 7, brought home from school a story that she had written, illustrated with a picture of the evergreen woods on Mount Shasta and a car hidden in the woods. The story is brief but reveals Clara's character. I kept it at home and here it is. "One stormy night, me and mom went to the woods. Mom got a heart attack. I was scared but strong. I pulled mom in the car. I called 911 and they came to get us. Our dog barked at a helicopter, and I waved the flashlight in the air. They saw the light and came for us. We were saved and we got safely back home. The End." The story shows that Clara is not only a strong character but knows her strength. Her teachers tell us that she is a natural leader.*

The souls of children "dwell in the house of tomorrow," said Kahlil Gibran's prophet. When the prophet was asked, "Tell of children," he replied: [Gibran(1964)][17–18]

> ...You may give them your love but not your thoughts,
> For they have their own thoughts.
> You may house their bodies but not their souls,
> For their souls dwell in the house of tomorrow, which you cannot visit, not even in your dreams....

22 November 2004
Dear Professor Dyson,
....We know that your family has top priority in how you spend your time. What advice would you give university students about to graduate, concerning priorities and expectations in balancing career with family life? How does this perspective in one's eighties compare with one's perspective on these matters at age 25?

30 November 2004
Dear STS class,
Thanks to you all for the Thanksgiving message and the three questions that came with it....
...I would not presume to advise any young person about priorities. As I learned from the Swiss nurse who helped deliver

my oldest daughter, "Some people like to go to church and other people like cherries." Each of us has the freedom and the responsibility to choose our own priorities. My first piece of advice is, do not get trapped in your first choice of a job or a career. Always leave yourself room to change your mind and do something different. A good example is my fourth daughter, who became a Presbyterian minister. She always wanted to be a minister and was very good at it. She did a fine job as a solo minister for a little church in Maine. She took care of her parishioners and their problems, and her congregation grew. Meanwhile she also took care of her growing family. But after her fourth baby was born, she decided that she was stretched too thin. Her church and her family each needed more of her time than she had to give. So she had to make a choice. She gave up the church and is now a full-time mother. She does not regret the decision. She will be a full-time mother as long as she is needed, and then she can go back to being a minister at another church later. Of course she could not have had this freedom if she did not have a supportive husband. The most important advice I can give you is, be careful who you marry. I was lucky to find a wife who was a full-time mother for my kids. On the whole, I do not find that my priorities have changed much between the ages of 25 and 80.

13 April 2009
Dear Professor Dyson,
I bring you greetings from the Spring 2009 section of the Science, Technology, and Society class...
Your New Year letter mentions your grandchildren. My oldest son and his wife made first-time grandparents of my wife and I last September. It's so much fun to see our six-month-old grandson discovering the world. We hope he always laughs as spontaneously as he does now.
For what would you like your grandchildren to remember you?

17 April 2009
Dear Dwight,
...I like my grandchildren to remember me as I am, a friendly old codger who enjoys watching his grandchildren grow. ...Congratulations to Dwight for his new grandson. I wish him as much joy as we have with ours. With best wishes for the future, for you and for him. Yours ever, Freeman.

The eloquent simplicity of this response was significant to a student named Matthew:

Last week...we received a reply from Freeman Dyson... He
simply said that he wanted to be remembered for who he was.
...He had nothing else to offer but himself... I think a
valuable lesson was learned from Professor Dyson...

1 May 2001
Dear Professor Dyson,
Once again as we near the semester's end, our Science, Tech-
nology, and Society class sends greetings to you and your fam-
ily....
What makes you laugh?
Thank you again Professor Dyson for teaching us so much. We
appreciate you, for yourself and your insights that you share
through your writings, and also for your willingness to partici-
pate in the life of our class. Best regards to you and Imme and
your extended family.
Warm regards...

3 May 2001
Dear Dwight, thank you for the May Day message and thanks
to the students for their list of questions. Please say a special
thank you to Beth B. for her personal letter...
Two misfortunes fortunately canceled each other out. (1) Your
list of questions came too late for me to answer before your
[end-of-semester] deadline of May 7, since my wife and I are
supposed to be in Texas with a gathering of high-school students
from all over the USA. (2) My wife collapsed suddenly with
acute appendicitis and is now in hospital recovering from the
surgery. As a result of (2), we canceled the trip to Texas and I
have time to answer the questions. As you can imagine, I am
a bit frazzled, and the answers may not be very illuminating....
What makes me laugh is mostly my grandchildren. I am lucky
to have three of them living close by. Also, when I am sitting
at the lunch table with the local astronomers talking shop, we
laugh a great deal. In a profession like astronomy, or music
or theater, with a large number of prima donnas, whenever a
group of experts comes together they will be making jokes about
the antics of the prima donnas.
That's all for tonight. I still have to visit my wife in the hospital
before going to bed. Thanks again for your questions, and all
good wishes for your futures.
Yours sincerely,
Freeman Dyson.

While Imme's illness may have facilitated getting our questions answered, we would have preferred that Imme and Professor Dyson could have attended the gathering of high-school students, for Imme's sake, and so the high-schoolers could have gathered some Dyson memories.

Professor Dyson continues to look to the future, even though he has a rich past of splendid experiences.

> 6 April 6 1999
> Dear Professor Dyson,
> Once again our "Science, Technology, & Society" class has reduced about a hundred proposed questions to five. If we may impose upon your graciousness once again... my Spring '99 students would like to present the following questions....
> ...We have been impressed with your many life experiences (e.g., being present at Dr. Martin Luther King's "I Have a Dream" speech) in addition to your scientific accomplishments. On what projects are you presently working, and what have you not yet done that you would still like to do?
> Thank you. The STS Class
>
> 10 April 1999
> Dear Dwight, thanks for your message, and thanks to the class for their good questions....
> Projects. I just finished the revised and improved second edition of "Origins of Life" and sent it off to the printer. That has been my main project for the past year.[225] It will be published by Cambridge University Press some time this year. Now, when I am finished with this visit to Gustavus Adolphus, I will go back to Princeton and think about what to do next.
> I am now 75 years old and have been retired for five years. These five years have been mostly spent traveling and teaching, visiting many places in the same way as I am now visiting Gustavus Adolphus. I have enjoyed these visits but I have spent too little time at home. I hope to stay home more in the next five years, see more of the grandchildren and perhaps write another book. That is all I can say about future plans.
> Yours ever, Freeman Dyson

His agenda was similar at age 90. Amazing.

---

[225] *Origins of Life* was published by Cambridge University Press in 1999, and is now in a second edition.

Walking with Grandfather

"To him whose elastic and vigorous thought keeps pace with the sun, the day is a perpetual morning." –Henry David Thoreau[226]

Joseph Marshall III closed *Walking with Grandfather* with stories of a long-bow and his grandfather, as an approach to reflections on wisdom.

When I was about six or seven, I watched my grandfather handcraft a bow.... From the perspective of a boy, the process of hand-crafting a bow was tedious and time-consuming... In the final process of curing and hardening, he didn't talk about the bow. He talked about life... [Marshall(2005)][109–113]

Marshall recalls several incidents when his grandfather taught him many lessons. His grandfather did not teach by telling young Joseph what to do. He taught by telling stories then letting Joseph make his own decisions so he could learn from experience. "My grandfather was giving back the gift that life had given him. Wisdom is life's gift."

Professor Dyson has given back life's gift of wisdom. In our journey with him he has tapped seventy to ninety years of life experience, and through his stories he has shared it generously with a full generation of students, about three thousand individuals across twenty years of STS classes. We are deeply grateful.

Marshall recalls how pre-reservation Lakota and Cheyenne societies had informal governance based on respect. The influential core was a council of elders. In Lakota this group was called *wica omniciyapi*, the "council of complete men." "Complete men" meant

...men who had experienced and accomplished much in their lives and who were unselfish, humble, and wise.... The council of elders did not pass legislation or issue edicts. Their primary purpose was to discuss each and every issue, concern, and problem at length. After discussion, the council would usually arrive at an opinion regarding the question or issue at hand. That opinion was revealed to the people, who accepted it as advice and counsel, rather than as a directive or an order. But the people understood that the council's opinion had the weight of several hundred years of life experience and the wisdom the council possessed individually and collectively... [Marshall(2005)][7–8]

From the Princeton Citizens' Committee to the Jasons, from delivering the Gifford Lectures to advising Senate committees, from teaching Robert

---

[226][Thoreau(1960)][62]

Oppenheimer how to do physics to answering questions from undergraduate students in a small Oklahoma college—all the while putting his family first—Professor Dyson has been a complete man. To we STS students, he has been our *wica omniciyapi*, our wise grandfather to whom we turn for counsel. He has lived a long and meaningful life, and has generously shared his wisdom—and himself—with us. Marshall closed *Walking with Grandfather* with a thought that we apply to our relationship with Professor Dyson:

There are still moments when I wonder if I will be as wise as my grandparents are. The answer is probably not. But close behind comes another thought: I can strive to be as wise as I can be. Now I understand, that was all they wanted me to learn. [Marshall(2005)][113]

Let us give the last words to Professor Dyson's grandchildren and the STS students. First, the grandchild, speaking for all the Dyson grandchildren. In 1999, Freeman and Imme's eldest grandchild, granddaughter Bryn, sent a birthday message to Imme, as told in the Dyson family New Year letter of 2000:

The year ended with some good advice from seven-year-old granddaughter Bryn in Maine. She wrote a letter for Imme's birthday: "Dear Omi, I Bryn hope and wish for you a very happy birthday... Remember that there are more years to come and I hope you spend them wisely."

In my speech at the Singapore conference to celebrate Professor Dyson's 90th birthday, I borrowed Bryn's wish for Imme's birthday and applied it to Professor Dyson's birthday: [Phua *et al.*(2014)][325]

Professor Dyson, I am sure that Bryn and her grandmother will not mind if my students and I, along with everyone here today, transfers Bryn's advice and birthday wishes to you. On behalf of an entire generation of STS students who are grateful to have shared in your wise grandfather spirit, we hope that you are having a good time at your birthday celebration. Remember that there are more years to come. We know you will spend them wisely! Thank you for being a person who cares. You continue to inspire us with your example of an undivided life filled with appreciation and awareness.
Yours ever,
Your STS students

Fig. 19.2 *Professor Dyson conversing with a student at the 2012 Sigma Pi Sigma Congress, Orlando, Florida, November 2012.* (author photo)

At the end of the Singapore talk Professor Dyson shook my hand and said "Thank you for allowing me to be part of your course." I replied, "Thank you for helping me teach it." The STS students later thanked Professor Dyson by letter:

> *24 April 2014*
> *...Thank you Professor Dyson for your contributions to our class, for helping the local professor teach it, and for being a friend to an entire generation of STS students. The STS class... wishes you joy and continued health, and extends our best wishes to Imme, to your children, and to all your wonderful grandchildren."*

Bibliography

Abrams, I. (1995). The 1995 Nobel Peace Prize for Joseph Rotblat and the Pugwash Conference on Science and World Affairs, http://www.irwinabrams.com/books/excerpts/annual95.html.

Agnew, H. M. (1985). What the Physicist Saw, *Time* **125**, 4, pp. 40–46.

Alpher, R. A. and Herman, R. (2001). *Genesis of the Big Bang* (Oxford University Press).

Alpher, V. S. (2012). Ralph A. Alpher, Robert C. Herman, and the Cosmic Microwave Background Radiation, *Physics in Perspective* **14**, 3, pp. 300–334.

Arbatov, A. and Dvorkin, V. (2011). *Outer Space: Weapons, Diplomacy, and Security* (Carnegie Endowment).

Barbour, I. G. (1990). *Religion in an Age of Science*, Vol. 1 (Harper Collins).

BBC News (2008). Wildlife populations 'plummeting', http://news.bbc.co.uk/2/hi/uk_news/7403989.stm.

Beevor, A. (1999). *Stalingrad: The Fateful Siege: 1942-1943* (Penguin).

Bethe, H. A. (1950). The Hydrogen Bomb: II, *Scientific American* **182**, pp. 18–23.

Bird, K. and Sherwin, M. J. (2005). *American Prometheus: The Triumph and Tragedy of J. Robert Oppenheimer* (Alfred A. Knopf).

Bohr, N. and Wheeler, J. A. (1939). The Mechanism of Nuclear Fission, *Physical Review* **56**, 5, p. 426.

Bronowski, J. (1973). *The Ascent of Man* (Little, Brown, & Co.).

Brown, D. (1971). *Bury My Heart at Wounded Knee* (Holt).

Brundtland, G. *et al.* (1987). *Our Common Future* (Oxford University Press, USA).

Car History 4U (2015). History of Motor Car/Automobile Production 1900-2003, http://www.carhistory4u.com/.

Carr, N. (2011). *The Shallows: What the Internet is Doing to Our Brains* (WW Norton & Company).

Carr, N. (2014). *The Glass Cage: Automation and Us* (WW Norton & Company).

Catton, B. (1965). *Never Call Retreat: The Centennial History of the Civil War. Volume Three* (Doubleday).

Chaisson, E. J. and Kim, T.-C. (1999). *The Thirteenth Labor: Improving Science Education*, Vol. 15 (Gordon and Breach).

Clymer, F. (1953). *Those Wonderful Old Automobiles* (McGraw-Hill).

Comins, N. F. and Kaufmann, W. J. I. (2000). *Discovering the Universe, Fifth Ed.* (W.H. Freeman and Co.).

Conklin, E. G. (1925). Science and the Faith of the Modern, *Scribner's Magazine* **78**, p. 452.

Crawford, M. B. (2009). *Shop Class as Soulcraft: An Inquiry into the Value of Work* (Penguin).

Dawidoff, N. (2009). The Civil Heretic, *The New York Times Magazine* **29**.

Diamond, J. M. (1999). *Guns, Germs, and Steel: The Fates of Human Societies* (Random House).

Dickens, C. (1957). *A Christmas Carol* (Junior Deluxe Editions).

Dickerson, R. E. (1990). Letter to a Creationist: Seeking the Middle Ground, *Science Teacher* **57**, 6, pp. 48–53.

Dickinson, E. and Franklin, R. W. (1999). *The Poems of Emily Dickinson* (Harvard University Press).

Dryden, J. (1958). *The Poems of John Dryden*, Vol. 4 (Oxford Clarendon Press).

Dyson, F. (1984). *Weapons and hope* (Harper and Row).

Dyson, F. J. (1949). The radiation theories of Tomonaga, Schwinger, and Feynman, *Physical Review* **75**, 3, p. 486.

Dyson, F. J. (1960). Search for artificial stellar sources of infrared radiation, *Science* **131**, 3414, pp. 1667–1668.

Dyson, F. J. (1979a). *Disturbing the Universe* (Basic Books).

Dyson, F. J. (1979b). Time without end: Physics and biology in an open universe, *Reviews of Modern Physics* **51**, 3, p. 447.

Dyson, F. J. (1988). *Infinite in All Directions* (Harper Perrennial).

Dyson, F. J. (1991). "To teach or not to teach," Freeman J. Dyson's acceptance speech for the 1991 Oersted Medal presented by the American Association of Physics Teachers, 22 January 1991, *American Journal of Physics* **59**, 6, pp. 491–495.

Dyson, F. J. (1998). Is God in the Lab? *The New York Review of Books* **45**, 9.

Dyson, F. J. (2000). Progress in Religion, `https://edge.org/conversation/ progress-in-religion`.

Dyson, F. J. (2002a). Book Review– Memoirs: A Twentieth-Century Journey in Science and Politics by Edward Teller with Judith Shoolery, *American Journal of Physics* **70**, 4, pp. 462–463.

Dyson, F. J. (2006). *The Scientist as Rebel* (New York Review of Books).

Dyson, G. (1997a). *Baidarka: The Kayak* (Alaska Northwest Books).

Dyson, G. (1997b). *Darwin Among the Machines: The Evolution of Global Intelligence* (Addison-Wesley).

Dyson, G. (2002b). *Project Orion: The True Story of the Atomic Spaceship* (Macmillan).

Dyson, G. (2012). *Turing's Cathedral: The Origins of the Digital Universe* (Vintage).

Einstein, A. (1956). *Out Of My Later Years* (Citadel Press).

Einstein, A. (1982). *Ideas and Opinions* (Three Rivers Press).

Einstein, A. and Calaprice, A. (2005). *The New Quotable Einstein* (Princeton University Press).

Einstein, A., Lorentz, H., Weyl, H. and Minkowski, H. (1952). *The Principle of Relativity* (Dover).

Eisenhower, D. (1961). Farewell address by President Dwight D. Eisenhower, *Box 38, Speech Series, Papers of Dwight D. Eisenhower as President 1953-61, Eisenhower Library.*

Else, J. (1981). *The Day After Trinity: J. Robert Oppenheimer and the Atomic Bomb* (Pyramid Films).

Federal Budget (2014). 2014 Federal Budget Submitted to Congress by President Obama, `http://www.gpo.gov/fdsys/pkg/BUDGET-2014-BUD/pdf/BUDGET-2014-BUD.pdf#page=193`.

Feller, S. and Sauncy, T. (2013). An Undergraduate Alliance Comes of Age, *Physics Today* **66**, 6, pp. 46–51.

Fermi, E. (2009). Physics at Columbia University: The Genesis of the Nuclear Energy Project, *Physics Today* **8**, 11, pp. 12–16.

Feynman, R. P., Leighton, R. B. and Sands, M. (1963). *The Feynman Lectures on Physics, Desktop Edition Volume I*, Vol. 1 (Addison-Wesley).

Findlay, J. (1908). *Humbugs and Homilies* (Whitcombe and Tombs Ltd.).

Finkenbinder, L. R. and Neuenschwander, D. E. (2001). The Chainsaw and the White Oak: From Astrobiology to Environmental Sustainability, *Radiations* **7**, 1.

Fitzgerald, W. W. and Merritt, R. F. (1968). *Ferrari, the Sports and Gran Turismo Cars* (Bond Publishing Company).

Frankl, V. E. (1963). *Man's Search for Meaning* (Washington Square Press).

Freedman, S., Siers, J. and Ngata, W. (1974). *Maori Songs of New Zealand* (Sevenseas Publishing Ltd., Wellington).

Freeman, C. P. (2012). Fishing for Animal Rights in "The Cove": A Holistic Approach to Animal Advocacy Documentaries, *Journal of Critical Animal Studies* **10**, 1, pp. 104–118.

Fukuyama, F. (2002). *Our Posthuman Future: Consequences of the Biotechnology Revolution* (Picador).

Geohive.com (2015). Current World Population, `http://www.geohive.com/earth/population_now.aspx`.

Gibran, K. (1964). *The Prophet* (Alfred A. Knopf).

Gilchrist, A. (1998). *The Life of William Blake* (Courier Corporation).

Gillon, T. (2003). Space Weapons, Policy Wars, *Astropolitics* **1**, 3, pp. 119–122.

Giovannitti, L. and Freed, F. (1965). *The Decision to Drop the Bomb: A Political History* (Coward-McMann).

Godwin, R. (2003). *Dyna-Soar: Hypersonic Strategic Weapons System*, Vol. 35 (Burlington, Ont.: Apogee Books).

Gombrich, E. (1995). *The Story of Art, 16th ed.* (Phaidon Press Limited, London).

Goodchild, P. (1981). *J. Robert Oppenheimer: Shatterer of Worlds* (Houghton Mifflin).

Gordon, D. and Plowden, D. (2007). Disappearing America: Interview of David Plowden, "The Story" by Dick Gordon, WUNC North Carolina Public Radio.

Gould, S. J. (1997). Drink Deep, or Taste Not the Pierian Spring, *Natural History* **106**, 8, pp. 24–25.

Grinspoon, D. (2009). Living Dangerously: The Same Forces that Make Earth Hazardous also Make It an Abode for Life, *Sky & Telescope* **69**, 2.

Grossman, K. (2011). *Weapons in Space* (Seven Stories Press).

Guth, A. H. (1981). Inflationary universe: A possible solution to the horizon and flatness problems, *Physical Review D* **23**, 2, p. 347.

Hachiya, M. and Wells, W. (1955). *Hiroshima Diary: The Journal of a Japanese Physician, August 6-September 30, 1945* (University of North Carolina).

Haldane, J. B. S. (1924). *Daedalus, or Science and the Future* (EP Dutton).

Harvey, E. N. (1958). Edwin Grant Conklin, *Biographical memoirs, National Academy of Sciences* **31**, pp. 54–91.

Hubbert, M. K. (1956). Nuclear Energy and the Fossil Fuels, `http://www.hubbertpeak.com/hubbert/1956/1956.pdf`.

Hubbert, M. K. (1971). Energy Resources of the Earth, *Sci. Amer. 224: No. 3, 60-70 (Sep 1971)* .

Hubbert, M. K. (1993). Exponential Growth as a Transient Phenomenon in Human History, *Valuing the Earth: Economics, Ecology Ethics. MIT Press, Cambridge, MA* , pp. 113–126.

Hubble, E. (1929). A relation between distance and radial velocity among extra-galactic nebulae, *Proceedings of the National Academy of Sciences* **15**, 3, pp. 168–173.

Hubble, E. and Humason, M. L. (1931). The velocity-distance relation among extra-galactic nebulae, *The Astrophysical Journal* **74**, p. 43.

Hugo, V. and Wilbor, C. E. (1943). *Les Miserables* (Blue Ribbon Books).

Irving, C. (1993). *Wide-body: The Triumph of the 747* (William Morrow & Co).

Jablonski, E. (1971). *Airwar: Terror from the Sky*, Vol. 1 (Doubleday Books).

Jahoda, G. (1975). *The Trail of Tears* (Henry Holt & Co).

Janson, H. and Janson, A. (2001). *History of Art* (Harry N. Adams).

Jerome, F. and Taylor, R. (2006). *Einstein on Race and Racism* (Rutgers University Press).

Kardashev, N. S. (1964). Transmission of information by extraterrestrial civilizations. *Soviet Astronomy* **8**, p. 217.

Kaufmann, W. A. (1963). *The Faith of a Heretic* (Doubleday & Co.).

Kelly, D. (2014). Drones create a buzz at store, *Colorado Springs Gazette, December 21, 2014, A1, A4* .

Khrushchev, N. and Talbott, S. (1974). *Khruschev Remembers: The Last Testament* (Little, Brown, & Co.).

King, M. L. and Washington, J. M. (1986). *A Testament of Hope: The Essential Writings and Speeches of Martin Luther King, Jr.* (Harper One).

Krist, B. (1987). *West Point: United States Military Academy* (Harmony House).

Kristensen, H. M. and Norris, R. S. (2010). Global nuclear weapons inventories, 1945–2010, *Bulletin of the Atomic Scientists* **66**, 4, pp. 77–83.

Kristensen, H. M. and Norris, R. S. (2015). Nuclear weapons stockpile report, `http://www.ploughshares.org/world-nuclear-stockpile-report`.

Leakey, R. E. and Lewin, R. (1978). *Origins: In Search of What Makes Us Human* (New York: EP Dutton).

Littmann, M. and Planetarium, H. (1976). *The People: Sky Lore of the American Indian* (Hansen Planetarium).

Lizhi, F. (1990). Physics, physics students, and Tiananman Square, *American Journal of Physics* **58**, 9, p. 809.

Lovejoy, T. E. (2010). Profiting from biodiversity, *International Herald Tribune*, p. 8.

Mandel, L. (1982). *American Cars* (Stewart, Tabori et Chang).

Mantsios, G. (1998). *A New Labor Movement for the New Century* (Taylor & Francis, Florence, KY).

Marklein, M. B. (1996). Pope accepts evolution, creates furor, *USA Today*, October 24, 1996.

Marshall, J. (2002). *The Lakota Way: Stories and Lessons for Living* (Penguin).

Marshall, J. (2005). *Walking with Grandfather: The Wisdom of Lakota Elders* (Sounds True).

Masters, E. L. (1916). *Songs and Satires* (T. Warner Laurie Limited).

Mayer, J. (2009). *The Dark Side: The Inside Story of How the War on Terror Turned Into a War on American Ideals* (Anchor Books).

Mayo, G. (1987). *Star Tales: North American Indian Stories about the Stars* (Walker & Co).

McKibben, B. (2003). *Enough: Staying Human in an Engineered Age* (Holt).

McLuhan, T. C. (1971). *Touch the Earth: a Self-Portrait of Indian Existence* (Touchstone).

Meitner, L. and Frisch, O. R. (1939). Disintegration of uranium by neutrons: a new type of nuclear reaction, *Nature* **143**, 3615, pp. 239–240.

Mello, G. (1997). New Bomb, No Mission, *Bulletin of Atomic Scientists* **53**, 3, pp. 28–32.

Meyer, M. W. and Bergel, K. (2002). *Reverence for Life: The Ethics of Albert Schweitzer for the Twenty-First Century* (Syracuse University Press).

Morozov, E. (2013). The Perils of Perfection, *The New York Times*, March 2, 2013.

Neihardt, J. G. (1961). *Black Elk Speaks* (University of Nebraska Press).

Neuenschwander, D. E. (2003). Rattlesnake University, *SPS Observer* **35**, 4, pp. 6–7, 14.

Neuenschwander, D. E. (2004). Sometimes I Feel Like Quitting: Some Facts About Student Depression and Suicide, *SPS Observer* **36**, 3, pp. 1–7.

Neuenschwander, D. E. (2006). Fear, and the Principle of Inconsistency, *Radiations* **12**, 2, pp. 16–18.

Neuenschwander, D. E. (2014). Mental Maintenance and Inner Unity, *Radiations* **47**, 4, pp. 14–17.

North, J. D. (1965). *The Measure of the Universe: a History of Modern Cosmology* (Clarendon Press Oxford).

Odum, E. (1959). *Fundamentals of Ecology* (W.P. Saunders).

Oppenheimer, J. *et al.* (1949). General advisory committee's majority and minority reports on building the h-bomb, `http://www.pbs.org/wgbh/amex/bomb/filmmore/reference/primary/extractsofgeneral.html`.

Oppenheimer, J. R. and Snyder, H. (1939). On continued gravitational contraction, *Physical Review* **56**, 5, p. 455.

Petersen, D. R. (1986). *Unlocking the Mysteries of Creation* (Creation Resource Foundation).

Phillips, K. (2005). *American Theocracy: The Peril and Politics of Radical Religion, Oil, and Borrowed Money in the 21st Century* (Viking).

Phillips, M. (1952). Dangers Confronting American Science, *Science* **116**, 3017, pp. 439–443.

Phua, K. K. *et al.* (2014). 'Dear Professor Dyson': Twenty Years of Correspondence Between Professor Dyson and Undergraduate Students, in *Proceedings of the Conference in Honour of the 90th Birthday of Freeman Dyson. Edited by Phua, K.K. et al. (World Scientific).*

Pirsig, R. M. (1999). *Zen and the Art of Motorcycle Maintenance: An Inquiry into Values* (Random House).

Plowden, D. (2007). *Vanishing Point: Fifty Years of Photography* (WW Norton).

Pope John Paul II (1997). The Pope's Message on Evolution and Four Commentaries: Message to the Pontifical Academy of Sciences, *The Quarterly Review of Biology* **72**, 4.

Preston, R., Johnson, D. J., Edwards, S. J., Miller, M. D. and Shipbaugh, C. (2002). *Space Weapons Earth Wars* (Rand Corporation).

Pryke, C., Halverson, N., Leitch, E., Kovac, J., Carlstrom, J., Holzapfel, W. and Dragovan, M. (2002). Cosmological parameter extraction from the first season of observations with the degree angular scale interferometer, *The Astrophysical Journal* **568**, 1, p. 46.

Quindlen, A. (2005). Life of the closed mind, *Newsweek*, 30 May 2005.

Quintana, E. V. *et al.* (2014). An earth-sized planet in the habitable zone of a cool star, *Science* **344**, 6181, pp. 277–280.

Regan, G. (1992). *The Guinness Book of Military Anecdotes* (Abbeville Press).

Rhodes, R. (1986). *The Making of the Atomic Bomb* (New York: Simon & Schuster).

Rhodes, R. (2005). *Dark Sun: The Making of the Hydrogen Bomb* (Simon and Schuster).

Rhodes, R. (2007). *Arsenals of Folly: The Making of the Nuclear Arms Race* (Alfred A. Knopf).

Rilke, R. M. (2011). *Letters to a Young Poet* (Penguin UK).

Rilke, R. M. (2015). *Ahead of all Parting: The Selected Poetry and Prose of Rainer Maria Rilke* (Modern Library).

Ritzer, G. (2011). *The McDonaldization of Society 6* (Pine Forge Press).

Russell, B. (1957). *Why I am Not a Christian* (Simon and Schuster).

Sagan, C. (1990). Guest comment: Preserving and cherishing the earth: an appeal for joint commitment in science and religion, *American Journal of Physics* **58**, 7, pp. 615–617.

Schewe, P. F. (2013). *Maverick Genius: The Pioneering Odyssey of Freeman Dyson* (Macmillan).

Schlipp, E., Paul A. (1970). *Albert Einstein: Philosopher-Scientist* (MJB Books).

Schlosser, E. (2012). *Fast Food Nation: The Dark Side of the All-American Meal* (Houghton Mifflin Harcourt).

Schultz, S. (1999). Looking for alien light, *Princeton Weekly Bulletin* **89**, 2.

Schweber, S. S. (1994). *QED and the Men Who Made It: Dyson, Feynman, Schwinger, and Tomonaga* (Princeton University Press).

Schweitzer, A. and Campion, C. (1949). *Out of My Life and Thought: An Auto-biography* (Henry Holy and Co.).

Segrè, E. (1980). *From X-Rays to Quarks: Modern Physicists and Their Discoveries* (WH Freeman San Francisco).

Serber, R. (1992). *The Los Alamos Primer: The First Lectures on How to Build An Atomic Bomb* (University of California Press).

Shermer, M. (1996). Guest Comment: Hope Springs Eternal–Why People Believe Weird Things, *American Journal of Physics* **64**, 10, pp. 1229–1230.

Shermer, M. (2004). The question of God: Why believe? http://www.michaelshermer.com/2004/06/the-question-of-god-why-believe/.

Shrier, W. S. (1961). *The Rise and Fall of the Third Reich: A History of Nazi Germany* (Secker and Warburg, London).

Shurcliff, W. A. (1947). *Bombs at Bikini: The Official Report on Operation Crossroads* (Wm. H. Wise and Co.).

Silver, L. M. (2002). *Remaking Eden: How Genetic Engineering and Cloning will Transform the American Family* (Harper Collins).

Solzhenitsyn, A. (1973). *The Gulag Archipelago*, Vol. 1 (Harper & Row).

Sorrell, S., Miller, R., Bentley, R. and Speirs, J. (2010). Oil futures: A comparison of global supply forecasts, *Energy Policy* **38**, 9, pp. 4990–5003.

Sousanis, J. (2011). World vehicle population tops 1 billion units, *Ward Auto World*, August 15, 2011.

Speer, A. (1970). *Inside the Third Reich* (Macmillan).

Spergel, D. N., Bean, R., Doré, O., Nolta, M., Bennett, C., Dunkley, J., Hinshaw, G., Jarosik, N., Komatsu, E., Page, L. *et al.* (2007). Three-year Wilkinson microwave anisotropy probe (WMAP) observations: implications for cosmology, *The Astrophysical Journal Supplement Series* **170**, 2, p. 377.

Stachel, J. (1998). *Einstein's Miraculous Year. Five Papers that Changed the Face of Physics* (Princeton: Princeton University Press).

Standing Bear, L. (1933). *Land of the Spotted Eagle* (University of Nebraska Press).

Stern, C. (1975). *Gates of Prayer: the New Union Prayer Book* (CCAR Press).

Sykes, C. (1989). *The Last Journey of a Genius* (WGBH).

Templeton, J. (1972). The Templeton Award, http://www.templetonprize.org/purpose.html.

Templeton, J. (1997). *How Large Is God?: Voices of Scientists and Theologians* (Templeton Foundation Press).

Thoreau, H. D. (1960). *Walden* (Boston: Houghton Mifflin).

Tracy, W. D. (1994). The question box, *Herald of Holiness* , December 1994.

Treaties Between the US and Costa Rica (1962). US and Costa Rica treaties, http://www.costaricalaw.com/Treaties/treaties-between-the-united-states-and-costa-rica.html.

Tropp, E., Frenkel, V. Y. and Chermin, A. (1993). *Alexander A. Friedmann: The Man Who Made the Universe Expand* (Cambridge University Press).

Turkle, S. (2012). *Alone Together: Why We Expect More from Technology and Less from Each Other* (Basic Books).

UN FAO (2015). Deforestation and net forest area change: FAO fact sheet, `http://www.fao.org/forestry/30515/en/`.

Volti, R. (2006). *Cars and Culture: The Life Story of a Technology* (Johns Hopkins University Press).

Waggoner, A. and Carey, D. (2015). Welcome to the History of Schilling A.F.B. Salina, KS, `http://www.40th-bomb-wing.com/schiling.html`.

Weinberg, S. (1988). *The First Three Minutes* (Basic Books).

Weinberg, S. (1992). *Dreams of a Final Theory* (Pantheon Books).

Weiner, T. (2005). Air Force Seeks Bushs Approval for Space Weapons Programs, *The New York Times* **18**.

Wiener, N. (1948). *Cybernetics* (Wiley).

Wiener, N. (1950). *The Human Use of Human Beings: Cybernetics and Society* (Da Capo Press).

Wiley, H. O. (1985). *Christian Theology*, Vol. 1 (Beacon Hill Press).

Will, G. F. (2005). The oddness of everything, *Newsweek*, 23 May 2005.

Woodbury, G. (1950). *The Story of a Stanley Steamer* (Norton).

World Bank Statistics (2015). Latin American and Caribbean Data and Statistics–World Bank, `http://www.worldbank.org/en/country/costarica`.

Yong, Y. D. T. (2004). Development of high-energy laser weapon systems in the United States, *Laser & Optronics Progress* **12**.

Zabel, R. (2014). *SNU Factbook 2014* (Southern Nazarene University).

Index

Ørsted Medal, 47
1066 and All That (Sellar & Yeatman), 62
60 Minutes (television program), 180
9/11 attacks, 125, 129, 134, 163, 190

A Question to Nature, 51
A Christmas Carol (Dickens), 81, 182, 251
A Room of One's Own (Woolf), 217
Aberdeen, Scotland, 313
abortion, 261, 262, 265, 272, 282
    and adoption, 263
accelerating universe, 303
Acheson, Dean, 160, 165
adult cells, 282
Advanced Research Projects Agency (ARPA), 195
adventure, 218, 287, 306
Aeropagitica (Milton), 273
Afghanistan, 111, 125, 179
Agnew, Harold, 153
Agnostic's Prayer, 370
agriculture, 28, 205
Air Force Space Command, 179
aircraft
    B-29, 117, 145
        Bock's Car, 145
        Enola Gay, 153
        Great Artiste, 153
    B-47, 165
    B-52, 127
    Boeing 707, 99
    Heinkel 111, 118
    Junkers 52, 118
    Lancaster, 120
    Mosquito, 127
    U-2, 166
    Wright Flyer, 87, 99
Alamogordo, New Mexico, 150
Albert Schweitzer Hospital, 257

Albuquerque, New Mexico, 93, 287
Aldrin, Buzz, 198
Alfred, Lord Tennyson, 328
All Night Vigil (Rachmaninov), 311, 370
Alpha Centauri, 203
alpha decay, 334
alpha particles, 138
Alpher, Ralph, 323–325
Alston, Wallace, 270, 361
ambiguity, 38
America, a Prophecy (Blake), 128, 200
American Association of Physics Teachers, 6
American Astronomical Society, 231
American Federation of Labor, 50
American Institute of Physics, 320
American Journal of Physics, 288, 292, 337
American Petroleum Institute, 97
American Physical Society, 112, 326
An Essay on Criticism (Pope), 336
Anders, William, 197
Anschluss, 139
Answers in Genesis, 318, 337
anthrax, 40, 171
anti-matter, 323
Antiballistic Missile Treaty, 179
Apollo 11, 194
Apostle's Creed, 370
Appalachia, 249
appreciation, 210, 237, 358, 359, 383
    as course theme, 13
    of cars, 87
    of place, 214
Arab Spring, 135–137
Arctic National Wildlife Refuge, 97, 241
aristocracy of the intellect, 114
Aristotle, 21

Arkansas, 273
Armed Services Committee, 175
Arms Control and Disarmament
    Agency, 166, 177, 178, 184, 191,
    308
arms race, 168
Armstrong, Neil, 198
Army Ballistic Missile Agency, 195
Arsenals of Folly (Rhodes), 168
art and science, 66, 286
As You Like It (Shakespeare), 200
Aspen, Colorado, 237
asteroid, 206, 219
astronomical habitat, 202, 229
    classic mode, 203
    conditions necessary for life, 203
    romantic mode, 209
atheism, 356, 370
atomic bomb, 115, 137, 138, 178, 291,
    294
Atomic Energy Commission, 159,
    212, 291, 293
attitudes, 256
Auguries of Innocence (Blake), 224,
    228, 237, 247
Autobahn, 93
automation, 28, 105
    deskilling, 108
    equivalent of slave labor, 106
awareness, 91, 233, 237, 356–358, 383
    as course theme, 13
    of cars' impact, 87
    of doubt, 331
    of weapons proliferation dangers,
        173
    present moment, 298

B61-11 (bunker buster), 157
baby
    as God, 365
    as part of God?, 350
    Christ Child, 350, 363
    closing scene of Disturbing the
        Universe, 359, 363, 365,
        367, 374
    in Christmas story, 350

Madonna and Child motif, 350
Bach, Johann Sebastian, 347, 364
Bacon, Francis, 348
bad causes becoming good, 129
Bagdhad, Iraq, 126
Baikonur, Kazakhstan, 238
Bailey the beetle, 259
Bainbridge, Kenneth, 150
Barbour, Ian, 313, 346
barium, 139
Bartlett, Albert, 250
Bashford, James W., 315
Battle of Britain (see also Blitz), 118
Battle of Stalingrad, 118, 171
Beach Boys, 87
Beatitudes, 336
Beatles, 84, 372
Beauregard, Gen. P.G.T., 116
Beijing University, 38
Belief in God in an Age of
    Science(Polkinghorne), 311
Bell Labs, 325
Bell, Eric, 64
Bergman, Ingmar, 367
Berkeley (U of CA), 77
Berkeley, California, 294
Berlin, 120, 151, 193
Berlin, Germany, 138
Bernard School, San Diego, 172
beryllium, 139, 144
Besicovitch, Abram, 65
Bethe, Hans, 142, 147, 286–288, 317
Beyond Belief: The Secret Gospel of
    Thomas (Pagels), 361, 362
Bible Institute of Los Angeles, 329
big bang cosmology, 303, 316, 319,
    335, 351
    accelerating universe, 351
    as a forensic science, 323
    CBR temperature fluctuations, 320
    closed universe, 351
    cosmic background radiation
        (CBR), 319, 324
    critical density, 351
    dark sky, 319, 320
    decoupling of matter and light, 324

detection of CBR, 325
element abundances, 319, 322, 323
evidences for, 319
expansion of universe, 319–322
 Hubble-Humanson data, 322
fine tuning, 351
flat universe, 351
fluctuations in CBR, 326
fluctuations in matter density, 326
inflation, 351
initial singularity, 322, 324
name "big bang", 325
Omega, 351
open universe, 351
prediction of CBR, 324
reliability of laws of physics, 323
structure formation, 322, 323
vacuum genesis, 325
velocity-distance relation, 321–323
Big Mac, 29
big-box stores, 249
Bikini Islands, 157, 161
Bill of Rights, 153, 163
biological weapons, 171, 285
Birmingham, England, 88, 364
Black Elk, 1, 349
black holes, 142
Blake, William, 128, 200, 224, 228, 237, 247
blastocyst, 282
Blitz, 118, 120, 130–133
Bloodhound Project, 199
Bohm, David, 162
Bohr, Niels, 33, 50, 140, 142, 314
bomb shelters, 158
Bomber Command, 89, 97, 119–121, 129, 150, 289
bomber pilots, 122
Bondi, Herman, 324
Bonnycastle, Stephen, 290
Boomerang (astrophysics), 327
Bormann, Frank, 197
brain as part of nature, 318
Brave New World (Huxley), 40
Bresee Hall, 51, 55
Bresee, Phineas, 329

Brigham Young University, 308
Brockett deer, 225, 227, 228
Bronowski, Jacob, 21, 113, 249
Bruntland Commission, 235
Bruntland, Madame Gro Harlem, 235
Brynes, James, 156
Buckingham Palace, 347
buffalo, 29, 243, 256
Bulgaria, 128
bulldoze, 249, 255
Bulletin of Atomic Scientists, 157, 166, 186
Burber, Martin, 42
Bush, Pres. George H.W., 175, 184, 185
Bush, Pres. George W., 125, 127, 179, 187, 192
Butler, Octavia, 274
Butow, Robert, 153

Calaprice, Alice, vii
California gold rush, 216
Cambridge Citizen's Committee, 284
Cambridge University, 323
Cambridge, England, 138
Cambridge, Massachusetts, 284
capital punishment, 263
carbon dioxide, 94, 243, 244
caring, 14, 24, 86, 232, 234, 248, 264, 286, 359
Carleton College, 72
Carr, Matthew, 108
Carr, Nicholas, 105, 218
cars
 and bicycle technology, 87
 appreciation of, 90, 94, 101
 as works of art, 89
 autonomous, 104, 108
 awareness of, 93, 94, 101
 cars designed for cities, 100
 cities designed for cars, 100
 compressed air power, 98
 early cars, 87, 88
 electric, 87, 98
 flywheel power, 98
 fuel cells, 98

gadgetization of, 107, 109
hybrids, 98
hydrogen fueled, 98
lack of dipstick, 107
solar power, 98
steam, 87, 98, 101
Casco Bay Conservation Society, 69
Castle Bravo test, 161, 176
Castro, Fidel, 291
Catholic Bishops, 208, 313
Catton, Bruce, 116, 138
Cavendish Laboratory, 88
cell phones, 15, 297
cemetery
Dalamar, Nevada, 221
Frisco, Utah, 214
Winchester, England, 79, 82
Center of Theological Inquiry, 361
Central Conference of American
Rabbis, 343
centrifuges (isotope separation), 143
certainty, 318, 356
at the price of honesty, 339
Chacón, 244
Chacón, Caridad, 225, 226
Chacón, Efrain, 225, 226
on owning axe, 231
on owning chainsaw, 231
orchard business, 225
success as dairy farmer, 225
trout fishing business, 225
Chacón, Marino, 225, 226
Chacóns
White Oak decision, 226, 227, 230,
232, 233
Chadwick, James, 138, 139, 144, 149
Chaffee, Roger, 197
chain reaction, 140, 142–145, 171,
172, 250
chainsaw, 26, 231, 260
chance, 357
Chandler, Arizona, 349
Charleston, South Carolina, 116, 138
Chartres Cathedral, 375
Chaucer, Geoffrey, 58, 202, 290
Chavalier, Haakon, 147, 294

checklist scientific method, 43
chemistry, 206
Chernobyl reactor, 142
China, 242, 244
Chiparopai, 254
Christmas, 139, 141, 197, 251,
348–350, 363
and children, 363
and Dyson family holidays, 58
Christmas story, 349
Nativity accounts, 350
Church of England, 81, 311
Churchill War Rooms, 119, 120
Churchill, Winston, 151, 158, 166
Citizens for Peace in Space, 111
Civil War, American, 116, 138, 249,
256, 312
Confederacy postwar religious
identity, 312
Civil War, Spanish, 118
civilization, 22, 29, 101, 207, 216, 256,
257, 259, 301–303, 311
Schweitzer's philosophy of, 257
Types 1-3, 301, 302
clade, 281, 309
classic mode of understanding, 24,
202
climate change, 94
clone, 281, 309
cloning, 253
Dolly, 275
human beings, 275
organ, 276
Coalition for Peace Action, 126
Coimbra, Portugal, 306
Cold War, 24, 165, 169, 171, 173, 178,
180, 198, 291
and fear, 158, 195
and hydrogen bomb, 158, 161
and space race, 195
costs, 166
effect on economy, 165, 168, 180,
182
immorality of, 169
populations held hostage, 138
start of, 157, 158

weapon stockpiles, 174
Collins, Michael, 198
colonizing space, 18, 239
Colorado, 255, 261
Colorado Springs, Colorado, 110, 111, 255
Colorado State University, 260
Columbia (Apollo 11), 194, 198
Columbia University, 142
Columbiad (Verne), 194
comets, 206
Commonwealth Fund Fellowship, 287
Communist, 24, 38, 118, 161, 162
community, 286, 362
complementarity, 314, 316
Comprehensive Nuclear Test Ban Treaty, 184
Compton, Arthur, 151
computers
    deskilling people, 104, 108
    hackers, 104
    John von Neumann, 104, 114
    medical records, 109
    quantum, 112
    reducing personal interaction, 105
    social engineering with, 104
    survelliance, 111
    ubiquitous, 104
Conklin, Edwin Grant, 315, 336–338
convenience, 237
Copenhagen, 140
Cornell University, 142, 286–288, 291, 296
cosmic background radiation (CBR), 319, 324, 325
    as probe of early universe, 327
    detection of, 325
    prediction of, 324
    temperature of, 325, 326
cosmic egg, 323, 325
Cosmic Mind, 72, 341, 359, 370
    existence of, 360, 362
Cosmic Unity, 75, 78, 79, 264, 289
cosmological eschatology, 18, 303
Cossel, Becca, 235
Costa Rica, 126, 224, 225, 297

"McDonaldland", 236
and deforestation, 231
and immigration, 236
Arenal Volcano, 230, 234
banana towns, 231
children's vote, 233
defense treaty with US, 233
Los Chiles, 232, 236
Los Quetzales National Park, 231, 235
Manuel Antonio National Park, 230, 232, 234
Monteverde, 230
national elections, 233
national parks, 233
Pueblo Nuevo, 230
Pura vida, 222
Quepos, 232
    and squirrel monkeys, 232
    building codes, 232
    development for North American tourists, 237
    ecotourism, 233
Quetzal Education Research Center (QERC), 227
relative stability and prosperity, 233
retirement communities in, 237
Rio Frio Wildlife Refuge, 232
Rio Savegre, 225, 227, 231, 235
San Gerado de Dota, 225, 226, 232, 244
San José, 236
San Luis, 230
Spanish explorers, 233
Tabacon, 230
Talamanca Mountains, 222, 224, 225, 235
council of "complete men", 382
Crabtree, Michael, 234
Cratchit, Bob (Dickens), 252
Crawford, Matthew, 107
Creation Resource Foundation, 333
creationism, 336, 343
critical mass, 144
Crowfoot, 216

CT scan, 266
Cullumber, Jim, 349
Curie, Marie, 20
Curie, Pierre, 20
Cybernetics (Wiener), 107
Czech Republic, 179

Daedalus (Greek myth), 267
Daedalus, or Science and the Future
    (Haldane), 267, 284
Dalamar, Nevada, 25, 221, 256
Dante, 304
Dante's Prayer (McKennitt), 210, 211
dark sky, 215, 320
Darwin Among the Machines (George
    Dyson), 90
Darwin, Charles, 336
DASI (astrophysics), 327, 351
Davey Crockett (weapon), 196
Davis, Chandler, 162
Dawkins, Richard, 341
de Hoffman, Freddy, 169, 171
DeFlore, Leonard, 318
deforestation, 30, 231, 236
    for North American fast food
            industry, 237
    global rate, 236
    green deserts, 236
    Haiti and Nicaragua, 236
    time to recover, 236
democracy of the intellect, 113
Department of Defense, 96, 168, 184,
    186
Department of Education, 168
Department of Energy, 100
dependence on technology, 104
designer babies, 275
development, 255
DeWeese, Robert, 46
Diamond, Jared, 12
Diaz, Manuel, 118
Dicke, Robert, 325
Dickens, Charles, 251, 350, 363
Dickenson, Emily, 327
Dickerson, Michael, 333, 342
differentiated cell, 280–282

dinosaurs, 205, 206
Director of Rapid Rupture, 142
Disney (corporation), 109
Disneyfication, 110, 232
district engineering, 167
Disturbing the Universe, 1, 14, 290,
    355, 356, 373
    chapters
        A Distant Mirror, 296
        A Ride to Albuquerque, 287,
            289
        A Scientific Apprenticeship,
            287, 289
        Aeropagitica, 273
        Clades and Clones, 281, 305,
            307, 308
        Dreams of Earth and Sky,
            350, 351, 354, 366
        Extraterrestrials, 300, 302
        Pilgrims, Saints, and
            Spacemen, 198
        The Argument from Design,
            313, 356, 360
        The Children's Crusade, 121,
            124, 126
        The Ethics of Defense, 182,
            183
        The Greening of the Galaxy,
            222, 239, 245, 305
        The Island of Doctor Moreau,
            266, 267, 285, 305
        The Magic City, 105
        The Redemption of Faust, 79
        Thought Experiments, 305
    diversity, 277, 281, 304, 331
        and interestingness, 306, 309
        biological, 110, 309
            conscious selection, 239
        cultural, 110, 306, 309
        genetic, 306
        in Costa Rica, 225, 226
        language, 306, 310
    Divine Mind, 356
    DNA, 31, 141, 172, 206, 267, 269,
        270, 273, 284, 285, 305
    Dolly (cloned sheep), 275, 281, 282

Donne, John, 258
doubling time, 250
  nuclear fission, 140
doubt, 327, 331, 348, 356, 369
  acknowledgment of, 338
  and faith, 332, 338, 370
  and honesty, 341, 361, 362, 370
  as precursor to understanding, 340
  necessity of, 341
  suppression of, 340
Doubting Thomas, 361
Dr. Strangelove (movie), 183
Drake equation, 299, 300
Drake, Frank, 298
Dream of Gerontius (Elgar), 364
Dreams of a Final Theory
  (Weinberg), 353
  "What About God?", 353, 354
driver education, 104
drones, 110, 111
Dryden, John, 318
Dukas, Helen, vii
Dylan, Bob, 18, 336
Dyson equations, 355
Dyson Family Chronicle, 63, 69, 80,
  237, 238, 362, 377, 383
Dyson QERC Scholarship, 233–235
Dyson sphere, 18, 301, 375
Dyson, Alice, 16, 62, 63, 80–82, 364
  and Catholicism, 70, 81
  as social worker, 81, 82, 262, 263
Dyson, Dorothy, 3, 5
Dyson, Emily, 3, 91
Dyson, Esther, 3, 9, 39, 72, 73, 80,
  238
Dyson, Freeman
  education, 58
  as "complete man", 383
  as grandfather to students, 2, 219,
    246, 379, 382, 383
  as optimist, 301
  books
    Birds and Frogs, 17
    Dreams of Earth and Sky, 17,
      220

Infinite in All Directions, 128,
  200, 303, 304, 313
Origins of Life, 381
The Scientist as Rebel, 242
Weapons and Hope, 121
essays
  "How Large is God?", 344
  "The Sell-Out", 121
  "The Two Windows", 314
  "Tolstoy, Napoleon, and
    Gompers", 50
Gifford Lectures, 313
giving back wisdom, 382
going strong at 90, 254
grandchildren, 286, 364, 372, 373,
  375, 379–381, 383, 384
  Aidan, 81, 182
  Bryn, 70, 383
  Clara, 378
  Donald, 5, 70, 74
  George, 5, 70
  Lauren, 70
  Liam, 70
  Marcus, 91
  Max, 70
  Randall, 70, 377
  Tess, 70
legacy, 254
ninetieth birthday, 375, 377, 383
on...
  9/11 attacks, 130, 134
  Abram Besicovitch, 65
  adventure, 72
  advice to the young, 72, 73,
    174, 379
  agnosticism, 341
  alternative ground
    transportation, 99
  Apollo missions, 198
  Apostle Thomas, 361
  Arab Spring, 136
  Arabs, 134
  art and science, 66, 106
  assisting Alice in social work,
    81
  atheism, 341

automation, 73, 106
babies, 364
babies and God, 367, 368
baby in closing scene of
  Disturbing the Universe,
  366
babysitting grandchildren, 373
balancing family and work,
  376, 378
being a good loser, 296
being remembered, 375, 379
biological weapons, 171
biology, 68, 74
Blitz, 130, 131
Bomber Command, 121, 122,
  150
bombing in Yugoslavia
  (Serb-Croat war), 125
British Empire, 130
Bush Administrations, 185,
  187, 192
capitalism, 39
career and convictions, 96, 185
careers, 72–74
cell phones, 297
changes (or not) in
  government operations, 192
choosing a profession, 67
Christianity and Western
  civilization, 312
Christmas and Easter, 363
church attendance, 333
civilization's long-term fate,
  303
climate change, 95, 96
cloning, 253, 281
complementarity, 314
complexity of frogs and stars,
  205
converting enemies into
  friends, 131
Cosmic Unity, 78, 264, 265
data mining, 112
death, 208, 253
denominations, 70
disagreements, 293, 298

diversity, 277
drones, 110, 112
duty, 68
Dyson sphere, 301, 375
e-mail, 297
educational systems, 46, 48
Edward Teller, 161, 170,
  292–294
Eichmann organization, 121
Elaine Pagels, 363
elementary school teachers, 42
Emma Epps, 294
energy, 242
ethics, 78, 79, 347
extraterrestrial life, 301
failure, 295
fairness in education, 48
Falcon rocket, 199
family, 17, 65, 219, 364, 376,
  377
favorite childhood books, 64
fear and siezing power, 291
fond memories of youth, 201
fossil fuels, 242
friendship, 179, 293
future, 201, 274, 304
Galápagos Islands, 219
gap between poor and rich,
  17, 39, 48, 76, 202, 242,
  274, 275, 347
genetic engineering, 253, 270,
  271, 274, 275, 280, 306
genetic manipulation, 76
genetic technology and
  priorities, 276
getting away from it all, 219
getting students to think, 42
God, 367, 368
good works vs. theology, 347
Gospels of John and Thomas,
  363
grandchildren, 379–381
gray and green technology,
  223
greatest hope, 174

greatest intellectual
community, 286
greatest inventions, 12
Hans Bethe, 288
Herbert G. Wells, 66
his mother's family planning
clinic, 262
his mother's influence, 65, 66
his mother's poetry, 62
his parent's religious beliefs,
341
holding babies as act of
worship, 367
homily at Gustavus Adolphus
College, 274
human rights, 77
humanists, 242
humanities, 66
humans living in space, 200,
304, 305
hydrogen bombs, 161, 176
ice ponds, 223
imposing rules, 362
inequality, 242
injustice, 76, 79, 202, 347
insanity, 242, 245
interestingness of universe,
208
interstellar travel, 302, 303
Iran and nuclear weapons, 137
Iraq war, 126, 134
Isaac Newton, 309
ISIS, 136
Israel, 134
Jacob Bronowski, 114
Japan, 341
Japanese kamikaze pilots, 134
Jason, 185, 187
Jesus, 69, 316
John Steinbeck quote, 173
John von Neumann, 114
Jonah, 274, 347
justice, 243
Kepler satellite, 199
Latin, 309

learning other languages, 308,
309
Libya, 136
life lessons, 67
limitations of language, 344
limits to science and
technology, 20
literature, 64
little red schoolhouse, 170–172
living in present moment, 298
London during World War II,
130, 131
Manhattan Project, 150
manned space missions, 199
market economics and human
labor, 106
marriage advice, 379
Martha and Mary, 69
meaning in his life, 377
medical access, 276
mind-body problem, 360
mind-universe problem, 360
missile defense, 184
Mormons and languages, 308
most important scientific
discovery, 269
most influential book, 64
most influential persons, 65
most pressing fear, 174
motorcycling, 89
museums, 49
music, 64
nanotechnology, 172
NASA, 199
naturalists, 242
New Jersey ecosystem, 245
night-climbing, 201
North Korean nuclear
weapons, 177
nuclear fission discovery, 141
nuclear fission technology, 169
nuclear medicine, 169
nuclear power industry, 170,
242
nuclear power stations, 169

nuclear weapon stockpiles,
    175, 176
nuclear weapons, 173, 174
nuclear weapons security, 175
nursing, 3
opportunities, 67, 72
opposing invaders, 191
origin of life, 300
Osama Bin Laden, 134
overpopulation, 253
Palestinians, 130, 134
Patriot Act, 163
playing God, 268
playing the violin, 64
poetry, 128
post-oil solar and nuclear
    energy, 240
prima donnas, 380
Principle of Maximum
    Diversity, 208
priorities, 376–378
private space ventures, 199
projects, 381
QERC, 234
qualitative decisions, 202
Quality, 25
quantum computing, 113
questions for God, 368
questions for which science
    has no answers, 319
randomness, 91
Reliable Replacement
    Warhead program, 187
religious creationists and
    scientific materialists, 347
rich and poor, 76
Richard Dawkins, 341
Richard Feynman, 65
Robert Oppenheimer, 294
Robert Pirsig, 298
Russian space travel, 238
Russian-Ukranian conflict, 178
Saddam Hussein, 187
Samuel Gompers, 50
school children, 44

science and religion, 34, 312,
    316, 347
science education, 44
science in distant future, 21
science's biggest mistake, 141
scientist's beliefs about God,
    341
scientist's response to
    McCarthyism, 162
search for optical flashes in
    sky, 171
secrecy, 112
shale gas, 96
silence, 217
Singapore, 39
smart bombs, 127
social justice, 242, 275
social reforms and sustainable
    energy, 242
socialism, 17, 39
solar energy, 242
souls, 91
speaking out, 96
stem cell research, 283
Steven Weinberg, 355
still small voice, 315
Stockpile Stewardship, 185
string theory, 68
student struggles with
    fundamentalism, 348
talking to enemies, 187
talking to generals and
    admirals, 114
technological lifestyle, 28
technology and ethics, 347
technology and personal
    separation, 297
technology he would like to
    remove, 169
terrorism, 131
The Children's Crusade, 121
The Day After Trinity, 147
the Resurrection, 333
timescales, 201
translators, 111

Truman's decision on atomic
bombs, 153
truth, 33
truth and loyalty, 121
two windows metaphor, 34,
312, 314, 347
Type 3 civilizations, 302
uncertainty, 333
US manned space program,
199
US of 1950s, 39
Victory through Air Power
(slogan), 183
weapons in space, 181, 183
what he might have done
different, 376
what makes him laugh, 380
William Blake, 128
writing *Disturbing the
Universe*, 376
writing laws, 270
young people and protest, 137
Zürich, 39
papers
Physics and Biology in an
Open Universe, 76, 354
Time Without End: Physics
and Biology in an Open
Universe, 303
quantum electrodynamics, 353
question to students, 189
Russian language, 178, 308
science club at Winchester, 58
signer of "Preserving and
Cherishing the Earth...",
317
speeches
"Science and Religion"
(Conference of Catholic
Bishops), 208, 313
"The Scientist as Rebel", 2
"The Seven Ages of Man", 200
"The Varieties of Human
Experience" (Witherspoon
Lecture), 362

"To Teach or Not to Teach"
(Oersted speech), 6, 47
Gifford Lectures (see also the
speech "Science and
Religion" and the book
Infinite in All Directions),
313
Templeton Prize, 70
study of languages, 58
Witherspoon Lecture, 362
Dyson, George (Freeman's father),
58, 63, 64, 76, 87, 131, 368
at Winchester College, 58
In Honour of the City, 58
music, 347
The Canterbury Pilgrims, 58
works performed at Three Choirs
Festival, 364
Dyson, George (Freeman's son), 3, 25,
80, 187, 203, 351, 355, 359, 365, 374
baidarka, 4, 27, 76, 234
books authored, 4, 90, 103, 113
engines with souls, 90, 91
on the end of science, 20
tree house, 4, 76, 77, 90, 292, 362
trees that think, 90, 91
Dyson, Imme, 3, 16, 63, 80, 91, 233,
234, 237, 238, 308, 309, 380, 381,
384
birthday message from Bryn, 383
Freeman's gratitude for, 379
influence on Freeman, 65
Dyson, James, 8
Dyson, Katarina, 3, 187, 355
Dyson, Mia, 3, 68–70, 81, 105, 130,
182, 187, 188, 355, 379
Dyson, Mildred, 58, 64, 66, 79, 80, 82
family-planning clinic, 262
influence on Freeman, 65
love of poetry, 60
on Cosmic Unity, 79
on good losers, 296
on world soul, 79
Dyson, Rebecca, 3, 80, 362, 378
Dyson, Sir Frank, 8

e-mail, 297
Eagle (Apollo 11), 198
Eagles (band), 237
Earth as niche for life, 357, 358
Eccles, Marriner S., 168
Ecclesiastes, 353
ecosystem, 230
    of proactive young people, 233
    symbiotic relationships, 231
    time to recover, 236
ecotourism, 232
Eddington, Arthur, 58
Editus, 222
educational system
    England, 48
    France, 46, 50
    Russia, 48, 50
    Soviet Union, 48
    USA, 44, 46
Educational Testing Service (ETS),
    48
efficiency, 29, 110, 122
Egypt, 205
Ehrlich, Randy, 260
Eichmann, Adolf, 121
Einstein on Race and Racism
    (Jerome & Taylor), 294
Einstein, Albert, vii, 8, 19, 33, 58,
    141, 149, 156, 311, 343, 353, 359
    1917 cosmology, 320
Eisenhower, Pres. Dwight D., 93, 167
electron, 322, 357
electroweak interaction, 353, 355
element abundances, 322
Elgar, Edward, 364
Elijah (Mendelssohn), 364
Elijah (Old Testament), 364
Else, Jon, 147
Eltenton, George, 294
embryo, 253, 280, 283
energy independence, 97
engine cadaver lab, 84, 85
engineered dependency, 107
English Channel, 119
Enola Gay, 145
Enough (McKibben, 279

environmental sustainability, 222,
    224, 233, 235, 241, 244, 245
    and economy, 236
    Bruntland commission definition
        of, 235
    White Oak Model, 231
Enya, 209
Epps, Emma, 270, 293, 295
escape velocity, 334
ethics, 30, 31, 77, 148, 160, 248, 254,
    258, 265, 267, 269, 272, 276, 280,
    285, 347
    and hydrogen bomb, 160
ethnic cleansing, 124, 259
Eugelab, 161
European Union, 179
euthanasia, 263
evil made anonymous, 123
evolution, 33, 315, 330, 336, 357, 358
    and Catholic Church, 318
    biological, 229
    in stars, 229
    natural selection, 338
    steered by humans, 243
existence, meaning of, 359
Exodus, 71
expansion of the universe, 351, 352,
    357
exponential growth, 250
extrasolar planets, 300
extremists, 348
    and insecurity, 340
    Position A, 333
    Position Z, 333
    shouting from, 333, 340
    vs. middle ground, 342

FAA Safety Alert to airlines, 105
Facebook, 111
facts, 335
Fado, 307
faith, 327, 331, 336, 348, 369
    and doubt, 369
    and honesty, 338
    and humility, 338
    as a choice, 338, 369

Kaufmann's definition, 338
reconciled to knowledge, 338
related to doubt, 332, 338
Russell's definition, 337
student definitions, 331
family first, 376, 377
Faraday, Michael, 353
Fascism, 138
fast food, 93, 109, 237
Fat Man, 30, 117, 119, 145, 150
Faust (Goethe), 60, 79, 350
fear, 291, 318, 340
  and Cold War, 158, 195
  and doubt, 339
  and fundamentalism, 339
  and McCarthyism, 161
  and Principle of Inconsistency, 340
  and seizing power, 291
  of Nazis building atomic bomb
      first, 147
  of Soviet building hydrogen bomb
      first, 159
federal budget, 2014, 168
Fermi, Enrico, 138, 139, 142, 145,
  151, 296
Ferrari, Enzo, 89
fertility clinics, 254, 270, 275, 276,
  282, 283
Feynman, Richard, 93, 120, 286, 289,
  290, 311
  and Tannu Tuva, 287
  influence on Freeman, 65
  on adventure, 287, 290
  on non-sciences, 315
  quantum electrodynamics, 353
Fifth Amendment, 162
Finkenbinder, Leo, 224, 225, 228
Finkenbinder, Zana, 225, 228
fire bombing, 117
  Dresden, 117, 133
  Guernica, 118
  Hamburg, 117, 120
  Tokyo, 117, 120
fission, 138, 140, 141, 145, 169, 176
Forbes (magazine), 72
Fort Sumpter, 116

fossil fuels, 239, 244, 245
franchising, 109
Franco, Gen. Francisco, 118
Frankenstein (Shelly), 21
Frankl, Viktor, 208, 363
Franklin, Benjamin, 67, 163
French Equatorial Africa, 257
Friedmann, Alexander, 321, 322
Frisch, Otto, 140
Frisco, Utah, 213
frog, complexity of compared to star,
  205
From the Earth to the Moon (Verne),
  194
Fukushima reactor, 142
Fukuyama, Francis, 279
fundamentalism, 312, 329, 340
  and fear, 339, 342
  in US South, 329
  religious, 318, 337, 339
  scientific, 318
Fundamentalist (proper noun), 329
fundamentalists, 318, 329, 330
  and the Principle of Inconsistency,
      339
  political, 339
  religious, 333, 336, 339, 341
  science, 333, 339
Furry, Wendell, 162
fusion
  in stars, 203, 206, 207, 229
      CNO cycle, 288
      iron synthesis, 207
future, 201, 202, 296, 298, 304, 309,
  381
  of life and intelligence, 303

Gabon, 257
gadget (nuclear bomb), 143
Galápagos Islands, 219, 238
galaxy, 206, 300, 305, 313, 320, 321,
  324, 326, 351, 364
  and diversity, 306
  and Drake equation, 299, 300
  colonization of, 303
  number of stars in, 299

Galileo Galilei, 33, 37, 273
Gallagher, Kevin, 69, 379
Gamow, George, 323, 325
Gandhi, Mahatma, 77, 124, 291
gap between poor and rich, 17, 39,
    48, 76, 274, 276, 280
gaseous diffusion, 143
General Advisory Committee, 159,
    176
General Atomic, 172
General Dynamics Corporation, 169
general relativity, 320
Genesis, 33, 197, 318, 330, 334,
    343–345
    "days" of creation, 345
    as poetry, 344
    as religious, not science, document,
        345
genetic engineering, 76, 141, 253,
    269–271, 275, 279, 304, 305
    and personal identity, 280
    germline, 279, 280
    policies, 275, 277–279
    somatic, 279
George Washington University, 323
Giberson, Karl, 369
Gibran, Kahlil, 378
Gifford Lectures, 313, 314, 382
Gifford, Adam, 313
Gilchrist, Alexander, 200
Gillmore, Gen. Quincy, 116
Glashow, Sheldon, 353
Global Strike, 199
global warming, 96
Glousester, England, 364
God
    as a baby, 365
    as love, 370
    concept of, 370
    existence of, 340, 348, 353, 354,
        356, 358–360
    in natural theology, 314
    meaning of, 353
    too-broadly defined, 371
God of Convenience, 237
God of Efficiency, 110

Goering, Hermann, 118
Goethe, 60
Golan Heights, 365
Gold, Thomas, 324
Gombrich, E.H., 286
Gomer, Robert, 187
Gompers, Samuel, 50
good causes becoming bad, 129, 134
Googie architecture, 93
Google, 108
Google Glass, 111
Gore, Al, 95
Gospel of John, 361, 362
Gospel of Luke, 69
Gospel of Thomas, 361, 362
Gould, Stephen Jay, 43
GPS, 28, 54, 127, 180
Grade Information Waiver, 45
Graham, Rev. Billy, 346
grandchildren
    borrowing from, 211
    stealing from, 236, 249
Grandin, Temple, 260
Grapes of Wrath (Steinbeck), 173
gravity
    and stability of infinite static
        universe, 320
    as curvature of space, 320
gray technology, 11, 90–92, 222, 238,
    267, 304
Great Basin, 213
Great Books, 74
Great Spirit, 359
green deserts, 231, 236
green technology, 11, 90, 92, 222, 239,
    267, 305
Greenpeace, 246, 251
Gresham, Loren, 55
Grissom, Gus, 197
Grossman, Lt. Col. David, 123
Groves, Gen. Leslie, 142, 149, 158,
    295
Guernica (Picasso painting), 118
Guernica, Spain, 118
Guns, Germs, and Steel (Diamond),
    12

Gustavus Adolphus College, 274, 277, 381

Hahn, Otto, 138, 139, 145
Haifa, Israel, 351
Haiti, 236
Haldane, J.B.S., 267, 284
Halliday, Nancy, 280
Halt, Peter, 362
Handel, George F., 364
Hanford, Washington, 144
Hanger, Howard, 371
Hardesty, Captain, 180
harmony, 243, 244, 359
    with nature's laws, 239
Hayes, Peter, 186
Hebrew University, 366
Hefley, Earl, 371
helium
    atmospheric abundance, 334
    from decay of uranium, 334
Hereford, England, 63, 364
Herman, Robert, 324, 325
Hickox, Richard, 58
High Wycombe, England, 119
high-speed trains, 100
Hine e hine (Maori), 306
Hiroshima, 115, 117, 120, 133, 138, 145, 146, 152, 153, 155, 160
Hiroshima Diary (Hachiya), 155
Hitler, Adolf, 22, 121, 138, 178, 193, 291, 368
Hoesch, William, 318
Home Depot, 104, 106
homogenizing of America, 101
honesty, 356
    and certainty, 339
Honolulu, Hawaii, 232
Hope Springs Eternal–Why People Believe Weird Things (Shermer), 337
Horgan, John, 20
horoscope, 19
horses, 101
House Committee on Un-American Activities, 162

House Subcommittee on Science, Research, and Technology, 273
How Large is God? (Templeton), 314, 344, 369
Howie, Fannie Rose, 306
Hoyle, Fred, 324, 325
Hubbert's Peak, 97
Hubbert, M. King, 97
Hubble Deep Field, 209
Hubble, Edwin, 321
Huber, Verena, 3
Hugo, Victor, 328
human expansion into space, 200
human genome, 267, 271
Humane Slaughter Act, 260
humanists, 242–244
humans as part of nature, 243
humans living in space, 306
Humanson, Milton, 321
Hussein, Saddam, 125, 187, 188
Huxley, Aldous, 40
hydrogen, 357
    automotive fuel, 98
    from dissociating water, 98
hydrogen bomb, 115, 158, 161, 176, 180, 195, 269, 291
    booster, 161
    Einstein-Russell Manifesto, 149
    GAC recommendation, 160
    lithium-deuteride, 161
    Super, 159
    Teller-Ulam design, 161
    Truman's decision, 160
    yield, 160
Hymn of Creation, 344
hypersphere, 321

I and Thou (Burber), 42
ice ponds, 223, 224
idiot lights/idiot park, 109
Illulisat, Greenland, 95
imagination, 199
In Honour of the City (George Dyson), 58
In Memoriam (Tennyson), 328

In Search of Authority (Bonnycastle), 290
incendiaries, 117
India, 242, 244
Indian Removal Act, 256
Industrial Revolution, 244, 249
inherent safety, 170
initial singularity, 323
insanity, 239–241, 245, 246, 305
Institute for Advanced Study, vii, 2, 17, 103, 114, 196, 201, 217, 223, 291
Institute for Creation Research, 318
Institute of Advanced Studies (Singapore), 375
Intelligent Design, 358
Interim Committee, 151
International Geophysical Year, 195
International Physics Olympiad, 38
International Space Station, 238, 239
Internet, 76, 92, 218
Interstate Highway Act, 93
interstate highways, 100, 101, 243, 255
Interurban, 100
Iowa, 246
Iran, 136, 157, 175, 177, 187
Iraq, 187
Iraq war, 125, 134, 163, 179, 186
Irish potato famine, 281
Iron Curtain, 158, 166
ISIS, 136
island ecology, 232
isotope, 140, 143
Israel Institute of Technology, 351
Italy, 273
Ithaca, New York, 93, 287
Ivy Mike (H-bomb test), 161
Iwo Jima, 146

Jablonski, Edward, 127
Jackson Hole, Wyoming, 237
Jackson, Pres. Andrew, 256
James, William, 362
Jansky, Karl G., 210
Japan's Decision to Surrender (Butow), 153

Japanese Emperor, 135, 152, 187
Japanese-Americans during WWII, 153
Jasons, 18, 178, 184, 186, 382
Javert, Inspector (Hugo), 328, 340
Jernigan, Charles, 330
Jerome, Fred, 294
Jerusalem, 269, 366
Jesus, 33, 69, 82, 114, 205, 312, 333, 336, 349, 361, 365
Jet Propulsion Laboratory, 91, 129, 195
Joan of Arc, 291
John (Apostle), 370
Johnson, Louis, 160
Johnson, Pres. Lyndon, 156, 186
Joint Quantum Institute (U of MD), 112
Jolmes, Marjorie, 349
Jonah, 274
Joos, George, 58
Jornada del Muerto, 150
Jubb, Daniel, 199
Jumbo (Trinity test), 196
Jupiter, 203

Kant, Immanuel, 335
Kardashev, Nikolai, 301
Kaufmann, Walter, 338, 339
Keillor, Garrison, 3
Kennedy, Pres. John F., 167, 198, 199
Kennedy, Sen. Robert, 156
Kepler 186f, 300
Kepler satellite, 199
Keynes, John Maynard, 22
KGB, 178
Khrushchev, Nikita, 158, 166
Kiev, Ukraine, 178
King, Dr. Martin Luther Jr., 77, 137, 381
kinship, 285, 297, 298, 307
Kreble, John, 83
Kutter Cheese Factory, 223

La Belle Jardiniére (Raphael), 350
Lacrimosa, 155

Laplace, Pierre-Simon, 335
Lawrence Livermore National
  Laboratory, 185
Lawrence, Ernest, 151
Lawson, Macey, 235
Leakey, Richard, 239
leatherback sea turtles, 231
Lee, Gen. Robert E., 116
Lee, Wen Ho, 163
legalism, 328, 330, 331
Leighton, Ralph, 287
Lemîatre, Georges, 323, 337
Lemay, Natalie, 235
Lembarené (Africa), 257
Lenin, Vladimir, 291
Lennon, John, 372
Leonardo da Vinci, 350
Les Misérables (Hugo), 328
Letter to a Creationist (Dickerson),
  333
Lewin, Roger, 239
Libya, 136
life
  and awareness, 358
  and temperature differences, 358
  extraterrestrial, 299, 300
  interestingness of, 208, 210
  length vs. depth, 208
  meaning of, 208, 363, 377
life belts around cities, 158
Life magazine, 158
life zone of a star, 203, 299, 300
light pollution, 30, 215, 241
Lilenthal, David, 160
literalism, 329, 330, 332, 338, 339,
  344, 345
  Genesis and age of Earth, 334
lithium-deuteride, 161, 169
Little Boy, 117, 119, 144, 145, 150,
  176, 196
little red schoolhouse, 170, 171
Lizhi, Fang, 38
London Institute of Tropical
  Medicine, 341
London, England, 118, 130
Longstreet, Gen. James, 116

Lord, Gen. Lance, 179, 181, 182
Los Alamos Boy's School, 142
Los Alamos National Laboratory,
  143, 163, 172, 185, 196
Los Alamos, New Mexico, 142
Los Angeles, California, 93
love, 315, 371
Lovejoy, Thomas, 23
Lovell, James, 197
Luftwaffe, 118
Luther Standing Bear, 256
  thoughts like Cosmic Unity, 265

MacArthur, Gen. Douglas, 122
machines and personality, 92
Madrid, Spain, 110
Man's Search for Meaning (Frankl),
  208
Manchester, England, 138
Mandela, Nelson, 77
Manhattan District, 141
Manhattan Project, 52, 142, 144–147,
  159, 171, 334
  assumed personalities of
      participants, 147
  cost in dollars, 152
  partipitation in, 147
  would students have used the
      bomb, 151
Maori, 306
Marley, Jacob, 251
Marshall, Joseph III, 2, 259, 382, 383
  his grandfather, 382
  on "complete men", 382
  thoughts like Cosmic Unity, 265
Martha and Mary (Biblical figures),
  68, 69, 71, 72
Marx, Karl, 106
Masters, Edgar Lee, 212, 331
Mather, John, 326, 327
Matthew (Apostle), 361
Maxwell, James, 353
Maxwell–Boltzmann distribution, 334
McBroom, Amanda, 344
McCarran Committee, 167
McCarthy, Sen. Joseph, 161–163

McCarthyism, 291
McCartney, Paul, 372
McCowan, Dean, 145
McCulture, 109
McDonaldization, 93, 109, 110
McDonalds, 109
McKennitt, Loreena, 210, 211
McKibben, Bill, 279, 280
McKibbin, Dorothy, 147
meaning, 280
    lack of, 208
    source of, 359
Meitner, Lise, 138–140
Memoirs: A Twentieth-Century
    Journey in Science and Politics
    (Teller), 292
Men of Mathematics (Bell), 64
Mendelssohn, Felix, 364
mental maintenance, 62
Meselson, Matthew, 284, 285
Messiah (Handel), 364
metabolism, 204
metallicity, 207
metaphor, 38, 344
    and Genesis creation account, 344
    and mystery, 344
    in Christianity, 344
    in poetry, 344
    in science, 344
    two windows (see also two windows
        metaphor), 34
meteorite, 206
methane, 94
middle ground, 346, 348
    vs. extremists, 343
Midler, Bette, 344
militarized economy, 168
military funding, 167
military-industrial complex, 167, 175
Milky Way, 194, 204, 215
Miller, Krista Olmsted, 350
Milton, John, 273, 290
mind
    and appreciation, 358
    and awareness, 358
    and consciousness, 357

and mind-body problem, 360
and observation in atomic physics,
    357
as religious mystery, 360
aware or our minds, 356
brain as scientific mystery, 360
Cosmic, 359
harmony and need for, 359
in our awareness of nature, 356
limitations of, 318, 340, 370
logical connection between levels,
    357
participant in events, 357
roles of mind in universe, 358, 360
third level of in universe, 359
universal, 359
mind-body problem, 360
mind-universe problem, 360
Ministry of Aircraft Production, 119
Minnesota, 273, 279
Minotaur, 267
Misner, Charles, 320
MIT, 218
molecular speed, 334
Monet, Claude, 372, 373
Mongolia, 287
Monsanto, 246
Montana State University, 46
Montgomery, Alabama, 77
Moore, Bob, 126
morale, 119, 120
Morris Island, 116, 138
Moscow, Russia, 178
Moses (Old Testament), 71
Mother Teresa, 341, 346
motorcycle, 87, 88, 101
Mount Horeb, 364, 365
Mount Rainier, 362
Mount Shasta, 362, 378
multipotent cells, 280
Murrah Building bombing, 132, 133,
    188
museums for education, 49
Musk, Elon, 99
Mutual Assured Destruction, 165, 169

Nagasaki, 30, 138, 145, 152, 155
nanotechnology, 172
Nanyang Technological University,
vii, 375
Napoleon, 50
NASA, 21, 96, 195, 197, 199
alternatives to, 198
Apollo, 197, 199
Apollo 11, 198
Apollo 8, 197, 198
Gemini, 197, 199
Mercury, 197, 199
moon mission, 197, 199
space shuttle, 197, 199
National Air and Space Museum,
198, 204
National Catholic Educational
Association, 318
National Defense Education Act, 195
National Institute of Health, 21
National Science Foundation, 21
National Security Administration,
111
Native Americans, 256
Algonquin, 194
and grandparents, 2
Blackfeet, 216
Cherokee, 11, 256
Cheyenne, 194, 382
Chickasaw, 256
Chippewa, 194
Choctaw, 256
Coeur D'Alene, 10
Lakota, 29, 256, 265, 382
Muscogee, 256
Navajo, 307
Paiute, 214
Potawatomi, 10, 256, 310
Seminole, 256
Sequoyah, 11
Shoshone, 214
Trail of Death, 256
Trail of Tears, 256
Wintu, 216
Yuma, 254
NATO, 124, 136, 178

natural theology, 313, 314
naturalists, 242–244
nature both beautiful and cruel, 238
Navajo language, 307
Naval War College Review, 180
Navy Reserve Officer Training Corps,
124
Nazis, 256
nebula, 203, 207
nebula condensation model, 335
Nesbit, Edith, 15
Neuenschwander, Evonne, 263, 265,
355
neutron, 138–140, 322
absorbers of, 142
source of, 139, 144
discovery of, 139
Nevada, 213, 217
Dalamar, 25, 221
Jackass Flat, 212, 213, 217
Patterson Pass, 214
Snake Range, 216
Steptoe, 214
New Guinea, 12
New Jersey, 245
New Jersey railroad, 217
New York Review of Books, 220
New York Times, 179, 182
New York, New York, 140, 262, 309
New Zealand, 260
Lake Rotorua, 306
Newton, Isaac, 22, 309, 353
Nicaragua, 232, 236
Nicene Creed, 370
Nigeria, 310
Nigerian languages, 310
NIST, 112
No War in Iraq petition, 125
NOAA, 96, 192
noise, 212, 218
Non-Proliferation Treaty, 177
North Korea, 157, 175, 177, 187
Northwestern University, 17
Norway, 114, 179, 235
NSC-68 (1950 national security
report), 165

nuclear energy, 240
nuclear explosion
  shock wave, 145
  temperature, 145
nuclear fission, 115
nuclear forces, 295, 296
nuclear fusion, 115
  in bombs, 159
  in stars, 159
nuclear physics, 138, 139, 357
  chain reaction, 140
  cross-section, 143
  liquid drop model, 139, 141
  stability of iron, 159
nuclear reactor, 142, 241, 294
  protests against, 240
nuclear weapons, 144, 145, 173
  Baratol, 145
  booster fusion bomb, 161
  Composition B, 145
  critical mass, 144
  damage radius, 160
  deployed, 175
  flash burns, 155
  implosion, 145
  initiator, 144, 145
  Jason Vietnam study, 186
  M-388 (and "Davey Crockett"
      rifle), 196
  stockpiles, 166, 174–176, 188
  student prior knowledge of, 146
  tamper, 144
  yields, 176

O'Neill, Gerard, 99
Oak Ridge National Laboratory, 96
Oak Ridge, Tennessee, 143
Obama, Pres. Barak, 168, 283
octane, 94, 305
Odum, Eugene P., 231
Oersted (Ørsted) Medal, 6, 37
Ogowe River, 257
Ohio Wesleyan University, 315
oil consumption, 97, 236, 241
Okinawa, 154
Oklahoma, 261, 279

  on personhood, 273
  religious culture, 312
Oklahoma Academy of Sciences, 231
Oklahoma City Philharmonic, 349
Oklahoma City, Oklahoma, 132, 210,
  239
Oklahoma Railway Company, 100
Oklahoma Supreme Court, 272
Oklahoma Territory, 256
Olympic Games, 178
Once Unique, Soon a Place Like Any
  Other (Whaley), 249
Operation Crossroads, 157
Oppenheimer, Frank, 147, 149
Oppenheimer, J. Robert, 138, 142,
  147, 150, 156, 159, 167, 176, 291,
  295
  advisor to Interim Committee, 151
  AEC hearing, 156, 291, 293–295
  and black holes, 142
  and GAC, 159
  and George Eltenton, 294
  Manhattan Project, 142
  on nuclear weapons control, 156,
    291
  opposition to hydrogen bomb, 161
  questioned by FBI, 295
Oppenheimer, Robert J., 383
oral tradition, 307
Oregon, 236
origins and identity, 319
Orlando, Florida, 134, 384
Orthodox Church, 311
Osama Bin Laden, 134
Our Posthuman Future (Fukuyama),
  279
overpopulation, 251, 253

Pagels, Elaine, 361–363
Paggio, H.T.H., 58, 72
Pakistan, 110
Palestinians, 129
Panama, 235
Patriot Act, 163
Peace Corps, 306, 308
peace of mind, 220

Pearl Harbor, 141, 153, 246
peer review, 286
Peirels, Rudolf, 88
pelicans, 233
Penzias, Arno, 325
People for the Ethical Treatment of Animals, 260
People's Republic of China, 38, 163
Permann, Gordon, 172
personhood, 272, 275
personhood legislation, 272
Petersen, Dennis, 333–337
Phillips, Melba, 167
Phoenix, Arizona, 210, 240
photon, 138, 322
photosynthesis, 204, 205, 229
physician-assisted suicide, 263
Picasso, Pablo, 118
Piedmont, Oklahoma, 13
Pierian spring (Pope), 336
Pike's Peak, 206
Pink Floyd, 10, 35, 207
Pirsig, Chris, 25, 86
Pirsig, Robert, 22, 86, 87
    "good" time, 101, 298
    classical/romantic modes, 202
    on caring, 24, 248
    on machines' personality, 92
    on mechanic-machine relation, 47
    on withholding grades, 46
    thoughts like Cosmic Unity, 265
Planck time, 322
planet-building, 203, 206
planets
    collisions, 206
    stability of orbits, 206
Plato, 316
Platonic ideals, 331
playing God, 265, 267, 269, 271, 284, 305
Plowden, David, 23, 240
pluripotent cells, 280, 282
Pluto, 204
plutonium, 140, 143, 144, 161
poet's war, 129, 197
poetry, 128

and metaphor, 344
Point Loma Nazarene University, 235
Polkinghorne, John, 311
Pontifical Academy of Sciences, 317
Pope John Paul II, 317
Pope Pius XII, 318
Pope, Alexander, 336
population, 250, 252
    statistics, 250, 254
Portland, Maine, 69
Position A (Dickerson), 333, 338
Position M (Dickerson), 342, 343
Position Z (Dickerson), 333, 338
postal service, 192
Potawatomi language, 310
Potsdam conference, 193
Potsdam, Germany, 151, 152, 156
power plants, 142
prairie dogs, 255
precision cosmology, 327
Preisner, Zbigniew, 155
Preserving and Cherishing the Earth...(Sagan), 317
Princeton Citizens' Committee, 270, 273, 284, 293, 382
Princeton Seminary, 361
Princeton University, 140, 171, 270, 294, 315, 325
Princeton, New Jersey, 126, 220, 246, 374
Principle of Inconsistency, 339
    and fear, 340
    and fundamentalism, 340
Pro-Choice, 261
Pro-Life, 261, 263
progress, 13, 257
Project Orion, 18, 99, 196–199, 212
prospector, 34
proton, 139, 322
Psalms, 209, 311
Pugwash Conferences, 149
Purgatorio (Dante), 304
Putin, Vladimir, 178

QERC (see Quetzal Education Research Center), 227

Quality, 25, 87, 90
quality of life, 248, 251
quantum computers, 112
quantum electrodynamics, 18, 287
quarks, 322
quetzal, 225, 227, 228, 230
Quetzal Education Research Center
  (QERC), 227, 229, 230, 235
  and community, 235
  Dyson Travel Scholarship, 233
  official dedication, 234
  student research, 235
  study abroad, 233
Quiet Cars, 217

Rabi, Isaac I., 147, 151
Rachmaninov, Sergi, 311, 370
Radiations (magazine), 292, 320
radio telescope, 210
radioactivity, 138, 196, 303
  alpha decay, 138, 139
  beta decay, 138
  gamma decay, 138
  half-life, 143, 334
radium, 20, 139, 144
Ramah Navajo Reservation, New
  Mexico, 307
Rand Corporation, 180
Raphael, 350
relationships, 36, 49, 91, 290, 359, 362
Reliable Replacement Warhead, 187
religion (see also "science and
  religion"), 32
Religion in an Age of Science
  (Barbour), 313
Remaking Eden (Silver), 254, 269,
  275
Requiem for My Friend (Preisner),
  155
respect, 14, 86, 94, 131, 152, 187, 192,
  210, 230, 244, 256, 257, 260, 265,
  284, 294, 313, 315, 339, 343, 347,
  354, 356, 361, 375, 382
reverence, 14, 257, 264, 317
Reverence for Life, 257–260
  and abortion, 261

  and Albert Schweitzer, 258
  and capital punishment, 261
  and end-of-life issues, 261, 264
  and ethics, 265
  and genetic technologies, 264
  and hunting, 261
  and livestock, 260
  and pressure of necessity, 258
Rhodes, Richard, 168
Richard Feynman: Last Journey of a
  Genius (documentary), 287, 289
Rilke, Ranier M., 10, 194
rocket
  Falcon, 199
  Redstone, 195
  Saturn, 195, 204
  V-2, 198
Rocky Mountains, 207
Roman Empire, 312, 316
romantic mode of understanding, 24,
  202
Rome, Italy, 100, 138
Roosevelt, Pres. Franklin D., 141, 151
Rosa Parks, 77
Rosenfeld, Léon, 140
Rotblat, Joseph, 149, 150
Rotterdam, Netherlands, 118
Route 66, 287
Rumsfeld Commission, 179, 182
Rumsfeld, Donald H., 179
Russell, Bertrand, 149, 337
Russell-Einstein Manifesto, 149
Russia, 127, 177, 287
Rutherford, Ernest, 138

Sacks, Oliver, 262
sacred, 257, 258
Sagan, Carl, 317
Sakharov, Andrei, 77
Salam, Abdus, 353
Salina, Kansas, 165
Salk Institute, 172
Salt of the Earth (song), 193
San Antonio, Texas, 50
San Augustin plain, New Mexico, 210

San Diego, California, 91, 169, 171, 363
San Francisco, California, 204
San José, Costa Rica, 126
Sandia National Laboratory, 185
sanity, 222, 239, 241, 245, 247, 284, 305, 306
Sankey, Peter, 201
satellite, 195
  as a weapon, 180, 181
  Cosmic Background Explorer (COBE), 325
  Echo, 197, 325
  Explorer, 195
  Kepler, 199, 300
  Planck, 327
  Sputnik, 194, 195
  Trios, 197
  WMAP, 327
Saturn, 196, 219
Saudi Arabia, 130
Saxe, John Godfrey, 35
Schilling Air Force Base, 165, 169
Schilling, Col. David C., 165
Schweber, Sylvan, 88
Schweitzer, Albert, 257, 259, 337
  Reverence for Life, 258
  thoughts like Cosmic Unity, 265
Schwinger, Julian, 353
science
  and art, 286
  as evidence-based reasoning, 340
  mechanisms within nature, 315
  no supernatural, 335
science and religion, 32, 311, 327, 332, 338, 348, 355, 359, 360, 369, 371
  and metaphor, 344
  conflict, 312, 313, 317
    on free will, 317
    on origins, 317
    on teleology, 317
  dialogue, 313, 317
  independence, 313, 316
  integration, 313
  reasons for study, 311, 312
  two windows metaphor, 313

Science, Technology, and Society course, 1, 14, 18
Scopes trial, 38, 338
Scribner's Magazine, 338
Scrooge, Ebenezer (Dickens), 251
Sea of Galilee, 365
Search for Extra-Terrestrial Intelligence (SETI), 299
second and third graders, 40, 56
self-checkout, 104, 106
Sellar, Water C., 62
Serber, Robert, 143, 146, 147
Serbia, 125
Shakespeare, William, 77, 200, 220
Sharp, Dover, 128
Shawn, William, 122
Shepherd, Matthew, 23
Sheridan, Gen. Philip, 256
Shermer, Michael, 337, 342
Shop Class as Soulcraft (Crawford), 107
Shore, Dinah, 84
Sierra Club, 246
Sigma Pi Sigma, 6, 16, 384
silence, 209, 210, 212, 215, 216, 218, 220, 230, 365
Silence (Masters poem), 212, 219, 221, 331
Silicon Valley, 24
Silver, Lee, 254, 270, 275
Simon Peter (Apostle), 361
Singapore, 39, 375, 383
Singer, Maxine, 284
six faces of science, 37, 40, 47, 76
Skeptic (magazine), 337
sky people, 194, 207
slave labor, 106
Sloan Foundation, 7, 67
Slovakia, 179
smart bombs, 126
smart house, 103
smart phones, 28, 103, 220
Smithsonian Institution, 204
Smoot, George, 326, 327
Snowden, Edward, 111
Snyder, H., 142

Socorro, New Mexico, 150, 210
Socrates, 57
solar energy, 240
Solar Impulse 2 (solar airplane), 99
solar ponds, 223
solar system, 335
  scale model of, 204
solutionism, 24
Solzhenitsyn, Alexander, 137, 346
somatic cell nuclear transfer, 282
somatic gene therapy, 279, 280
Song of Solomon, 132
Sophocles, 253
soul, 90, 91, 128, 214, 315, 336, 340
Southern Baptist Convention, 329
Southern Nazarene University, 316, 329
Soviet Union, 153, 156, 166, 173, 195, 294
  and Cold War, 166
  and Iron Curtain speech, 158
  buffer states, 157
  fission bomb, 158, 159
  fusion bomb, 161
  student protests in, 137
  WW II war on Japan, 153
Soyuz, 238
Space Race, 195
space superiority, 179
Space, Time, and Gravitation (Eddington), 58
SpaceShipOne, 198, 199
Speer, Albert, 119
Spicer, Paul, 63
squirrel monkeys, 232
St. Alban's School, 372
St. John's College, 74
St. Louis, Missouri, 205
St. Petersburg, Russia, 178
Stalin, Joseph, 137, 151, 156, 158, 166, 291
standard candles, 322
standardized tests, 43, 45, 47
Standing Bear, Luther, 210
Stantis, Scott B., 31
Stapleton, Olaf, 301

Star Maker (Stapleton), 301
Star Trek, 18, 301, 375
stars
  Cepheid variable, 322
  collisions, 206
  death of, 206, 207
  evolution, 229
  formation, 203
  fusion, 324
  life zone, 203
  lifetime, 204
  red giant, 206, 208
  stability, 204, 205
  supernova, 207, 322
  white dwarf, 206, 207
START treaties, 166, 174
steady state cosmology, 324, 325
steered from afar, 105, 240
Steinbeck, John, 173
stem cell research, 297
  2001 Presidential order, 283
  2009 Presidential order, 283
stem cells, 264, 272, 282
  embryonic, 282
Sterling, Robert, 349
still small voice, 315, 364
Stimson, Henry, 117, 120, 151, 152, 156
Stockpile Stewardship, 163, 185
Stoner, Richard, 140, 141
Strassman, Fritz, 138, 139
Strategic Air Command, 165, 169
strategic bombing, 120, 123, 127
Strategic Defense Initiative, 183
Strickland, Douglas, 213, 214, 221
Strickland, Dudley, 213
strong nuclear force, 357
STS Museum, 247, 362
student depression, 62
student life
  career selection, 71
  intellectual and emotional challenges, 57, 74
student suicide, 57
Sulzman, Bill, 111
sun

death of, 207
energy source, 204
lifetime, 204, 207
luminosity, 204
Sunrayce, 98
Swamp Angel, 116, 119, 138
Sweden, 138, 179
Swedenborg, Emanuel, 335
Switzerland, 39
Syria, 136
Szilard, Leo, 294

Taiji, Japan, 257
Taiwan, 38
Talamanca Mountains (Costa Rica), 222
Tannenwald, Nina, 186
Tannu Tuva, 287
Taylor, G.I., 88
Taylor, Maxwell, 187
Taylor, Rodger, 294
Taylor, Ted, 196, 223
technically sweet, 183
technician's war, 129
technology and moral code, 111
Teets, Pete, 179
Teller, Edward, 142, 161, 291–293, 295
  advocate of hydrogen bomb, 159
  AEC hearing, 291
  autobiography, 292
  Triga reactor, 170
  visit to West Point, 292
Templeton Foundation, 344, 369
Templeton Prize, 70, 346, 347, 372
Templeton, John, 314, 346
Tennyson, Alfred Lord, 370
Terentius Afer, 60
terrorism, 131
terrorists, 135, 173
Test Ban Treaty, 181, 196
The Moody Blues, 56
The Ascent of Man (Bronowski), 21, 113
The Astronomical Basis of Life on Earth (course), 224, 228

The Beginning or the End (motion picture), 158
The Canterbury Pilgrims (George Dyson), 58, 63, 76
The Canterbury Tales (Chaucer), 58, 60
The Cove (documentary), 28, 257
The Day After Trinity (documentary), 147, 149, 152, 288, 289
The End of Science (Horgan), 20
The Faith of a Heretic (Kaufmann), 338
The First Three Minutes (Weinberg), 320, 352, 353, 356
The Fundamentals: A Testimony to the Truth, 329
The Glass Cage: Automation and Us (Carr), 105
The Gnostic Gospels (Pagels), 361
The Greening of the Galaxy, 241
The Human Use of Human Beings (Wiener), 106
The Island of Doctor Moreau (Wells), 40, 284, 305
The Last Resort (The Eagles), 237
The Lord of the Rings (Tolkien), 213
The Magic City (Nesbit), 15, 64, 105, 110
The Meaning of it All (Feynman), 311
The Mechanism of Nuclear Fission (Bohr & Wheeler), 141
The New Yorker, 121, 122
The Origin of Species (Darwin), 318
The Parable of the Sower (Butler), 274
The Poem of the Dawn, 344
The Question of God (Shermer), 342
The Road From Los Alamos (Bethe), 288
The Rose (McBroom), 344
The Science Teacher, 333
The Self-Tormenter (Afer), 60
The Seventh Seal (Bergman), 367
The SPS Observer, 320

The Virgin of the Rocks (da Vinci), 350
theology, 312
  and history of science, 312
  Greek influence, 312
  natural, 313
theory, 54
  word as meant by scientists, 335
  word misused by non-scientists, 335
Third Reich, 22
Thomas (Apostle), 361, 362
Thompson, Frank, 127, 128, 257
Thoreau, Henry David, 28, 57, 208, 211, 219, 221, 222, 237, 245, 257, 382
  thoughts like Cosmic Unity, 265
Thorne, Kip, 320
Thornton, Rep. Ray, 273
Three Choirs Festival, 63, 80, 364
Tiananmen Square protests, 137
tides, 230
timescales, 35, 143, 200, 201, 204, 207, 297, 300, 303
Tiny Tim (Dickens), 252
Tokyo, Japan, 200
Tolkien, J.R.R., 213
Tolstoy, Leo, 44, 50
Tomonaga, Sin-itiro, 353
Tonobungay (Wells), 40
tornado, 210
totipotent cells, 280, 282
Tracy, Wesley, 343, 344
Trail of Death, 256
Trail of Tears, 256
trains, 104
Tranquility Base, 198
Treaty of Versailles, 118
Triga reactor, 18, 169
trilobite, 215
Trinity test, 150, 151, 156, 196
Truman, Pres. Harry S.
  at Potsdam, 151, 193
  decision to build hydrogen bomb, 160, 180
  decision to use atomic bomb, 117, 153

  not telling Stalin about Bomb, 156
truth, 33, 34, 329, 334
tularemia, 171
Tull, Jethro, 369
Turing, Alan, 103
Turkle, Sherry, 23, 218
Twitter, 111
Two From Galilee (musical, book), 349, 350
two windows metaphor, 34, 312–317, 340, 347, 348, 355

Ubi Caritas (hymn), 371
Ukraine, 142, 177
Ulam, François, 147
Ulam, Stan, 113, 142, 147, 161
uncertainty, 34, 53, 284, 333, 340, 342, 370
uncertainty principle, 325
unified forces, 353
United Nations, 184, 235, 236
United States Military Academy, 122, 292
universe
  and our coming, 357
  as participant in, not spectator of, 211
  as pointless, 352, 354
  interestingness in, 358
  needing life, 358
University of Birmingham, 291
University of Chicago, 142, 296
University of Colorado, 250
University of North Texas, 231
University of Oklahoma, 235
University of Wisconsin, 142
Unlocking the Mysteries of Creation (Petersen), 333, 335, 342
unsustainable behavior, 236
uranium, 139, 140, 142–144, 179, 334
Uranus, 204
urban sprawl, 93, 101
USA Today, 318
Utah, 213, 216
  Confusion Range, 214
  Frisco, 213

House Range, 214
Notch Peak, 214
Sevier Lake salt flat, 214
Swasey Peak, 214, 215, 230
Week's Canyon, 214

V-E Day, 151
Valjean, Jean, 328
values, 36, 319
Vanishing Point (Plowden), 240
Vermeer, Johannes, 38
Verne, Jules, 194, 199
Very Large Array, 210
VfR (early German space travel
   society), 196
Victory through Air Power (slogan),
   120, 183
Vietnam, 122, 127, 179, 185, 186
Vinita, Oklahoma, 287
Virgin and Child Enthroned between
   Saints and Angels (Byzantine
   painting), 350
volcanoes, 230
Voltaire, 29
von Braun, Werner, 195–197
von Neumann, John, 103, 113
Voyager 1, 209, 298
VSE (Velocity, Silence, Efficiency), 99

Wal-Mart, 104, 106, 246
Walden (Thoreau), 219, 265
Wales, 307
Walking with Grandfather
   (Marshall), 2, 382, 383
Wall-E (motion picture), 109
Warsaw, Poland, 118
Washington National Cathedral, 347,
   361, 372
Washington, DC, 203
Washington, George, 291
Wataghin, Gleb, 103
Watanabe, Tomone, 341
Water Lilies (Monet), 372
Water Meadows (Winchester), 80, 82
Waterman, Susanna, 270
wave-particle duality, 33, 315, 357

weapons in space, 161, 179
   air of inevitability, 180
   China, 180
   Global Strike, 179, 199
   lasers and radio beams, 179
   parity, 182
   Rods from God, 179
   space superiority/supremacy, 179
   US Air Force, 179
weapons modernization, 157
Weinberg, Steven, 187, 320, 352–354,
   359, 370, 371
   electroweak theory, 353, 355
   on belief, 354
Wells, H.G., 40, 66, 267, 284, 305
Wesley, John, 329
Westminster College, 158
Whaley, Abe, 249, 257
Wheeler, John, 140, 161, 320
Whermacht, 118
White Oak Model of environmental
   sustainability, 231
White, Ed, 197
Why I Am Not A Christian (Russell),
   337
Wiener, Norbert, 106
wildlife habitat, 255
Wiley, H. Orton, 344, 345
Wilkin, Dan, 235
Wilkowske, Matthew, 235
William of Wykeham, 202
Wilmut, Ian, 281
Wilson, Jane, 147
Wilson, Robert, 147, 325
Winchester College, 58, 64, 127, 201,
   202, 296
Winchester, England, 16, 58, 70, 79,
   80, 82, 262, 296
wind turbine, 239, 241
wisdom, 382, 383
Witherspoon Lecture, 362
witholding grades, 46
WMAP (astrophysics), 351
Woodbury, George, 101
Woolf, Virginia, 217
Worcester, England, 364

world soul, 79, 80, 82, 359
World Trade Center, 131
World War I, 257
World War II, 138, 141
   arguments for using atomic bombs
        on Japan, 152
   casualty rates, 153
   invasion of Poland, 118
   kamikazes, 134
   opposition to occupation, 191
   postwar economy, 93
   precision bombing, 127
   strategic bombing, 123
Worlds Apart: The Unholy War
  Between Religion and Science
  (Giberson), 369
Worley, Karla, 349
worship as poetry, 370
Wright, Courtenay, 187
Wright, Thomas, 313
Wright, Wilbur, 105

Yager, Chase, 235
Yeatman, Robert J., 62
Yeshiva University, 17
yom (Hebrew), 345
Yugoslavia, 124, 125, 128

Zürich, Switzerland, 39
Zen and the Art of Motorcycle
  Maintenance (Pirsig), 22, 202, 298
Zovath, Mike, 318
Zworykin, Vladimir K., 212